The
Desert
World

The

Desert

World

ALONZO W. POND

THOMAS NELSON & SONS

Edinburgh   **NEW YORK**   *Toronto*

DESIGN BY FRANK KARPELES

Library of Congress Catalog Card Number: 62–16355

MANUFACTURED IN THE UNITED STATES OF AMERICA

IN APPRECIATION OF THEIR PATIENCE WITH MY LONG ABSENCES IN ARID
LANDS, *The Desert World* IS DEDICATED:

To Dorothy, who shared many of the desert experiences;

To Chomingwen, whose first sand pile was in the Sahara duneland;

To Art who has listened attentively to our tales of desert survival.

Foreword

THE DESERT WORLD IS NOT A PLACE THAT ONE CAN DEFINE WITH boundaries, or even limit with descriptive terms, and, yet, those travelers who have seen it with their hearts and minds as well as with their eyes and ears know that it exists. I think it exists, not in one place but in many places, each with its special character, each with some similarities to other corners, but never like any other part of the desert world in every aspect. Always it is a strange land where plants have thorns for leaves and four-footed animals drink no water. Its climate is harsh on man, beast, and plant; its weather varied and unpredictable. The land itself is always marked by abrupt hills, or majestic canyons, or sand heaped up in sweeping waves, or glistening, flat-floored basins, and plains of infinite monotony; but, of course, it is not always marked by all of these.

I have known the physical aspects of this desert world for nearly two score years. The Sahara, the Gobi, our own southwest, Libya, Egypt, the Negev, and the oil-rich deserts of Arabia have been within my travels. In each of them I can call some person "friend." On foot and horseback, from camel-back and motorcar, by aeroplane and helicopter, I have seen the startling contrasts of the desert world. For ten years it was my job with the U.S. Air Force to prepare material for those who might be stationed in desert areas or who might find themselves survivors in that unfamiliar world. During this time the journals of explorers, the diaries of survivors, and the papers of botanists, zoologists, climatologists, and physiologists were my textbooks to help me to better understand the desert world so that I could help to make airmen know it as a habitable world and relieve them of their fear of this fantastic place.

Even though we cannot define it; even though it differs for each man who dares to try to solve its mystery, the facts about the desert world are worthy of attention. We can describe the physical features of the arid wastes. We can identify its plants and animals. We can analyze its climate and describe its weather. We can even explain how man has adjusted to its harsh reality. All this is necessary background for an understanding; but those who know will tell you that the desert world is much, much more than our eyes and ears and sense of touch can recognize.

I know the desert as a strange world of awesome terror and satisfying peace; of vivid contrasts, contradictions and contemplation. It frightens and repels. It fascinates and pulls. To know the desert world is to hate it and revile it; to love it and to bless its infinite sublimity. But above all else, the desert world is a place of freedom, a last realm of individualism, where even a slave is more truly free and equal than a citizen of a modern democracy. I would like to have you meet the desert as I have known it.

ALONZO W. POND

Contents

The
Desert
World

I

. . . .

. . . .

. . . .

. . . .

. . . . .

What Is the Desert World?

THE DESERT WORLD IS A COMPLEX WORLD COMPOSED OF DIFFER-
ent geographical regions. Together they make up about one fifth of
the land area of the earth. No two of these regions are alike, but
they all have some features in common, some characteristics, which
in varying degrees, justify their inclusion in the desert world.

Desert regions are found on every continent, and most of them
bear names which, like Sahara and Gobi, just mean desert or arid
waste in the language of the local inhabitants. To the linguist,
therefore, it is redundant to say "the Gobi Desert" or "the Sahara
Desert." I often use the names that way because it sounds better.
However, a Frenchman or an Arab living near the Sahara will talk
about "the Desert" or "the Sahara" but almost never say, "The
Sahara Desert." In America either "The Sahara" or "The Sahara
Desert" is good usage.

Some of the desert names apply to local regions which are really
only parts of larger deserts. The Libyan Desert, for example, is
part of the Sahara, and there are some geographers who consider
even the great Sahara only part of the Palaearctic Desert extend-
ing from the Gobi in Asia, with side branches into India, through
Arabia and North Africa to the Atlantic Ocean.

These pieces of the desert world range in size from the little

500-acre Desert of Maine in northeastern United States to the 3,000,000 square miles of the Sahara in Africa. The latter covers almost half the continent of Africa and stretches from the Atlantic Ocean to the Red Sea. In the north it touches the Mediterranean Sea and reaches away south to the shores of the Niger River and Lake Chad in Central Africa.

North and east of the Sahara the Arabian Desert covers about 500,000 square miles of the Arabian peninsula. Some desert geographers like to say that it is just a northeast "bay" of the Sahara. Perhaps they are right but there are important differences in the land and weather and in the customs of the people. Although it is really joined to Africa by the Isthmus of Suez, most of us think of Arabia as belonging to Asia rather than to Africa.

In South Africa the Kalahari of Bechuanaland is an arid region of 200,000 square miles. Those who think of deserts in terms of the central Sahara or Death Valley, U.S.A., say the Kalahari is not a true desert because the grass grows high and human beings, like the Bushmen, can find edible roots, fruits, and even some game. There is enough wild food to support small family groups without the aid of agriculture or domestic animals. This is impossible in most desert areas.

Much of the interior of Australia is desert in the usually accepted sense of the word, and that part called the Great Sandy Desert, alone, covers about 160,000 square miles.

Another of the famous deserts is the Gobi of Mongolia. Much of its area, 125,000 square miles, has been made known to the western world by the expeditions of Dr. Sven Hedin and Dr. Roy Chapman Andrews. Parts of the Gobi have grass enough to support herds of horses and flocks of sheep, but over most of the area there is not enough wild food to support even a lone hunter.

On the west coast of South America the Atacama covers 70,000 square miles. It holds the world records for the lowest annual rainfall and the longest period without rain. Official records show fourteen years without precipitation at Iquique, Chile, and average annual rainfall at Arica, Chile, as only 0.02 inches, but unofficial reports indicate that parts of the Atacama have received no rain for as long as fifty years.

In North America, surrounding the Gulf of California, is the Sonora Desert. Farther east in Mexico is the Chihuahuan Desert. The United States has many geographical areas which are named deserts. The Mojave Desert in southern California, the Painted Desert in northeastern Arizona, the High Desert in Oregon, the Great Salt Desert in northwestern Utah, and the Black Rock Desert in northwestern Nevada are all parts of the Great Basin area. Even the names of these various parts of the desert world in the United States give evidence that deserts are not all alike.

Individual deserts have such distinctive characteristics that it is almost impossible to give an exact definition for the desert world, but many geographers have attempted definitions for regions properly called "desert." Some definitions have been based on the distribution of certain drought-resisting plants. Others use the ratio between average annual rainfall and the potential loss of moisture through plants and evaporation. Subdivisions in desert definitions are based on temperature of certain months and the time of year in which rain comes, but the most common criterion is rainfall. Any region usually called desert has less than ten inches of rainfall (including melted snow) in an average year. In many deserts the average is even less than four inches a year; and in some, several years may pass with not a single drop of rain or snow or hail. A few geographers would limit a true desert to a region in which a twelve-month period has occurred, at least once, without any precipitation.

At Themed in the Sinai Desert, on the Arabian Peninsula, during twenty-three years of record keeping, there have been three twelve-month periods without rain and one of those stretched to twenty-three months! Along the Arizona-Mexico border in the Sonora Desert clouds sometimes pile up black and ominous—rain falls but often doesn't reach the ground. The air is so dry that the rain evaporates in mid-air.

Some geographers have used the 10-inch or the 4-inch isohyets (rainfall lines on a map) as limits for their definition of desert areas. Of course, such lines shift back and forth from year to year. Then, too, there are many parts of the sea which get as little rain as four inches. Large areas of the Arctic are equally dry. Obviously it takes more than just rainfall to define a desert.

The recent Homoclimatic maps of the Eastern and Western Hemispheres prepared for UNESCO by Professor Peveril Meigs are based on a formula which recognizes that rainfall alone is not enough to determine the boundaries of the desert world. In addition to the amount of precipitation an area receives per average year, the formula includes the amount of moisture which could be lost from the area by drying winds and by transpiration from plants. It recognizes that no matter how much moisture an area receives it will be an arid land if the moisture is lost too quickly by evaporation and plant use. In other words, to avoid desert conditions, there must be enough rain to take care of evaporation loss and still supply plant cover with the moisture needed for its normal growth. On the basis of this evapo-transpiration formula, the new maps divide desert lands into extremely arid, arid, and semi-arid regions with many subdivisions. I consider *all* of these divisions as part of the desert world.

Only in recent years have statistics on rainfall, temperature, and relative humidity been available from enough stations in desert regions to work out evapo-transpiration figures. However, botanists have recognized that certain plants can grow in desert regions and others cannot. Robert Capot-Rey selected two plants, *cram-cram* (*Cenchrus biflorus*), a prickly weed, and *had* (*Cormacula monocantha*), a scrubby thornbush, and used their presence to define the southern boundary of the Sahara. He placed that line in the area where *cram-cram* is found farthest north and *had* grows farthest south. But these two plant zones overlap so that the *cram-cram-had* boundary for the southern Sahara is a broad band instead of a distinct line.

Even though species do overlap so that in some areas it is not easy to tell where the desert begins and the non-desert stops, there are other desert borders where the vegetation line is so distinct that it can be recognized by anyone even if he doesn't know the difference between an apple tree and alfa grass. In the Sahara, the vegetation boundary is sharp along the Nile River and on the north where a range of mountains makes the northwestern border with Morocco. The northwest side of the mountains has trees, bushes, and grass. As you fly over the crest, you see the desert side bare of vegetation. Along the Nile, too, the line between "here is desert— there is not" is as sharp as that between silence and the din of a boiler factory.

On other desert borders, grasslands just get thinner and poorer until finally there isn't any grass, only barren rock and gravel. One year there may be more rain and the grass will move farther and farther out onto the arid land. Another year, with less rain, the desert will encroach upon the grassland.

This is especially true at the Sahara's southern edge. There the green is like a majestic tide. When the rains come along the Niger River and water the southern desert, grass and flowers sweep north a thousand miles to Bidon Cinque, a military post in the desert so remote that it is becoming legendary—a synonym for utter isolation and complete desolation. As the sun and summer heat advance, the grasses die. The Green Tide flows back and the desert claims a land of skeleton grasses. They wither and disappear and leave the land bare until another rain, in another year, will sweep the Green Tide north again.

In the desert of Mongolia, the Green Tide is less spectacular but just as real. For many decades Chinese farmers have moved out into the Gobi grasslands to plant their crops. If the rains have been heavy for a year or so, the grasslands crowd north and west toward the desert. Then, some spring finds the Chinese plowing fields a little closer to the desert, pushing and crowding the Mongol herdsman from his range, just as the American Indian was pressured from his hunting grounds. But in the Gobi the rains fail eventually. Then the desert reclaims the plowed land, and the farmer in his turn retreats before the herdsman. Wherever there's a desert, there's a rhythmic advance of vegetation on the edges, a halt, and then retreat—all depending on the rhythm of the rainfall.

In Australia, C. T. Madigan says, "Any area that is difficult and dangerous to cross with camels may surely be called a desert, and though not scientifically exact, I find this a very useful criterion to apply." With this exception, animals, unlike plants, have not been used to define boundaries of any desert, but some of them, the kangaroo rat and the gazelle, are found only in desert regions. They have so well adjusted their living habits and modified their physiology to meet desert conditions that they are not found elsewhere. They are as much a part of the desert world as the human beings who have made their homes in the arid lands. Physical features of the desert, buttes, waterless river channels, and mountains rising abruptly from flat plains, are not included in definitions of a desert either, but they are part of the desert world and have played an important role in its creation.

Scanty rain and high evaporation, plains, mountains, and sand dunes, drought-resisting vegetation, and animals capable of enduring or avoiding intense heat are all characteristic of desert areas, but the desert world is more than all of these. While it is a section of the earth, it is also a scene of life and action—a state of existence different from any other on this earth. It is a dead world, but it is also vibrant with living change. It is a land of emptiness and monotony, of sudden violence, and breathless beauty. Above all, the desert is ruthless, relentless, and never compromising. In the desert world every living thing, man, beast, or plant is always on guard; ready to use the slightest advantage, or to seize the tiniest favor. Despite its ruthlessness, the desert is a most restful place for those with courage enough to live alone with their thoughts and not afraid to depend upon themselves. Such people love the desert and gain satisfaction from its continuous challenge. They find that the silence, the peace, the complete emptiness of the land make the stars seem close. These are the people who take time to know the vastness of the desert. They take plenty of time, because the desert world is no place for the man in a hurry.

The automobile has made some desert areas easily accessible, but at fifty or one hundred miles per hour these parts of the desert seem unreal. The auto must travel the less rugged routes and sweeps across plateau to plain so fast that the passenger fails to get the sense of their infinity. Instead, there is only a feeling of monotony and fatigue, or a sense of mild and unimpressive contrast between the gently rolling desert plain and the table-flat plateau. Only when you slow to a camel's pace of two and one half miles per hour do you really see the desert and understand the immensity of it.

At first the task of crossing such endless space seems hopeless, but if you are a true desert person the sight of that empty landscape tempts you onward. You see the wisdom of the Chinese proverb, "The journey of a thousand miles begins with one step." When you have taken that one step you are of the desert world.

But there are others who fear the desert. Some oasis dwellers, born and raised within the boundaries of the arid wastes, never dare to leave the safety of their wells and irrigated garden plots. These timid ones shun the desert because its great expanse terrifies them. They are afraid to risk the thirst, the burning sun, and blinding dust storms. They cannot meet the desert's challenge and so they live their lives close to others, fearful like themselves, who travel only from house to well to garden patch. They are *in* the desert, but they are not *of* the desert world and have no desire to know the satisfactions of its long journeys.

There are many long journeys in the deserts of the world. It is a thousand miles from Kalgan, China, across the Gobi to Uliassutai, Mongolia, and close to three months' journey as the caravans must travel. From the Atlas Mountains at the northern edge of the Sahara to the great bend of the Niger River in the south is 1,200 miles; and it is 3,500 miles across the Sahara from the Atlantic Ocean on the west to the Red Sea at the eastern edge of the greatest desert of them all.

Distances like these are not trifles even in this age of swiftly flying aircraft, and any flight, even with the best of planning, may leave you at the mercy of the desert. Not long ago I flew from Morocco over part of the Sahara I had crossed on foot in 1925. We started soon after dawn in beautiful weather, but by ten o'clock a dust storm had blotted out the earth. Minutes later the sun, too, was lost in somber yellow dust above us. For two hours we flew with neither sun nor earth in sight. Eventually we climbed above the yellow cloud and seemed to hang motionless between two worlds—one brilliant blue above, one murky yellow below. But they were separated along a line as sharp as one could draw on paper. Even there, 10,500 feet above the earth, the desert made no compromise between the gorgeous blue of the open sky and the yellow gloom of earth dust. Our navigator took a series of solar observations which showed that in just two hours we had been blown forty miles off course. Not until we were almost over Timbuktu and the Niger River was the air clear enough for us to see the ground.

Only three days before our flight a British passenger plane crossing the Sahara was 600 miles off course! It crashed onto desert mountains. With native help and modern equipment it was nearly a week before the survivors were brought to safety.

Modern means of transportation have shortened the time of many desert journeys, but the automobile and the airplane have not changed the desert or modified the rules for survival in the arid lands. Desert wells and caravan trails are as necessary today as they were two thousand years ago, when only camels and men on foot brought the wealth of the Orient to the western world. Passengers of a crashed plane or a stalled auto, who walk away in search of help, will die of thirst when their water is gone today, just as surely as did the hundreds of gold-seekers who, without adequate water, took the short-cut across the Sonora Desert to California at the turn of the century. In the desert there are no short-cuts to survival, for there is life only where there is water. The desert has made harsh and rigid rules which plants, animals, and men of the desert have learned, but any newcomer can survive by following the example of those already adapted to the rules.

Perhaps it is because of their austerity, their uncompromising climatic sternness, the constant, unrelenting challenge they offer man that deserts have been so important in the past. Great civilizations have flourished on the edges of the desert or along great desert rivers. The Nile, crossing the Sahara in Egypt, the Tigris and Euphrates, crossing the desert north of Arabia, the Colorado, flowing through the desert in the southwestern United States—all have nourished the crops of ancient people and supported large populations. Along every one of these streams ancient people learned to use the river water to irrigate the desert and make crops grow where almost nothing grew before.

The Colorado, Nile, Tigris-Euphrates, all cross the desert and reach the sea only because they start where huge supplies of water give them volume enough to overcome the great stretch of empty dryness. It is their water from the land of plenty which makes the desert bloom. If man falters, even a little, in applying that foreign water, the desert snatches back its land.

For some the desert is a soul bath, washing away the importance of the material world. Something about the emptiness, the infinite distances, the everlasting and unbroken silence stirs their minds to deeper thoughts than are common in lush valleys or rolling, grassy prairies. Whatever the reason, the desert has produced three great religions. Judaism, Christianity, and Islam were all born in the desert; and even today desert people are the great believers of the world. Their sense of right and wrong is clear cut and sharp like the desert line between oasis life and sterile sand.

Desert people also have been great warriors in the past. The Mongol hordes of Genghis Khan swept out of the deserts in Asia and destroyed much of Middle Eastern civilization. That wave of desert-toughened warriors flowed to the edge of Europe itself before it receded; and centuries later other desert armies under the religious banner of Islam conquered all North Africa and Spain before they, too, were stopped. After that, deserts lost their importance to the Western World. Commerce with the Orient found other routes and knowledge of the desert world was lost to Europeans until the Sahara, the Arabian sands, and the Gobi became a world of mystery and fear.

Within the past half-century deserts have again become important to people of the West. During World War I the deserts of the Arabian peninsula became combat areas made famous by Lawrence of Arabia. In World War II the Sahara was a principal battleground, and American deserts became training centers for soldiers scheduled for the Sahara theater of war. The discovery of huge oil deposits in the desert kingdoms of the Near East has brought thousands of westerners to the arid lands and created commerce far greater than anything ever known in the ancient desert world. Even outside the oil-rich desert areas, airplanes carry mail and passengers or rush air freight to every corner of the earth over routes which cross desert wastes. On the ground, oil wells, pipelines, and exploration parties seeking new mineral and oil deposits have made the deserts necessary travel routes and business areas for engineers, scientists, executives, and diplomats. Even mechanics, road-builders, motion picture crews, and soft drink salesmen have business in the desert today.

In spite of this new importance of deserts in the modern world, most people living in temperate climates know little about them. For example, popular opinion generally places all deserts along the equator, or at least mostly in the tropics. The fact is that the northern edge of the Sahara is about as far north as Charleston, South Carolina, or Memphis, Tennessee. The Gobi, the great desert of Mongolia, is as far north as Wisconsin and Montana. All deserts in the northern half of the world are located between 15° north and 45° north, and those of the Southern Hemisphere are no closer to the center of the Torrid Zone.

One common belief about deserts is true, however. They are sparsely inhabited. Although 20 per cent of the earth's land area is desert, only 4 per cent of the population lives in arid lands. This small percentage of the world's population has cloaked its homeland in mystery and wrapped it with mythical terrors of sandstorms and mirages, but with all its real and fanciful dangers the desert is a fascinating place to know. Its barren rocks have majestic grandeur, and its dry stream beds etch patterns on the landscape as lacily intricate as the tracing of a bettle's tracks on dunes of sand. The desert sunsets are not marred by wires or poles or other evidence of civilized conveniences.

If deserts are to bloom again or play an important part in the modern world, we must know them better and understand them as they are today—not only know their beauties and their terrors but their limitations and potentials. Although they vary so much that hard and fast boundaries cannot be described for the desert, a working definition is possible if we recognize that many of the differences between parts of the desert world are degrees of variations and not true differences in character.

On this basis, the desert world may be described as a land where contrasts, contradictions, and spectacular extremes dominate the landscape. It is a place of drying winds and cloudless skies, a place where river beds are dry for years and then, suddenly, are bursting with flood waters which race in torrents for an hour or two before they disappear or spread out into ephemeral lakes, never reaching the sea. It is a land of great daily extremes of heat and cold, a land whose plants and animals have had to develop ways of protecting themselves against these extremes or of avoiding them and limiting their activities to favorable periods only. A place where man is free to be himself and certain that in the eyes of God he is equal to all others of his kind.

II

The Face of the Sahara

THE DESERT LANDSCAPE INCLUDES HILLS, MOUNTAINS, VALLEYS, plains, plateaus, broad basins, river beds, and some huge deposits of sand called dunes. All of these features, even the sand dunes, are found in more humid regions, and all are formed by the same geological processes common to such features in other parts of the world. But in the desert world, arid climate and desert weather have given them a distinctive character.

Some of the desert characteristics are more pronounced in one desert than in another, and some are lacking in certain small desert areas, but the Sahara has everything, at least in some degree. Sand dunes are part, although a very small part, of the Sahara, but they are so spectacular, their formation so interestingly complicated, that they warrant a chapter to themselves.

Inland basin drainage systems are another feature common to the desert world. Some of these are found in the Sahara, but they are more pronounced and better developed in the deserts of Central Asia than elsewhere.

Most features of the Sahara, however, are representative of desert landscape in any part of the earth. When you know those features well, you will recognize them as familiar scenery in any part of the desert world.

The face of the Sahara is flat, but it is slashed here and there by steep-sided canyons and precipitous escarpments. In a few isolated areas, like the Tibesti on the southern border of Libya and the Hoggar region in the Algerian Sahara, the flat surface is pierced by jagged mountains, some of them reaching nearly 10,000 feet above sea level. These highlands were once the headwaters of ancient rivers which cut channels out into the desert. Some of their dry beds can still be seen, but quite as often they are lost or blended into the flat landscape far beyond the mountains. There are also billowy cushions of deep sand—a half dozen large areas scattered over the Sahara from Egypt to the Atlantic Ocean. And, finally, there are wrinkled sheets of sand like the thin sand ridges of Erg Chech in the southwestern Sahara.

The graceful curves of the big sand dunes make beautiful pictures, but sand covers such a small part—only about 10 per cent—of the Sahara, that it would be a distortion to call it a "Sea of Sand." We are safer in making the generalization that the face of the Sahara is flat. Mountains, canyons, and escarpments are scattered over the flat desert just enough to be "exceptions that prove the rule." They only emphasize the flatness of the desert.

When you see the Great Desert on foot or from the back of a slow-plodding "swift-riding camel," it stretches on and on; a flat, gravel floor reaching, it seems, to the end of the world. There a straight-line horizon marks the ultimate jumping-off place you always see but never reach.

I first saw the Sahara from its geographical north rim in 1925. The immensity of the view frightened me. I was planning to cross that vast expanse, and even though I knew thousands had journeyed that way before me, the distance I could see ahead was overwhelming.

There at the edge of the Sahara, I stood on great masses of flat rock turned on edge and crumbling. A few hundred feet below were scattered more domes of crumbling rock and then the flat Sahara stretching on and on. Some irregular blotches of black-green were splashed on the reddish-brown floor. At that distance they looked quite flat, like ink spots in a Rorschach test, but they were really

groves of date palms towering sixty to eighty feet above the desert
floor—with their heads in eternal sunshine as the Arabs say.

More than a quarter of a century later and 500 miles farther east,
I looked down on Hamada el Hamra, the red desert plateau, from
the comfort of a U.S. Air Force Rescue plane, to watch men in a
desert survival field test on that red rock, Sahara plateau. There
the desert was a flat floor, too, but dotted with green-speckled
saucers. The men who had walked forty miles across the plateau
said that they had seen only a couple of the shallow saucers. The
desert is so flat that a slight depression doesn't show unless you are
almost on its rim.

Another time, while crossing the Great Desert by auto, we
traveled all day as if we were rolling over a pebble-covered dance
floor. There was nothing to interrupt our view. Then there came
days when we saw flat-topped buttes and mesas, the remnants of
old plateaus. Canyon walls and plateau escarpments exposed the
flat "layer cake" structure of Sahara bedrock. Even amidst the dune
lands of the desert, the valley floors, or *gassi*, so often followed by
caravans because they are easier to walk on than the more picturesque dunes, are almost perfectly flat.

A geologist would point out that the Atlas Mountains bordering
the Sahara on the north and northwest are a young mountain chain
comparable to the Alps, but the Sahara itself is very old and to be
compared with the Canadian shield or the Siberian plateau where
the oldest rocks in the world may still be seen.

Back when this earth was young, there were mountains which
rose high in parts of the Sahara. During thousands of centuries,
storms and raging torrents, heat and cold, all the forces of nature
beat against those mountains and shattered the rocks. Gradually
the mountain masses were reduced to little stones and fine sand.
Rivers and the wind carried the debris of those shattered mountains
to the ocean floor. Eventually the once-high mountains were reduced to a gently rolling landscape which geologists call a peneplane.
Then great earth disturbances built other mountains, and seas
swept over the plains which had once been high and dry. The new

mountains in their turn met the onslaught of weathering agents and, like all the rocks before them, they too were reduced to sand and mud. Old land, now sea bottom, became covered with this refuse from the new mountains and from lands around the sea. Time and time again the process has been repeated, not only on that part of the earth we call the Sahara, but in every corner of the desert world and in the non-deserts surrounding it.

Sometimes the disturbances warped and twisted the ancient ocean floors as they were heaved above sea level into mountains. Sometimes the rising of the land or the deepening of the ocean basins left still flat the old shallow sea bottoms when they were raised high above the water. The sandstone, shale, and limestone rocks, so common in the world today, all once were the sand, the mud, the sea shells and precipitated lime that formed the bottom of some ancient sea.

All of those ancient seas have been named by the geologists. During the existence of each one there were certain kinds of plants and animals, fish, shellfish, reptiles, amphibians, and birds living on the land or in the sea. When these life forms died, they were sometimes buried in the sea bottom and so became fossils in the rocks later formed by the sand and mud and slime. Because the life forms differed during the time of each named period, these fossils enable the geologist or his close colleague, the paleontologist, to identify the rocks of each period. Each of these periods lasted millions of years, and during that time there were often local and minor variations which can be identified. Taken all together the list of names for the different periods is called the geologic column (see p. 28). These are the foundation for the desert landscape.

Over perhaps half of the Sahara these ancient, sub-basement rocks are covered by a veneer of more recent deposits. There are cretaceous limestones all the way from southern Algeria to Cyrenaica, and the Nubian sandstones of western Egypt belong to the same period. In the desert back of the Egyptian coast and west of the Nile there are some Miocene limestones. Here and there geologists find evidences of mountains weathered down to the roots of their ancient folds, ancient peneplanes showing through the veneer of later rocks—the skeleton, you might say, showing through the skin that covers it.

The Geologic Column and Time Scale

Eras and Dominant Life	Periods	Epochs	Duration in millions of years	Millions of years from the present since each began
Cenozoic (Recent Life) Man Mammals Flowering Plants	Quaternary	Recent Pleistocene	2	2
	Tertiary	Pliocene Miocene Oligocene Eocene	15 20 10 13	17 37 47 60
Mesozoic (Middle Life) Reptiles (Dinosaurs)	Cretaceous	Upper Cretaceous Lower Cretaceous	41 21	101 122
	Jurassic Triassic		31 27	153 180
Paleozoic (Early Life) Giant Ferns	Carboniferous	Permian Pennsylvanian Mississippian	36 47 36	216 263 299
Fish Invertebrates First abundant fossils	Devonian Silurian Ordovician Canadian Ozarkian Cambrian		44 26 42 23 27 79	343 369 411 434 461 540
Proterozoic (Earliest Life)			??	1,600??
Archeozoic (Oldest Known Rocks)				2,000

All of these flat-lying rocks and later sediments of the Sahara were laid down on the bottom of ancient seas. In that respect they are no different from the limestones and sandstones found today in

America or Europe or Asia. Many people find it difficult to believe
that the Sahara really was under the sea once. Yet the truth is that
parts of it were submerged not once but many times, although
other parts have been desert since Silurian time.

A more surprising fact is that the area has risen above sea level
so many times without bending or warping out of shape these flat
rock layers. The Gorge d'Arak, northwest of the Hoggar, and other
straight-walled gorges of the desert give testimony that the rocks
rose slowly, while ancient rivers scoured and cut down their beds
into the rock just about as fast as the rocks were rising.

Today only two rivers worthy of the name, the Nile and the
Niger, reach the sea through the Sahara. They are transients of the
desert, for each gets its water from areas of heavy rainfall far outside the Sahara. The Nile is fed by the White Nile and the Blue
Nile whose headwaters are in tropical highlands far south of Egypt.
The Niger rises only a few miles from the Atlantic Ocean, but it
takes a circuitous route through tropic, rain-soaked regions to the
edge of the Sahara, and then back into the rainy regions before it
empties into the ocean 2,600 miles from its starting point.

The great volume of water collected before it reaches the desert
gives the Niger the momentum to carry it through the Sahara and
on to the sea. Even so, it shrinks so low where it passes through the
desert that in June herdsmen camp and pasture their cattle in the
river bed. Farther south it picks up tributaries from the tropical
highlands of Nigeria. At least one of those streams of tropical
Africa, the Benue, some day will cut through the shallow divide
which separates its headwaters from those of the Lagone which
flows into Lake Chad. Then the Benue will have captured the
Lagone, and Lake Chad, the Sahara's only important fresh-water
lake will become even shallower than it is today, for much of its
present drainage will flow through the captured Lagone and the
Benue to the Niger and the sea.

Lake Chad is in a shallow basin with no visible outlet, but in
contrast to other closed-basin desert lakes it has fresh water. Apparently the water drains underground to another flat basin out in
the desert nearly 500 miles farther north. Europeans have mapped

the Chad in detail many times, but its shore lines, its swampy
borders and its many islands are always different. The whole body
of Lake Chad does not move to a completely new location the way
Lop Nor does in Central Asia, but then Chad covers about thirteen
times as much desert as Lop Nor. It is also somewhat deeper, and
it gets more water from outside the Sahara. Still, if it should lose
the water of the Lagone, then Lake Chad might become a "wandering lake" like Lop Nor.

Although the Sahara covers nearly half a continent it has almost
no drainage that reaches the sea except for those transient rivers
we have mentioned. True, there are some very short streams and a
few gullies that empty into the Mediterranean or the Atlantic. But
even within a few hundred yards of the Mediterranean there are
gullies which start just back of the coast, and when they do carry
water after a rare rain, that water flows deeper into the desert
rather than draining into the near-by sea. Such streams eventually
fill the desert basins with silt and sand, and they make the desert
still flatter by raising the low places instead of carrying the debris
from weathered land far out to sea.

We can, however, still recognize the skeleton of an ancient drainage system across the Sahara: dry river beds which disappear under
sand dunes or run into salt lakes. These stream channels are remnants from the days when rains were heavier and more frequent
than they are today. Those humid days were thousands of years
ago when glaciers covered much of Europe, Asia, and America.
The common name for one of these dry river beds in the Egyptian
Sahara is *wadi*, but in the rest of the Sahara the name is *oued*.

Some of those ancient stream beds started in the Atlas Mountains along the north and northwest edge of the desert and flowed
south. Others began in the Hoggar and Tibesti Mountains to flow
north and south. Old channels are still recognizable over parts of
their length; but where they broadened out into flat valleys the
wind has blown away the fine silt of their flood plains and obliterated the channels, and in other places dunes have blocked the old
watercourses. In some years, when there has been an unusually
heavy rain in the Atlas Mountains, the *oueds* flood to great tor-

rents. Eventually those waters disappear far out in the Sahara, but a few days later and many miles beyond their disappearing point in the desert the plain is covered with white patches which glisten in the sun.

What happens is this: waters from the flood overflow their usual subterranean channel and follow another older, buried course. Along this old channel there is a salt deposit, some of which is picked up by the seeping water and carried out into the desert. When the momentum of the flood is finally lost, capillary action brings part of the salty water to the surface of the desert, and evaporation then leaves the salt to glisten in the sun—a silent witness that water from the Atlas has penetrated 350 or 400 miles into the Sahara.

Another skeleton drainage system is the Oued Igharghar. It has been traced from the Hoggar Mountains of Central Sahara north to the Chott Melrhir near Biskra, an airline distance of six or seven hundred miles and a drop from an altitude of 6,500 feet above sea level to 167 feet below. This is the ancient drainage system that includes Oued Mihero, where European explorers found a live crocodile. One of these explorers, General Tilho, a Frenchman, was told by the natives at Archei on the Ennedi Plateau, southeast of Tibesti, that little crocodiles existed in the area; and writers on the Sahara have ever since accepted these crocodiles as survivors from the days of abundant water in the Sahara's rivers and as proof that the present swamps and old river beds were once connected with the waters of the tropics. I cannot vouch for the crocodiles, but I *have* seen fish in irrigating canals which take their water from tunnels having no connection today with permanent surface rivers.

Although the dry river beds draining south from the mountains of Central Sahara are not as well known as those to the north, it is quite evident that some of them, like the Oued Tamanrasset, were once tributaries to the Niger.

Not all the dry watercourses of the Sahara are "fossils." There are also young stream beds formed by the rare torrential downpours which occasionally flood the desert. These youthful stream beds etch the landscape with delicate patterns. They cut into the dark rock or compact soil and are outlined by blown sand trapped in the channels. The contrast between the sand of stream channels and the rock of the desert floor is so neat and sharp that the stream channels look like drawings in a geology textbook. Some systems are close together and the tiny branches of one system almost touch those of its neighbor. It is easy to see how the next desert flood could enable one system to "capture" its neighbor.

Near the edges of some plateaus are circular buttes, surrounded by channels that radiate in all directions like the spokes around the hub of a wagon wheel. Water falling on these buttes runs off in all directions. But out on the flats of these limestone plateaus, underground waters have dissolved away the rocks below the surface and left round sinkholes. There the drainage channels are also arranged around a center, but that center is a basin which gathers the waters instead of a high mound which disperses them. The sinkhole basins lead to cracks and crevices in the limestone deep below the desert floor, so the water disappears underground as fast as it drains into these holes, and it is seldom on the surface long enough for desert plants to make use of it. These sinkhole features, as far as I know, are found only in distant or inaccessible parts of the Sahara, far from the sea or bordering mountains.

Closer to the edges of the desert, or near inhabited oases, many closed basins, *chotts*, or salt lake beds are found, which collect the water from desert floods. After a storm these may have several inches or even a foot or two of water, but this dries up in a few weeks. Wind carries away the fine silt washed into the basin by the flood, and the place becomes just a smooth spot on the desert floor. Such salt pans are the flattest of all the flat desert floors.

Sometimes, especially if the basin is also fed by seepage water, salt and mud form a crust which is baked hard by the sun. Underneath that crust there may be a foot or two of soft, thick mud, and woe to the automobile that tries to cross that smooth boulevard! The crust may hold it up, but it may also break and drop the vehicle to its axles. Often the edge of the salt flat is as hard as a race track, firm enough for an airplane to use as a landing field, and sometimes only the very center of the area has the underlying soft mud.

Although there are no permanent streams in the Sahara, only a few shallow lakes, and little rainfall, nevertheless much of the face of the desert has been shaped by water. The straight walls of the Gorge d'Arak, north of the Hoggar, the steep-sided canyons in Libya dug by ancient floods, the plateau edges gouged and furrowed with deep rain gullies—all are water cut, all expose the flat layers of the desert bed rock, all are evidence that the flat face of Sahara has a long history from sea floor sediment through millennia of climatic changes to the present time of drying sunshine and rainless decades.

The infinite monotony of desert plains, the uniform height of buttes, mesas, and the straight lines of plateau escarpments have a hypnotic beauty for the desert traveler.

But there is another side to the face of Sahara. In a few regions like the Tibesti and Hoggar, already mentioned, volcanic masses have thrust up through the horizontal beds of sedimentary rocks to form towering mountains; majestic slag heaps from eternal fires below. The mountains of the Hoggar are better known than those of Tibesti because they are on the route of French exploration between the Mediterranean and the Sudan.

I saw the Hoggar many years ago. Other desert landscapes have impressed me too; but nothing has quite equaled the black peaks and slopes of the deep Sahara, and my memory of the first sight of them is still fresh.

All day long we could see mountains far to the south of us. We were traveling about twenty miles an hour, but the long, purple horizon seemed to keep its distance. Then, suddenly, it was closer, as if we had finally brought it into focus with powerful glasses. Such masses of solid rock! Huge domes—bare, black formidable-looking monsters! There were twisted forms and broken massive boulders. Many of the rocks resembled strange futuristic statues and all were massive, black, and terrible. We had planned to climb some of the Hoggar peaks, but the higher domes looked too mean and nasty for us amateurs. They showed no footholds at all when we studied them with binoculars.

A turn on the trail brought us to Tesnou, like a stone pachyderm resting on the desert floor. There was no blending, no gradation between the mountain and the plain. We stepped directly from the swept gravel floor of the desert onto the solid granite dome of the mountain.

Seven years before our visit our guide had spelled out "Tesnou" with small rocks on the desert floor. The letters were still intact. They had not been buried by sandstorms sweeping over them; nor had other small stone markers been disturbed in ten and fifteen years since he had placed them. Out on the plains we had seen the tracks of the first autos to penetrate the Sahara seven years before us. They looked only week-old fresh. Somehow these tracks seemed to help us to grasp the vastness of the ages which had passed since the ugly rocks were thrust through the desert floor.

As we left Tesnou our trail twisted through forbidding black rocks. There were great piles of broken stone heaped high or scattered in masses over the plain; and we knew that thousands of square miles around us were covered with black slag heaps from the infernal blast furnaces. Not a spear of green nor brown; nothing but bare, jagged, black rock jutting up abruptly from the light yellow of a sandy waste, shimmering with the heat.

Now and then the trail would turn and the wind would be directly behind us. In a sudden gust, a blast of hot, stifling dust would hit us like some puff of fire that burns the face of a stoker in the hold of a coal-burner.

We drove for hours through those broken black rocks. Then, late in the afternoon, we saw the famous Peak Illaman. It is like a short-necked bottle standing out above the great mass of Hoggar.

A few days later I rode a camel for fifty miles through those mountains. Much of the time the trail was a little shelf on a steep, rock-covered slope. At camel speed I could really study the landscape. How could there be so much angular black stone without any break in color? At home on the ash heaps and slag piles there are scraggly weeds and clumps of grass, but here on the Hoggar rocks there was nothing. Only when the trail crossed a dry river bed did I see a few scattered clumps of grass.

We made camp in one of those dry drainage channels. For a few minutes after we turned from the trail we saw the sunset. In low-angle light a kaleidoscope of gorgeous colors glided over the black rocks. In the sky, sunset colors were soft pastels and, as so often happens in the desert, the very best display was in the east. I don't know why. Only after a dust storm or, more rarely, when storm clouds gather in the west, have I seen brilliant desert sunsets where they should be; in the western sky.

Only a few minutes afterwards the sun dropped out of sight; it was night. There was no twilight, no border zone between day and night.

That evening we had violated one of the cardinal rules of camping and were bedded down for the night in a *oued*. Guides for desert travelers all warn of sudden floods starting on the mountains and sweeping down into the desert to drown anyone sleeping in their path. We had ignored the rule partly because there was no other place either flat enough or smooth enough to lie down.

We had gotten comfortably huddled in our sleeping bags when the stars were blotted out by great black clouds. Lightning flashed in brilliant streaks to silhouette the grotesque rocks. It was a nightmarish sight with appropriate sound effects, for thunder cracked and rattled in the crags above us. Then the downpour came! Three huge drops of rain—nothing more.

The sky cleared. Stars pierced the blackness. Before I fell asleep the moon came up behind a great blue-black mountain, but the jagged edges of the rock looked soft and rounded in the moonlight. The Hoggar was less harsh to look on in the silver light of an October moon.

The rugged scenery of the Hoggar is an awesome contrast to the flat monotony of Sahara's gravel-covered plains, but even the flat plains have interesting details when you look sharply or scratch the surface just a little. For instance, the black gravels are spread so evenly over the desert surface that they look like some coarse-grained pigment spread with a giant's brush. Their even spacing is the result of wind action, as we shall see in the chapter on the Dunes, but the pebbles themselves are round and water worn. Their rounded shapes tell the story of long water journeys, during which the once-angular stones were tossed and rolled and bumped against each other by countless waves and swift currents until their sharp edges were all worn away.

The pebbles are all black or very dark brown, and they give a somber uniformity of color to the already monotonously flat surface of the desert. But only the upper surface of the pebbles is black. Turn one over and the light gray underside is in sharp contrast to the top. They have lain for so many centuries in one position, exposed always to burning sun, that minute traces of mineral in the stone have been drawn to the surface and oxidized. Then the surface is polished by the wind and the passing blasts of sandstorms. The polish and the oxidized surface together are called "desert varnish." You'll find it on all exposed rocks in the desert, but the contrasting faces of pebbles from the gravel plain are the most easy to recognize.

Some sections of the desert floor are known as desert pavements. These are not the same as the gravel plains. The desert pavements which I have recognized were areas covered with small angular pieces of harder stone than that on gravel plains. Agates, and many forms of quartz and chalcedony once scattered through the soil of the desert mantle are left on the floor when the finer soil is blown away. The shiny stones fall one by one to fit themselves into a smooth mosaic that glistens in the sunlight.

"Sand roses," as the name implies, look like flowers. They are a desert formation that you will find only in the sand of dunes after a hard rain and then only in a region where there exists quantities of gypsum, a soft rock from which plaster of Paris is made. These "roses" vary in size. Some simple ones are no bigger than a quarter. Others are many-petaled and a foot or so across. Apparently rain water dissolves the gypsum sand; then when the water evaporates below the sand dune surface, the concentrated gypsum re-deposits in its characteristic crystal form, which resembles the arrangement of flower petals.

When you are looking closely at the pebbles on the desert floor, you will find some that are split as neatly as if cleaved with an ax. These are called "sun-split stones." The theory is that the intense heat of the desert sun has expanded the pebbles beyond the point of greatest stress which the material can stand, and so it breaks along the bedding planes of the original rock from which the pebble came.

Temperature changes certainly account for much desert weathering. In the Sahara the usual difference between a thermometer reading at just before sunrise and one at about one o'clock is at least 45° or 50°F. Rock temperatures in the sun have been checked as high as 176°F. Such high daytime heat causes the rocks to expand. Then a few hours later they contract in the cool of the night. This daily expansion and contraction—kept up day after day, month after month and year after year—eventually breaks the rocks. Sometimes huge blocks are broken from the mesa tops and escarpment faces. Some of these are further shattered as they fall, and continued daily heat and cold will break them again and again. So, through the centuries, the rocks of the desert are reduced to tiny fragments.

Once, deep in the Sahara, we were sitting just below the crest of a butte in a sort of cave formed by a tumbled mass of huge quartzite blocks. They were bigger than quarried stones but just as angular.

"Do you know anything interesting about this Gara Cheurfa?" I asked my Arab friend. Gara Cheurfa is the Butte of the Cheurfa.

"Yes," he said. "It sometimes shoots. It makes a loud noise like a gun."

"When does the Gara shoot?" I asked.

"Oh, it generally shoots in the fall, when the summer heat is gone. It doesn't shoot every year, though. Only those years when something important happens like the time soldiers took In Salah."

"Gara Cheurfa is a sort of prophet, then," I said. "When is the last time you heard it shoot?"

"This fall. Just a month before you came to us," was the Arab's answer.

Different kinds of rock respond to heat and cold in different ways. The shattered blocks on Gara Cheurfa are red quartzite and the breaks are all angular. Other kinds of rock like granite and the volcanic rock of the Hoggar peaks break off in curving flakes or scales with thin edges and thicker centers. Rocks which scale off in this manner are said to "exfoliate." In the process, thin flakes, splinters, and even sheets loosen from the parent stone and eventually fall away. Dome-shaped rocks and rounded boulders on desert mountains have been shaped by exfoliation, but they are also shattered into angular pieces by the heat and cold.

Desert cloudbursts also break the rocks. When a deluge of cold rain is suddenly dumped down on sun-baked rock, the stone is shattered even more spectacularly than from the monotonous daily heat and cold. Over the centuries all of these forms of desert weathering are at work—breaking down the mountains, the escarpments, the buttes, and the mesas.

In non-desert regions where rain is more abundant and dependable, the refuse from eroding hills is held in place by vegetation, so that the hills are rounded and their slopes more gentle. The landscape in such country becomes rolling, a gradual blending of hills and plains.

Not so in the desert. There the too scanty vegetation cannot hold the smaller particles of crumbling rock against the wind or keep the floods from moving larger stones. Wind sweeps the sand away almost as fast as weathering reduces the rocks to movable grains. The debris of "talus slopes," heaps of broken rock and coarse sand which accumulate at the foot of buttes and mountains, is spread far out on the desert floor by torrential rains. That is why there are so few gentle slopes between desert plain and mountains. This fact, together with the lack of vegetation which could hide the angles between plain and hill, makes the contrast between them as sharp as that of buildings rising from a city street. Abruptly rising mountains are as characteristic of the desert as its flat face.

If you are short of stature, as I am, and have ever faced a Sahara sandstorm, then you know the cutting force of wind and sand. The tiny sharp particles of stone feel like countless needles on your face and bare hands.

Automobile windshields can become frosted glass during the few hours of a sandstorm and a car body sanded down to bright metal. Such terrific force suggests that winds and sand have been the major agents in desert weathering. And, in fact, wind-borne sand has cut fantastic shapes in isolated rocks. It gouges soft stone from between harder layers and "cups" pebbles into many facets to form *dreikanter*—as such pebbles are called. Standing stone columns are undercut until they look like stone mushrooms. The lower stones of some Egyptian temples show the marks of such sand and wind erosion, and this evidence of the cutting action of sand in motion through the air is quite impressive. But in the great scheme of desert erosion it is not as important as other forces like rain or range in temperature.

The real contribution that winds have made in shaping the face of the Sahara is as transporting agents. By moving the finer particles produced by other agents, wind has obliterated river beds, flattened the shores of lake basins, and kept the line sharp between plain and mountains. It has built gigantic hills of sand and filled in hollows. Above all else, it is the housekeeper who lets no soil accumulate on plain or plateau. It sweeps clean the mesa tops and buttes. It keeps the face of Sahara flat.

III

. . . .

. . . .

. . . .

. . . .

. . . . .

The Dunes

ON THE FLAT GRAVEL PLAIN, OR *reg,* OF THE SAHARA TINY
dunes, symmetrical as well-ground lenses, are found after the wind
of a sandstorm dies. They move on with the next hard wind, but
until then they are round, gray dots on the black *reg.* Their small
size, perhaps six to ten feet across and a foot or so high, in comparison with the vast plain around them emphasizes that the desert
world is not a sand world by any means. These small, moving sand
piles are not the picturesque dunes which bar the route for travelers
and appeal to popular imagination, but eventually they will move
on and become a part of the great fixed dunes. Fixed dunes are the
spectacular hills with sinuous, knife-edged crests which tower two
or three hundred feet above the valley floor; in Arabia they are
even six or seven hundred feet high.

There are many kinds of sand deposits, like the barchan dunes,
sif dunes, and sand shadows, to mention a few, but wherever you
find them in the desert world the sand deposits are the most interesting features of the landscape. The dunes of the Gobi and the
dunes of the Sahara have been in their present locations for many
thousands of years. In both deserts prehistoric people camped
among the dunes, because then, as now, those were the areas which
held the moisture and let plants grow. Small animals like rabbits

found food and shelter among the plants and in their turn served
as food for Stone Age man. Neither as old nor as fixed in the landscape as the rocks of ages, still the dunes have lasted in many locations since long before the memory of man or his written records.
Some sand still moves in the desert world, but it is in small amounts
and it soon lands in the fixed dune areas where only the shallow
top layers shift back and forth like ocean waves.

Our first good view of sand dune masses was in October, 1925,
at Ouargla, about 325 miles south of the Mediterranean in the
Algerian Sahara. We had climbed to the top of a butte just for the
view. From that vantage point the familiar image of a "sea of
sand" did not seem farfetched. The landscape *did* look like a
stormy sea suddenly petrified. The crests of waves curling over were
stilled, just on the breaking point before the whitecaps form, making long lines of knife-edged curves on top of rhythmic swells.

Two months later and 400 miles deeper in the desert, we were
on camel back east of In Salah when we rode past great dunes of
yellow sand which contrasted with the distant gray rock cliffs.
Ahead of us was the level desert plain, but a fair east wind carried
away the crests of the dunes on our right. It made the crests stream
out like smoke ribbons from the sharp line of the summits.

"The dunes are smoking," said the guides. "There'll be a change
in weather."

Toward sundown the shadows of our camels stretched long
toward the dunes. Wisps of gauzy clouds were streaks of orange,
red, and rose in the western sky. We reined in our riding camels
and let the others pass so that we could watch them silhouetted
against the distant skyline. For a few minutes, as the sun dropped
below the plain, the camels, their riders, even the pebbles on the
desert floor, were colored copper by the sunset.

The next day was cold and gray. As the guides had predicted
there was a change in the weather. A stiff wind out of the northeast
made our sheepskin coats, buttoned and belted, just right for
warmth. Wind drove sand in snaky streamers across the hard
desert floor just as it blows fine snow over a hard-packed crust.
Sometimes the sand rose a little higher or, when we stumbled

and kicked loose a few more grains, whirled away in clouds. In a little while the air cleared around us. The wind held steady but it carried no dust except that stirred up by our stumbling feet.

Later that day we stopped at a well where a couple of adobe buildings gave shelter for passing caravans. Sand had accumulated near the buildings, but close to the walls there were trenches cleared by wind eddies. When we came into the area, the wind lifted the sand in great clouds a foot or two above the ground, hiding the lower half of our *barraked* camels, the buildings, and the legs of the guides. Again the cloud settled soon after we reduced our movement in the sand. At 4:15 that afternoon we rode into the oasis of In Rhar. Around the palm grove the sand was piled into high, smooth-sloping dunes. We rode between them to an avenue of date palms—tall, slender columns topped by clusters of gigantic ostrich plumes. We had left the dunes, but we had begun to understand a little about the movement and accumulation of wind-blown sand.

The simplest of the sand formations is called a sand shadow. A pebble larger than those around it, a bit of vegetation on the desert floor, anything prominent enough to reach up into the wind and check its force will cause a sand shadow. Stopped in its forward movement by the slowed air stream, the sand builds a tapering little streamer from the obstacle like the low-angled shadows of late afternoon.

When the wind is checked on a larger scale, the sand piles in drifts reaching to the top of the obstacle, perhaps a butte, or mesa, especially if the butte has a cleft or a draw oriented with the prevailing wind. I've seen such drifts as smooth and rounded and as gently sloping as the awning-covered gangplank leading to an ocean liner. Walls or buildings may also start a sand drift, and as the drift grows it causes eddies and direction changes in the wind, which in their turn alter the shape of the drift.

Recently formed dunes can sometimes be distinguished from old dunes by their color. The younger deposit is usually gray or light tan, whereas the older dunes are distinctly yellow or even almost orange. This is because each grain of sand contains some iron, and long exposure to the sun and desert heat eventually changes it to iron oxide and gives the sand the rich color of the old dunes. Sand which only recently has been produced from the parent rocks has not had time to change its color.

There are many kinds of sand, and although the most abundant are grains from the great variety of quartz rocks, they may also include considerable quantities of other minerals like mica, gypsum, limestone, etc. After long exposure to the weather those materials easily soluble in rain water are washed away, or they may be washed deeper into a dune and there act as cement to hold the grains of less soluble sand in a soft stone. But even the hard, almost insoluble quartz sands come from different kinds of rock, such as red, brown, or green chalcedony, black flint, gray chert, or red jasper. There are, accordingly, white sands, dark-red sands, and black sands, whose color does not change with age. Any of these may form bands, lenses, or pockets, if not whole dunes, but their presence is no guide to the age of the deposit because their color does not change.

In the southwestern Sahara there are long sand ridges that stand out sharp against the flat, dark, rock floor. They seem to run for miles in straight, parallel lines so that the desert looks like a gigantic, corrugated washboard. In other areas the sand lies in sheets without any special shape. If the sheets are very deep, the area is slow-going for automobiles. Some of these sheet-like sand beds are well sprinkled with tufts of grass or other vegetation, and as the vegetation grows it traps more sand until solid mounds of sand and plant roots are built up. These are not true dunes because their shape is governed by the plant roots which hold the sand in place and not by the direction of the winds which bring the sand to the mounds.

The type of dune most often seen in photographs and motion pictures is the "barchan." Its crescent shape, with sharp-pointed horns, thick, convex back toward the wind, and steep, concave face on its lee side, is the basic dune form. It is developed by wind blowing continuously from exactly the same direction. In the Egyptian part of the Sahara, where the wind blows from the northeast 303 days of the year, there are barchans in chains fifty or sixty miles long. Barchans are not so numerous in other parts of the Sahara because winds are not as constant as in that section of Egypt. In Algeria, wherever the barchan form exists, it is located below extensive plains on which very little sand is found. The type is well known in the Arabian Desert and many of the most spectacular recent photographs in magazines have been made in that area. The barchan has such a beautiful shape and such graceful curves that it is always photographed wherever it is found in any part of the desert world, but its perfect form is the exception among dunes rather than the typical. When you do find a symmetrical, crescent-shaped sand dune, you may be sure that the prevailing winds are also persistent winds.

Another common dune form is the "sif." This is developed from the typical barchan when strong winds or sandstorms come from a different quarter than the less violent prevailing wind. Wind from the new direction acts on one wing of the barchan to distort it, or to start it toward a new barchan shape. When the wind again returns to the prevailing direction, the distorted shape adds a new influence to the sand flow. The end result is the sif dune, an elongated hill with a sinuous crest.

The great dune areas, where sand masses are deep and cover many square miles, are called *ergs*. These are true "seas of sand" with waves on the surface. Like the waves of the sea, the surface curves of dune areas change their form as strong winds change direction, but the mass of the dune retains its fixed position.

In among the great sand hills are flat, sand-free floors, called *gassi*. They are followed by the caravans whenever possible and each one is known or easily recognized by desert men. When one sees dunes smoking or feels the sharp sting of a thousand sand grains driven by a sandstorm, one wonders how these broad floors among the dunes can stay open year after year, but they do.

Newcomers to the desert are generally hard to convince that the big dunes don't move. They point to abandoned date groves with trees half-buried in sand, or to ruined houses with sand accumulating along the walls. They can see the sand blowing from the dune tops and look at "snow fences" of palm leaves which gardeners place along the tops of dunes to guide the shifting grains. Desert roads are clear one day and blocked with sand the next. Naturally the desert tenderfoot believes that all these facts prove that the dunes march straight before the wind across the desert to the sea. He may have read, too, that dust from the Sahara has been identified in the Cape Verde Islands nearly 500 miles west of the African desert.

In contradiction, there is a whole series of facts which show that the main outlines of topography in the great dune areas are static. The *ergs* are fixed features of the desert scene. The surface of the great hills may change a little with shifting winds, but hundred-year-old maps of the Great Ergs are still usable. A guide will identify the big hills of sand, or the *gassis* between, as easily as an Alpine guide will recognize the peaks and valleys of the mountains. Even wells have seldom been lost under dunes. If a well is left open it might fill with sand, but a stone slab or planks across the well mouth will let the sand blow over it and protect even a shallow well.

Many oases, like that of Beni Abbes, lie on the edge of the great sand sea. It was as free of sand when I flew over it in 1952 as it was when I rode my white camel into it in 1926.

The medieval city near the stronghold, Ksar Charaba, in Fezzan, is surrounded on three sides by dunes of the Erg de Mourzouk. Both the stronghold and the city have been abandoned for a hundred years, but there so little sand has accumulated that you can still walk the ancient streets. Sedrata, just outside of Ouargla in Algeria, was destroyed in the eleventh century but you can still identify the town. If the dune had shifted, there would be no trace of Sedrata today.

The massive sand dunes of the desert world are fixed today, but if we go back before historic records we can see that they were not always in their present locations. Great rivers once flowed in channels now blocked by dune masses, and careful study of ancient shores, such as the shores of Oued Saoura in northwestern Sahara, clearly indicates that the Western Erg, now fixed in its present location, was, before the ice age, far to the east. In the distant past, the great dunes were small, active or live dunes similar to those moving today about thirty or thirty-five feet a year.

These slowly shifting heaps do not yet belong to the great dune masses which justify the name "sea of sand" and have been fixed in their present locations since the last geological epoch of heavy rains. The few sand masses which move are not large and are the result of new supplies of sand generated upwind.

It is this new material, let loose to the wind by newly made garden plots, by a road across the desert, or by some other disturbance of the stabilized desert surface, which piles up around buildings and over the course of many years may bury isolated palm trees. Such deposits move on and in a few years uncover the obstacle, so that eventually the new sand will be blown into the fixed dune area. If you look carefully at the dunes that have stood for ages next to an oasis, you will note they have the rich color of old dunes, while the sand moving in from new sources is the light gray of recently broken rock or material which has not been exposed to weather. One of the most common sources of such new material is a flood rushing down from the mountains. These torrents carry sand and silt to stream beds and desert deltas, and when the deposits dry out, they are prey to hard winds until they have become stabilized.

The moving dunes are found on open plains where there are no obstacles to stop them. When the sand masses, reaching basins or valleys excavated by ancient rivers, encounter the irregular terrain of those low places and are trapped, the flat floors between "islands," or irregularities of the valley floor, continue to be swept free of sand and form the *gassi* between the dunes.

Besides such obstacles which trap the sand, moisture accumulating in the low places holds the sand against the wind. It sometimes leaves a crust of mineral matter which also keeps the wind from disturbing the surface. Where there is enough moisture for plants to utilize, their foliage checks the wind action, and when the leaves dry up the roots continue to net the loose grains of the dune and hold them against the wind.

Eventually, the tops of the dunes dry out and the sand grains can be pushed around by the wind. They move from crest to crest of the sand waves, and back again with changing winds; and the finer particles of dust eventually move on out of the desert area. The surface sand moves but the dunes are fixed.

Perhaps this sounds like quibbling, but desert specialists are pretty touchy on the subject. Perhaps the reason we are so sensitive is because of the popular belief that sandstorms "pick up the dunes and plunk them down on unsuspecting caravans—to bury alive the men and camels." People have died in sandstorms, and indeed whole caravans have perished in them, but not because they were buried alive. They lost their way in the storm, their water supply was exhausted, and they died of dehydration.

Sandstorms, of course, are dramatic. They strike suddenly. Your first warning may be a thick wall of blackness rolling toward you across the plain. This black cloud is composed of the coarse sand grains and the fine dust particles of weathered rock from desert buttes and mountains. In a moment every unprotected part of your body feels the sting of a thousand needles jabbing against your flesh. Fine particles penetrate your clothing and drive into your watch and your camera. Nothing seems secure enough against the penetrating wind-driven dust. But even a violent storm will rarely leave more than a few inches of accumulated sand at any one point.

The driving sand may settle or drive on past you in a little while, and it never flies much over six feet above the ground. This isn't true of dust, the minute particles of broken rock which were stirred up by the storm. Dust can fly high and blot out the sun for hours. It may even dim its brightness for days.

On a flight to Timbuktu we began to hit dust just as we were over Gara Cheurfa. I happened to look straight down and recognized the butte, but already the dust was so thick that I couldn't see the village or the palm grove half a mile from the butte. A few minutes later we were in the yellow cloud. Finally the pilot climbed to 10,500 feet, and we floated on top of a yellow sea.

Although we flew for several hours in that "sandstorm," the fine desert powder caused no damage to the motors. After the flight they were torn down and checked, but the high-flying dust was apparently as soft as the talc mothers use to dust their babies' tender skins. This is quite in contrast to the blast of sand on the desert floor, which will polish off the finish of automobiles and makes frosted glass of windshields.

The fine dust may float for days high above the desert, and during that time sunsets and sunrises are most beautiful, but eventually the air clears and the dust settles, sometimes far from the desert. This settled dust is called loess. It forms thick beds of clay in many parts of the world. I have seen it in China, in Mississippi, and in Europe. Unlike water-deposited clay, the loess beds weather in straight-sided cuts such as the famous sunken roads around Natchez, Mississippi.

Once in Tunisia, on the edge of the Sahara, we drove our truck up a valley that had been inhabited by the early Romans. The old truck could hardly pull through the soft soil. The wheels made straight-sided ruts only two or three inches deep, but our progress was agonizingly slow. We had never encountered anything that packed so well but was so hard on the motor. Eventually we drove back over the same route. As long as we could keep our wheels in the identical tracks made on the way out, we sped along as if on a boulevard; but the least deviation slowed us and made the motor labor. Finally a tiny whirlwind lifted the dust into a spiral. Then I recognized the formation. It was a loess valley. Fine powdered clay from desert duststorms was deposited on that valley floor as evenly as one could spread paint on a porch. In its fresh, unconsolidated form, loess held the straight-sided track of our wheels as free of slopes as the thick, well-packed deposits at Natchez laid down by the glacial winds many thousands of years ago.

Dust and sand are moved by the wind in vastly different ways. The fine dust is so light that it floats in the air and rises thousands of feet above the desert floor. At high altitudes winds may transport the powdery stuff hundreds of miles before it finally settles to the floor of some distant basin or even to the ocean floor. Sand, on the other hand, moves along the desert floor in an entirely different manner.

Studies in different parts of the world have brought to light many interesting facts about sand and the movement of sand. One of the most complete studies was made in Britain by R. A. Bagnold.* He experimented with various sizes of sand grains in wind tunnels and checked his results by sandstorm observations in the Egyptian Sahara. His findings summarize the facts about sand dune growth and the travels of sand grains in the desert.

Rocks can be broken into smaller and smaller pieces by temperature changes, but this process cannot reduce the rocks to grains small enough for the wind to move. Apparently the sands of the desert reach wind-movable size by water action. Rare rain storms scour the talus slopes of buttes and mountain sides; they tumble rocks and pebbles along stream beds grinding the particles smaller and smaller. When the storm waters finally sink into the desert, a new supply of sand is left behind for the winds to play with and to smooth or round the grains still more.

Most people think of wind as air moving steadily in one direction at a time, but in reality it is a very complex movement with eddies and crosscurrents going up, down, sideways, and backwards within the mainstream. If sand particles are so tiny that complex air movements can overcome the pull of gravity, they are called dust and will stay in the air for long periods. Sand grains are heavier. The force of gravity pulls them to the ground soon after they have been lifted into the wind.

When dust particles settle to the ground, they are trapped, because the wind cannot pick up individual dust grains. It can move groups of dust particles, such as the projecting heaps on the sharp edges of footprints or automobile tracks.

Most of us have noticed that when a strong wind blows over a dust-covered road, no dust flies until a passing automobile breaks the surface. The dust cloud follows the car, but the wind raises no

* R. A. Bagnold, *The Physics of Blown Sand and Desert Dunes.* (William Morrow and Co., New York, 1941). The balance of this chapter is based largely on Bagnold's work.

dust from the undisturbed deposit because it has quickly smoothed off the sharp edges left by the passing car. On the edge of the desert a flock of sheep or a camel caravan may disturb the surface in the same way.

Sand grains do not begin to move until the wind reaches a speed of eleven miles an hour, but at that speed the grains begin to roll along the ground. As they gain speed, a few grains bounce off the ground. When they bounce into the air stream, the wind pushes them forward a little, but they soon fall back to the ground. If, in their fall, they hit sand-covered ground, they splash other grains into the air. When they hit rock or hard pebbles, they themselves, bound back into the air stream and are carried forward another jump. When the falling sand grains kick up other grains, these in turn are carried forward until they, too, fall back. In other words, the sand grains act like ping-pong balls driven by the wind, bouncing over hard surfaces and kicking up other "ping-pong balls" when they fall on a surface covered by others of their kind. The bouncing grains are said to be "in saltation" or to move "by saltation."

When a falling grain splashes into other grains, only a few are kicked up into the air far enough to begin saltation on their own, but many others are pushed ahead. Bagnold's experiments show that a bouncing sand grain has force enough to move a pebble 200 times its weight and six times its diameter! So while the lighter bouncing grains are speeded on their way by the wind, the coarser and heavier grains are being pushed jerkily along the surface of the desert floor. This jerky movement is called "surface creep," and it accounts for one-fifth or even one-quarter of sand movement. Saltation moves the other three-quarters to four-fifths of the material.

Surface creep produces sand ripples because of its uneven or jerky movement. The grains pile up into ridges so that the lee slopes become steeper and high enough above the trough to be noticed. Ripples become ridges when the wind is too feeble to move the coarse grains which have been pushed to the top by creep. Ridges are commonly two feet high and sixty-five feet apart. They are, of course, at right angles to the wind and extend for considerable distances in nearly straight parallel lines.

When the bouncing grains move over a surface covered with pebbles or grains too large to be splashed up by the falling sand, the surface creep stops. The sand grains striking pebbles bounce higher into the wind, upward eddies check their fall, they approach suspension, and are carried forward farther at each bounce. These form the sand cloud that moves over the desert at the beginning of a sandstorm and hides the lower parts of buildings and the legs of men and camels. It is also the true sandstorm which cuts away the lower parts of desert rocks and concrete signposts. This cutting will reach higher on a gravel plain or rock plateau than in a sandy region. The bouncing grains are not generally lifted more than forty inches above the desert floor, but some sand cutting shows as high as six feet on desert rocks. Where evidence of the sand blast is higher than that, it indicates that the cutting was done before the desert floor was worn down to its present level.

Any wind will drive sand faster over a hard or pebble surface than it will over sand-covered ground, because more grains are bounced into the air from sand and they all take energy for their movement out of the wind. This loss of energy slows the wind and accordingly allows sand to fall and accumulate over sand, while the same wind strength would be able to move the sand across a hard surface.

Increased wind strength rapidly speeds up the movement of sand. The finer grains are carried first. If the wind holds steady, as it often does, these smallest grains are soon blown away and the surface is stabilized—that is, it is left covered only by grains too large to be moved by that wind. The fine grains lying between or below the immovable ones are protected from the wind. If the wind becomes strong enough to move the next largest grains, these are carried away until the surface is again stabilized. Stabilization means that both saltation and surface creep have ceased for the given wind strength.

In the desert there are three ways in which wind deposits accumulate. The first is sedimentation, or the gentle falling of light particles such as the deposit in the loess valley mentioned earlier. The second is accretion, caused when the wind slackens, or the surface over which it blows changes, and allows the moving sand grains to stop in the nearest hollow or protected position available. The third method of deposition is encroachment. When the moving sand meets an obstacle such as an abrupt step—either a step up or down—the grains in saltation move over the obstacle but the surface creep is halted. On a sand dune, grains reaching the top edge roll over and fall down the slip face where they are protected from the bouncing grains passing over the dune crest. This is why the coarse grains are found on the downwind side of a dune, instead of at the top as in the ripples.

Every unevenness of the surface over which the wind moves causes changes in its surface direction, as well as changes in the angles at which saltating grains strike. Such uneven spots in a sand surface are accentuated by saltation and may be the start of a ripple.

The desert surface is never composed of *only* fine sand unprotected by coarser grains, but it is often a storage place for sand on its way to the dunes. Every pebble which has been uncovered by gentle winds and sticks up above the plain enough to form a wind shield protects the sand around it. The next strong wind may remove the stored sand in a few minutes and so create another stable condition. As the wind slackens, a new supply of sand will come to rest, to be stored in the wind shadow of the pebbles ready to supply the next sandstorm. When the upwind sand supply is eventually exhausted, the gravel plain is swept clean.

A strong sand-laden wind moving over a uniformly rough surface tends to deposit the sand in long strips. Such a chance sand patch grows from each side, as well as at the windward edge, because the wind hitting it is slowed and the sand stream is split. The result is a series of long, parallel strips of sand, the desert between being swept as clean as a dance floor. In Egypt such strips have been formed by a sandstorm on a featureless plain, and some extend as much as one-third of a mile. I once saw these strips northwest of Timbuktu on a perfectly flat desert floor.

This type of dune may disappear after a storm, because the wind, no longer saturated, will scatter the fine sand, or perhaps small pebbles from the area may creep over and bury the sand. It is possible, of course, that several storms in rapid succession may build up the sand strips thick enough to outlast other weather and become a chain of dunes.

Dunes build up to a knife-edged crest because the sand accumulates on the windward slope until that slope is so steep the wind cannot follow over its edge. Then the sand accumulates still faster. Eventually the slope is so steep that it passes the angle of repose and the sand avalanches down the slip face on the side opposite the dune's windward slope. The mass of sand falling away leaves a sharp break. The slope then builds up again until the mass again breaks loose. Sand grains bouncing over the sharp edge of the dune are also trapped in the slack air below where they fall onto the slip face and help advance the dune.

If the wind shifts to blow from the opposite direction, or against the sharp edge of the dune, it rounds off the top and destroys the picturesque knife edge. It may, of course, continue in the new direction long enough to make a new slip face and knife edge.

Bagnold says that the dunes in the Egyptian Sahara reach 325 feet in height, and some dunes in Libya are reported to be 600 feet high; but apparently the highest sand piles in the world are found in Iran, where they reach 700 feet from base to summit. In general the base of a dune is six times its height.

Dune masses have definite patterns controlled by long-period winds and they are little influenced by local features of the terrain. If a traveler knows the long-term pattern of prevailing and secondary winds, he can usually orient himself in a big dune region, especially if he is traveling by plane. But Bagnold found an area in northeast Africa where dune groups only a few miles apart differed in direction as much as fifty degrees.

Some observers, noting the fixed directions of dunes in a few localities, have assumed that they followed global prevailing winds. These observers suggested that airplane pilots be taught that sand dunes were weather vanes for westerly winds. The dunes are indeed

excellent weather vanes for their particular locality, but a pilot, familiar with dunes in the Algerian Sahara, would be quickly lost if he assumed that the dunes in Egypt were on the same wind system. Eventually the map makers may designate dune areas with symbols to indicate their orientation, but at the present time there are too few detailed surveys of dune regions to rely on world maps or flight charts for their orientation.

Apparently the reason for the change in orientation of the dunes is only a slight difference between the strong and gentle winds. Even a little shift in their relative velocities will let them take each other's place and change the dune pattern.

The longest and largest dune chains are found where the desert is open and featureless. These chains may be from thirty-five to sixty-five miles long. Each chain is broad at the windward end and tapers to a point downwind. There may be several such chains in a group, but each chain retains its individual form. This pattern of the big chains seems to be quite general because maps of the dune areas in Egypt, the French Sahara, and Australia are all much alike. This similarity is more remarkable when one realizes that there is no vegetation in the Egyptian area and considerable plant cover in Australia. Also the Australian dunes are younger, much smaller, and their corridors are sand-free, while the corridors among the older Egyptian dunes are sand-covered.

Sand dunes are not built of sand grains of uniform size. Winds of different speeds sort the grains as efficiently as standard mesh screens could, but the winds vary in strength so that a dune is built up by thin layers of different-sized sand. These layers are not visible to the eye in their natural state, but they can be recognized if part of the dune is moistened and carefully excavated. The water will hold the layers intact long enough to be observed and identified.

Such a study shows that the windward side of the dune, built up by saltation and creep, is composed of compact, hard layers where each grain has fitted snugly into its safe resting place. Experienced desert auto drivers develop a sixth sense at locating this hard surface sand. The slip face of the dune, built up by avalanching sand, is soft and loose. The grains are placed pell-mell, with plenty of air space between them. Deposits of this sort form the desert quicksands or dry quicksands, into which an auto can drop to the axles as quickly as if the road had fallen from under the wheels.

This laminated structure in one part of the dune and pell-mell deposit in other parts explains the uneven distribution of dune vegetation, as well as spotty distribution of moisture which so puzzles many observers.

When a shower wets a dune area, water falling on the compact sand doesn't sink in very far but runs sideways and stays close to the surface where it soon evaporates. Water which reaches the slip face of a dune runs down the old cut faces left by sand avalanches, and so goes deep into the loose sand to accumulate below the level affected by changing temperature and evaporation.

Desert natives know that moisture accumulates in some places and not in others, although they do not know all the reasons. Immediately after a shower someone will dig down in the right location to see if the sand a foot or so below the surface is wet. If it is, he knows that in due time these patches will sprout green plants and there will be pasture for the camels.

Sand is a poor heat conductor and even the great daily extremes in desert temperature are not felt eight or ten inches below the sand surface. Above that, depth air between the sand grains is changed regularly. During the heat of the day, the air in this upper layer expands and rises out of the sand; and at night, cold dry air is sucked back in. It takes but a little while after a shower for the upper layer of sand to lose its moisture, but that which sinks below the area of daily change will remain for very long periods.

It often puzzles desert travelers to dig down in the sand to a wet layer and then discover, as they dig deeper, that the sand is again "dry as a bone." Such wet patches are often far above the desert floor and still farther above the water table. Some observers have supposed that desert sand holds some secret power and that it can draw water up fantastic distances by capillary action. The surface tension of sand grains is capable of lifting moisture about 15½ inches, but that is far too little to account for the damp spots in dunes which occur scores of feet above the water table.

Others have assumed that deep water evaporated into air between the sand grains above it, that this saturated air then moved up, and the moisture condensed at higher levels. The only source of energy for such action would be the daily changes in temperature, and anyone who has left a thermometer buried a foot below the sand surface knows that sand at that depth just is not affected by the wide daily fluctuations in temperature.

As long as desert winds can reach individual sand grains of movable size, then the dune, the ridge, or the tiny ripple will move forward. If the wind direction is reversed, the sand deposit will come back. But if the sand becomes permanently damp, as may happen when it fills an old river basin; if vegetation gets a start; or even if 10 per cent of the surface is covered by pebbles too large for saltation to move—then the sand deposit will become fixed. These pebbles or vegetation which "kill" a dune may, of course, be covered by later sand deposits. This new layer will continue to "live" as long as the upwind supply of sand lasts, but the body of the dune remains fixed like the great *ergs* of the Algerian Sahara.

Whistling sands and booming dunes are rare sounds. At least, the booming of desert dunes is so rare that it has entered the realm of legend. Desert people have called it the song of a siren who lures the traveler into the waterless wastes to his death, and there are those who believe the sound, which suddenly shatters the desert silence, is the voice of an angry *jinni* expressing displeasure.

Whistling sands are found on some beaches. Bagnold reports hearing them on the island of Eigg in the Hebrides and also on the coast of North Wales. I have myself heard the sand whistle as I walked along the beach at Gulf Shores in Alabama.

The beach sands seem most likely to whistle close above high-water level, and when they have just dried after a rain. At Gulf Shores these conditions were met in the snow-white sand. The material there is apparently pure quartz, at any rate it is used in carload lots by one of the glass manufacturers.

Bagnold says that the shore sands whistle in "a frequency between 800 and 1,200 vibrations per second if there is a rapid disturbance of the dry top layer, such as is caused by walking over it, sweeping it quickly with the palm of the hand, or plunging a stick vertically into it." When whistling sands are removed, they soon lose their singing voice. Their quality varies, but all "singers" are in better voice immediately after being washed and dried. At least the sound is louder and more easily made at that time.

Bagnold says that he heard the booming dunes in Egypt start suddenly in the still of the night, and that the sound was so loud it drowned out his voice so that he had to shout to be heard. The first disturbance set others going—with a note so close to the first sound "that a slow beat was clearly recognized." This weird chorus was continuous for more than five minutes; then "silence returned and the ground ceased to tremble."

The sound somewhat resembled that of an airplane in steady flight, and it was produced in the lower part of a sand avalanche on the slip face of a high dune. Sand may start slipping spontaneously during or after a sandstorm, if the slope is unstable, because of surface temperature changes. It may also be started by a push from a foot or hand, and Wilfred Thesiger was able to start a dune to singing in that way when he was in the Empty Quarter of Arabia. The booming starts when the front of the sand avalanche begins to be slowed by a change in the dune slope near the bottom and the sand from above is telescoped into it.

Attempts to learn why and how the sands of beach and dunes sometimes boom and sometimes sing have found only partial answers. Singing sands from various sites have been collected and compared, but they seem to have no observable characteristic in common. In fact, the samples from booming dunes do not appear to differ from sands of dunes that do not sing.

Generally the whistling beach sands are clean and free of dust, but those from the booming dunes in the Libyan desert are dirtier than average—some grains were even rough with red iron oxide.

What is it that sets some rare dune avalanches to roaring like thunder, while others are silent? Do the moving quartz grains generate tiny charges of electricity which accumulate? Do the sand grains slipping over each other develop varying air volume between them? Does air pressure play a part in setting up vibrations? Do the sands moving at a critical speed set the grains to vibrating in unison? Or do the desert *jinns* strike the dune with their fairy wands and set the sands singing?

Only 10 per cent of the desert is sandy. Statistically this is not a very impressive figure; but the grace and beauty of the sand dunes, the unsolved mystery of their noises, the complexity of their formation, and their ability to trap and hold moisture for vegetation—all these make the dunes one of the most interesting and important features of the desert world.

IV

. . . .

. . . .

. . . .

. . . .

. . . . .

The Gobi Basins

ALL DESERTS DO NOT LOOK ALIKE, ALTHOUGH SOME DESERT FEA-
tures are duplicated in many parts of the world. I remember that
when I looked at the deepened, twisting channel of an ancient river
in the Libyan Sahara, which geologists call entrenched meander
gorges, I thought, "These are replicas of the famous Goosenecks of
the San Juan River in the American desert—almost, but not quite."

In the Negev of Israel there is a desert pavement which is almost
the duplicate of one from which I collected colored pebbles in the
Gobi of Mongolia—but not quite as flat and with more vegetation.
The sand dunes of Death Valley make perfect stand-ins for the
dunes of Arabia—until you look at the vegetation. Flat-topped
mesas, abruptly rising buttes, mountains, stream channels that lose
themselves in the desert plain or end in dead-end salt lakes, and
long, empty views to distant horizons are common to all deserts.
But each desert of the world also has its own individuality, and, to
me, the Gobi is a land of basins.

Out there in remotest Asia, between Tibet and Siberia, is a vast
undrained region where mountain streams lose themselves in desert
plains or end in shallow salt lakes, but almost never reach the sea.
High mountains bound the area and shut out moisture from all the
seas. Within this mountain-bounded area are five great basins:

the Ala Shan and Ordos, the Tarim, Dzungaria, the Valley of the Lakes, and the Gobi. All are deserts and most of them are austerely bleak. Each is separated from the others by one or more mountain ranges, but one basin, the Central Gobi, joins them all by broad, lowland gateways. Perhaps that is why so many people refer to any desert of Central Asia as the Gobi.

If you isolate the five basins and their adjacent mountain ranges on the map of Asia, the area looks somewhat like the side view of a medieval jester's boot, with its pointed toe and flaring, fluted top. The rounded heel is to the south; the toe to the northeast; and the fluted upper, which would extend high on the jester's leg, is composed of alternating mountains and basins flaring out to the west. Bounded by mountains, the Gobi Basin makes the foot and ankle. The Ala Shan Desert, with the Ordos and big bend of the Yellow River forms the heel. The upper part of the boot is the Valley of the Lakes, the Dzungari Basin, and the Tarim Basin which includes the Takla Makan Desert and the Turfan Depression. The deepest point of this depression is 890 feet below sea level, and only about 100 miles away, the top of Topotar Auliye towers 18,000 feet above the sea. This is one of the widest ranges in altitude anywhere in the world within so short a distance.

The whole series of desert basins and mountains is a geographical unit, but this chapter will emphasize that section, called the Gobi, which is located within the political state of Outer Mongolia, now called The Mongolian Peoples Republic, and part of Inner Mongolia which is claimed by Red China.

Geologists call it a huge warped saucer of desert and semi-desert country, 600 miles across and 1,000 miles from northeast to southwest. However, it is also a plateau as well as a basin; from all sides it is approached over a mountain rim.

In 1928 I came into the Gobi on the south, or China side, with Roy Chapman Andrews and the Central Asiatic Expedition. We had a Chinese Cavalry escort from Kalgan, China, to the edge of Mongolia, but the horses traveled only about five miles an hour. We couldn't be discourteous and race past our "hosts," so our motors labored and boiled during the whole long drive to the edge of the plateau 5,000 feet above sea level.

In the north, up where the drainage cuts through the Arctic Divide, the plateau is 6,000 feet in altitude, but in the middle, at the bottom of the saucer, the Gobi is only 3,000 feet above the sea.

This gentle, general slope of six feet per mile to the southwest is important to the geologist, for it tells much about the geologic processes which shaped the region; but to the eye of a traveler, the Mongolian Plateau is a rolling, upland country, so far to the horizon in any direction that he feels lost in empty space. It is by no means a level plain, however, and the horizon is seldom the straight unbroken line so characteristic of the Sahara.

Within the general saucer-like depression of the Gobi there are several smaller warped basins called *talas*. These are separated from each other by broad rolling hills. *Talas* is a Mongol word meaning "open country between the mountains."

The *talas* include still smaller, weathered hollows called *gobis*. These are another prominent characteristic of Mongolia, and American scientists chose the Mongol word *gobi* for them because it means "flat desert floor." These *gobis* range from little depressions 200 yards in diameter up to important basins 100 miles across. In depth, typical *gobis* vary from 20 feet to 400 feet. Some of them are nearly level floors; some are gently rolling; and still others are studded with granite boulders, rock outcrops, and deeply dissected badland exposures. In the bottoms of many such basins are salt lakes and *playas*. In others there are sand dunes. Some of these dunes are modern and the sand is loose. Others are ancient dunes and the sand is as compact as soft sandstone.

This list of the features in the Mongolian desert may make it sound like a varied landscape, but as a desert traveler I got a very different impression. It is often so far between the various features that the general impression is one of monotony, and this impression is further emphasized by the absence of trees or bushes. Even the rocks and hills are so old, weathered, and rounded that they seem to increase the sameness of the plateau instead of giving it contrast.

Lack of those features which would give scenic contrast makes it possible for automobiles to travel in all directions, for an expedition can detour the few sections of difficult terrain or occasional obstacles so easily that our hunters even chased antelope at forty or fifty miles an hour and rarely had a breakdown.

There are not many lakes in the Gobi, and those few become more rare as you travel south and west. In fact, open water of any kind is scarce. Except in the north, real rivers are non-existent but there are many short river beds which carry water for a few days after a storm. These all start near the rim of the basin. Sometimes they lose themselves at the foot of steep slopes, and sometimes they reach a salt lake or *playa;* but all of them flow toward one of the numerous basins or *gobis*. Accordingly, the drainage pattern resembles the spokes of many wheels rather than the veins in a maple leaf, the pattern most common in non-desert parts of the world.

After a hard rain out on the plateau, away from its mountain rim, the landscape is dotted with small ponds. Every little hollow collects the runoff and holds it until it either sinks into the ground or is lost by evaporation. But there is never enough continued rainfall to let these ponds overflow and unite with others to form a connected drainage system. There are a few exceptions to the wheel-and-spokes pattern. In the far northwest, the Tola River gathers its tributaries and flows through the city of Ulan Bator (Urga). Eventually these waters reach the Arctic Ocean. In the northeast, another river, the Kerulean, collects a few small streams and flows east. Some years it reaches Dalai Nor, an inland lake, but in other years the waters sink into the desert before they reach the lake. In times of unusually heavy rains the lake waters are drained into the Hailar-Argun system and flow through the mighty Amur to the Pacific Ocean.

In the south the Ala Shan Desert Basin has one transient, the Yellow River, which, like the Nile, the Niger, and the Colorado, gets its volume of water from outside the desert but flows through the arid basins to the sea.

The desert streams of Central Asia have two high-water seasons. The first is in the spring, when melting snows in the highlands fill the drainage systems. The second is in summer following the rains. This summer high-water generally has greater volume because the desert has more rain than snow.

Lakes are not as scarce as real rivers in the Gobi, and in the eastern part of the plateau we saw many salt lakes. They are usually shallow and their size varies as the rainfall changes from year to year. One of them actually dried up and disappeared while our topographer was mapping its outlines. Even the fairly large lakes are completely dry at times, but salt deposits mark their location and at a distance the salt may deceive even experienced travelers. These dried lakes, or the dry shores of those still containing some water, are sources of salt for the native Mongols. Some are such good sources that they supply salt for export to China.

The Valley of the Lakes in the far northwest has several enclosed basins with large permanent lakes. This valley has the same basin structure as other parts of the Gobi, but there is more moisture. Accordingly, more of the lakes are connected by rivers so that the wheel-and-spokes drainage pattern is supplemented by some leaf-vein drainage systems.

Although open water is scarce in Mongolia, the natives have dug wells all over the country. Along the main caravan trails they are found every ten or fifteen miles, and pasture lands between the trails are also supplied with wells. Every trail in Mongolia will lead you to a well sooner or later, and many trails will lead you *only* to a well.

In this land of rolling hills and flat-floored basins, the sculptured badlands, granite boulders, rock outcrops, level-topped buttes and mesas are all readable pages in the history of the earth. They tell the story of how Mongolia and the Gobi came to look as they do today.

Two distinctly different groups of rock foundations are easily recognized. The first group is called the "later sediments," and it includes all those deposits which lie nearly flat and rest in the "Gobi" basins. All of these later sediments have been deposited since the Jurassic period, 155,000,000 years ago. In many parts of the desert they have been warped and faulted, that is, subjected to some uplift or sinking but not to mountain folding. The second group of rock foundations is the "old rock floor." These older rocks are buried beneath the later sediments but are visible as outcrops in large areas. Wherever you see them, they are folded and often cut by igneous rocks which were forced through them as hot, molten masses. Contact with the heat and pressure from the igneous rocks has, of course, metamorphosed or changed the character of the surrounding formations.

In other words, the floor of Mongolia is a very complicated series of rocks which belong to geologic ages ranging from the Archean period (at least 1,800,000,000 years ago) to Jurassic time. The ancient rocks have been folded and raised into mountains many times, and since the last mountain-forming disturbance (in the Jurassic period) extensive weathering has leveled the peaks and ridges. During that weathering, broad rivers carried quantities of material to ancient seas outside the region, so that the rugged terrain was reduced to an almost smooth, gently rolling peneplane. Technically it is known as the Mongolian Peneplane. It is the surface which forms the floor of the Gobi and separates the later sediments from the old rock. After the leveling which formed the Mongolian Peneplane, the Gobi was warped gently into the series of shallow basins.

Into these low places the sediments from surrounding highlands were carried. Only a few of these deposits are rocks made up of coarse, unsorted gravel or conglomerates. Most of the sediments are clay or sand, which means that they came from land that was neither high nor rugged, and that the beds of streams which distributed them sloped gently. There were only a few swift mountain torrents which carried coarse gravel to the basins.

These "new" basin deposits are the fossil beds for which Mongolia and the Gobi are so famous. Eventually, in late Pliocene times some of them were tilted and warped into still other basins. Then swift rivers deposited coarse gravels at the base of the mountains and spread finer pebbles far out over the plain. Again the highlands were eroded away—this time to another flat surface called the Gobi Peneplane. It forms a plain on top of tilted and faulted rock formations, and is the flat top of buttes and mesas so characteristic of Mongolia.

A still later geological feature of the region is the surface of undrained hollows carved from the Gobi Peneplane. During rainy epochs of the Pleistocene, rivers made broad valleys in the Gobi. In the dry periods which followed, the river systems disintegrated; undrained hollows formed, and little rivers lost themselves in sandy deltas or ended in shallow salt lakes, just as they do in the Sahara and in many other deserts. Closed drainage basins are as typical of the desert world as scanty vegetation.

Winds of the desert pick up the fine dust from the floors of these undrained hollows and flat *gobi* plains to carry it out of the region. Small pebbles are left behind, and these give the Gobi a mosaic floor. Over the centuries the mosaic is polished by the desert winds until it glistens in the sunlight.

In reality, the Gobi is a rock desert—a rock floor with never more than a thin, superficial covering which varies from a few inches to a few feet in thickness. Some of this rock floor is formed of almost unconsolidated sediments not unlike the sands themselves. Such soft rock makes easy digging for the fossil hunter, and the absence of vegetation makes his hunting easier than in lands of more abundant rainfall. This is why the paleontologists like to make expeditions to the Gobi.

The thin soil left on the rock floor of the Gobi is enough to support a scanty bunch-grass vegetation and furnish pasture to the Mongols' herds. But as you travel from the center of the great Gobi Basin toward its mountain rim, the soil mantle thickens. It also becomes darker and richer. Rainfall, too, increases as you get closer to the mountains. Increased moisture and more fertile soil produce better and better pasture until near the edge of the plateau there is a strip of land suitable for agriculture. This is where we saw Chinese farmers when we came into Mongolia. It is also the range of bandits, who lie in wait for caravans returning from their desert journeys with rich cargoes.

There are swampy strips along some of the stream beds of the

Gobi, particularly in the northeast section drained by the Kerulean River. Occasionally the terrain near a stream bank will appear to be solid ground, but actually it is only a thick crust.

North and east of P'ang Kiang, which is between Kalgan, China, and Ulan Bator, in the Mongolian Peoples Republic, there is a large area (100 miles or so) of sand dunes which range from 40 to 300 feet in height. This patch of sand also extends to the southwest of P'ang Kiang, but it is widest to the east. These dunes are crossed in a narrow section by the Kalgan-Ulan Bator road. The sand hampers motor traffic, but camels and oxcarts travel through it without too much difficulty. A Japanese expedition visited the region during the 1930's and called it the Kunshantagh Desert, but I have not seen the name used by anyone else. We considered it just a part of the Gobi. The Japanese reported that there were more Mongols here than in other semi-desert regions. They also stated that they found willow and elm trees in the eastern part of the dune area.

In the southwestern corner of the Mongolian plateau, the Central Asiatic Expedition found sand in patches which could be crossed with difficulty by motorcar, but as we traveled west the dunes became higher until they were too difficult for motor traffic. In the basins north and west of P'ang Kiang there are other, relatively small patches of dunes, but none of the Gobi dune areas are as vast as the great *ergs* of the Sahara.

Throughout Mongolia short-lived streams carry silt into the basins where it spreads over the lake bottoms. As the lakes dry up, winds lift the dust and move it to the dune areas nearby. Sometimes this wind-borne sand collects around tufts of vegetation and forms small hummocks which are only a few inches high. They make a very uneven surface for motor traffic, but they are not a really serious hazard like the dunes. You get a pretty bouncy ride, though, if you chase antelope through such terrain.

In other places the hummocks are larger, and the motorcars have to pick and choose a route. Some of these hummocks are three, five, or even ten feet high, as in the case of tamarisk mounds. Careful study of such close-packed heaps of sand shows that the original mound accumulated around small plants like grass or peas. Later these were replaced by deep-rooted tamarisk, willow, or dune plum trees. Vegetation-held dunes are often jagged and irregular; never are they the graceful sand hills which make the background for desert motion pictures.

On the uplands above the valleys, sand is less abundant. There it tends to form a thin sheet over the terrain. It also covers the windward slopes of hills and protects the formation from wind erosion.

During really dry weather, when the days got hot and almost still in the Gobi, we saw many little dust devils begin to dance and whirl across the flat basins. These were not true dust storms, but little whirling funnels started by the intense heat of the burning sun on the bare desert floor. When the sun beats down on flat earth bare of vegetation, the hot air rises so fast that cooler air must rush in from all directions. In its haste to replace the hot air, the moving mass becomes a "whirling dervish" that sucks up the dust from the dry lake bottom and tosses it into the upper atmosphere where it drifts away from the playa. We used to laugh at these whirling funnels— that is, until one of them danced out of a grassless playa, caught a stack of thirty-seven empty five-gallon gasoline cans, and hoisted them into the air before dropping and tumbling them over the plain. Then we realized how powerful those little air funnels could be if they built up over extensive areas and became real tornadoes. In the course of months and years they remove quantities of fine dry soil from the basins.

The other deserts of Central Asia are, like the Gobi, basins surrounded by mountains. All are farther than the Gobi from the nearest seas, and most of their mountain boundaries are higher. These facts account for the smaller amounts of precipitation and make at least one basin, the Takla Makan, a much drier desert than the Gobi. High mountains surrounding the depressions, on the other hand, supply more water to their drainage streams and send those streams farther into the desert basins. These streams make habitable oases possible on the edges of the basins, but out in the center they are as inhospitable as any desert basins in the world.

One of these holds the shallow lake, Lop Nor, which Dr. Sven

Hedin called the "Wandering Lake." Apparently its basin is so shallow that sediments carried in by wind and tributary streams fill the lake and move its waters to other parts of the basin from time to time, very much in the way that channels change from day to day in rivers carrying heavy loads of silt.

As you travel into the western Gobi and get closer to the other Central Asian deserts there are more sand dunes, more tamarisk mounds, and more sandstone rocks. The Ordos and the Ala Shan, too, are more sandy than Mongolia, so that fewer inhabitants find a living out in the west where vegetation is reduced to sparse camel sage scattered over rolling, sandy hills.

The Etsin Gol in the Ala Shan, is one of those rivers that starts with rain and melting snow in high mountains to the south. It was once a fertile valley—at least, Marco Polo so described it—but the members of Hedin's Swedish expedition who traveled that way in the late 1920's and early 1930's say that they could find only "niggardly wells, reeds and tamarisk." They saw only a few nomad families, raising goats and camels, who called the region home; but the salt lakes of Etsin Gol valley are a rest stop for migrating birds. The expedition reported that one of the most spectacular sights of the desert world occurred when a single shot was fired. The noise shattered the desert silence so abruptly that thousands of birds rushed into the air and "the sky was blackened with ducks, gulls, swans and cranes."

Part of the expedition took the hard way from Etsin Gol to Hami. This is the trail through the Black Gobi and along the edge of the Turfan Depression. On the worst stretch there are only two wells: one after four dry marches, four long days of travel without water; the other after three dry stages. Out there the desert trails are indistinct, and it becomes quite a feat of navigation to hit so small a target as a desert well when you travel by compass and the stars instead of following a well-worn camel path. They could find no one who would lead the party through the Black Gobi, but they did meet a Chinese caravan which had been robbed by bandits. None of the men who had just covered the route would turn back as guides; but one of the expedition members got a dog from the

Chinese, and they kept the animal thirsty so that he led them straight to the last well. Hedin's scientists describe the region as one of "savage desolation, a sterile desert with no trace of life, nothing but ugly hills and outcrops of gray stone."

South of the Black Gobi, on the eastern edge of the Takla Makan, the group entered the predominantly sandy Lop Desert, and when they reached the Tarim River they found that the hot April winds had dried it up almost completely. Only a few water holes and pools remained, and these became fewer as they went south. Eventually the sand desert gave way, they tell us, to "desolate, dead stone plain between belts of undulating clay-sand." In some places a white powder of salt covered the ground, and in others there were long ridges of loose sand. The men were finally rewarded for their hardships in crossing this desolate region, for the desert is fringed with oases. Luscious fruits and vegetables grow profusely in the irrigated gardens at the foot of high mountains.

Closed basins surrounded by mountains are a common characteristic in many areas of the desert world, but in the Gobi the basin topography reaches such a high development that there are basins within basins. The edges of the major depressions may be bordered by grasslands and in Central Asia even circled by oases, but in the center every Gobi basin is a recognizable desert.

V

···································
··································
·····························
···················
·········

Desert Climate

DESERTS ARE WHERE THEY ARE BECAUSE OF WINDS AND MOUN-
tains and currents of the ocean. Most of the desert world has been
desert since the earth began whirling in its present orbit, setting up
the seasonal pattern of prevailing winds and driving ocean currents
in circulation on their present courses. When the mountains have
been raised up in the path of steady winds, deflecting the movement
of great air masses, the area where desert climate prevails has
expanded on the earth. When huge quantities of the ocean's moisture became locked in glaciers about the poles and so lowered the
level of the seas, the climate of the desert world became more arid.

If the axis of the earth should turn to a new position, if prevailing
winds should take up new seasonal patterns, if the ocean currents
should shift from their courses, then our deserts will change their
character. But other deserts will appear to fit the new circulation
pattern of prevailing winds and ocean currents. If the glaciers melt
and raise the level of the seven seas so that more rains water the
earth, the deserts of today may become somewhat smaller. They
will still, however, be deserts or semi-deserts in relation to their
surrounding areas, as they have been in past geologic ages, when
glaciers were building about the poles and heavy rains were common
beyond the glacial borders.

Climate makes deserts. Mountain barriers, prevailing winds, and ocean currents make the climate. So far, man has not been able to alter those basic geophysical features on a scale grand enough to change the climate. He may flood the desert with sea water, but unless the flood gives up its moisture to the air in quantities, and unless that new moist air lies in the path of winds which will carry it over the barren wastes and drop the moisture—as rain—where it is needed, the flooded desert will not grow a tree nor sprout a seed. Moisture in the air will make no desert bloom. Only effective moisture, in the form of precipitation which plants can use, will carpet the desert floor with green.

It is often stated that deserts are in "rain shadow." This is the technical way of saying, "It doesn't rain in deserts." Much of the desert world is located 15 to 35 degrees from the equator, and this corresponds in part to the doldrums or horse latitudes over the ocean, an area of perpetual high pressure and cloudless skies lying between the prevailing westerlies and the trade winds. Even over the ocean this region gets little rain.

Many of the deserts extend beyond the horse latitudes and lie in the path of the prevailing westerlies. But these are all bordered by mountains. The moisture-laden winds from the ocean must go up over the mountains to reach the desert lands; and in going up the air is cooled, and cooling causes the air to drop its moisture on the windward side of the mountains. When the drier air descends on the desert side it is, of course, compressed by the weight of the atmosphere above it. Compression warms the air so that it flows over the desert as a hot, dry wind. Some deserts, like the Gobi, are so far from the ocean that the prevailing winds lose all their moisture long before they reach the desert.

But even the prevailing westerly winds cannot pick up much moisture from a cold ocean, because heat is necessary to evaporate the ocean water and give it to the air. In the Pacific the cold Humboldt Current flows north along the west coast of South America, and the west coast of that continent is desert even high up in the mountains which face the ocean. Similarly, the cold Canary Current, flowing toward the equator along the Atlantic coast of West Africa, gives up very little moisture to the winds that blow over those parts of the Sahara called Desert ed Djouf and Desert d'Ouara. Below the equator, the Benguela Current flows north along the Atlantic coast of South Africa. Little moisture is carried from that cold water by the westerlies blowing over the Desert d'Omaheke and the Desert de Sable on the coast, or the Kalahari farther inland.

The combination of the cold Oyashio Current in the Pacific Ocean, the horse latitudes, and the mountain borders make the southwestern United States and northwestern Mexico a desert area. But the winds from the warm Gulf of Mexico sometimes sweep up behind the mountains to bring some winter rains and soften the arid harshness. If you have ever seen the "flag of clouds" streaming out to the east from the pass at Colorado Springs when all the skies both north and south of the pass are cloudless, you will have realized that the air east of the mountains sometimes has a little moisture and only needs the cold air from off the mountain tops to condense it into clouds or precipitation. This can happen over American deserts as well as on the plains opposite Pikes Peak.

Winter rain falls on the northern edges of the Sahara if moist air from the Mediterranean Sea gets carried in behind the Atlas Mountains or is moved south from the eastern Mediterranean. Out in the Gobi, where prevailing winds are from the far-distant Atlantic, moist air from the Pacific sometimes reaches the desert on easterly winds in the summer. All of these are examples of air circulation contrary to the prevailing winds. The chances of rain in the desert world, accordingly, depend on the probability of exceptionally moist air getting through the normal or prevailing circulation pattern.

In those parts of the desert world where rainfall records have been kept over a period of years, the average annual precipitation ranges from ten inches to 0.02 inches. Unfortunately for those who try to raise crops in the desert, this does not mean there will be ten inches, or 0.02 inches—or, indeed, any precipitation at all—in a particular year. It means that the total precipitation for the number of years on record has averaged that given number of inches per year. For example, the average at Ulan Bator on the northern edge of the Gobi in Outer Mongolia is ten inches a year; but there have been many twelve-month periods when only four inches of rain have fallen, and other years have had twelve or fourteen inches and have pulled up the average. The climate of the desert world has a precipitation pattern of such contrasting extremes that annual averages are practically meaningless.

Not only are deserts in rain shadow but, as the song says, "the skies are not cloudy all day" and desert air usually contains less moisture than the air of more temperate climates. There are spectacular exceptions, however.

Meteorologists express the amount of moisture in the air either as "relative humidity" or as the "dew-point temperature." Relative humidity is the percentage of moisture in the air compared to the amount that air could hold. Dew point is the temperature to which that air must be reduced before the moisture will condense. A low figure in either case means exceptionally dry air. For example, at Stove Pipe Wells in Death Valley, relative humidity has been as low as 2 per cent and the dew point at that time was 8.6°F.

The amount of moisture in desert air varies a great deal from one arid region to another. It even varies so much between parts of the same desert that exceptions are more characteristic than any general comment. However, relative humidity in the desert world is often between 30 per cent and 70 per cent. In the Gobi, where official records are available for the edges of the desert only, the range is frequently between 35 per cent and 50 per cent. There are a few readings as low as 4 per cent and even 2 per cent. When such readings were reported thirty or forty years ago, they were considered of questionable accuracy or regarded as meteorological freaks. Modern equipment and trained observers, however, have recently obtained similar readings for the Sahara, the Negev, the Arabian Desert, and the southwestern United States. In January the Negev relative humidity is usually between 20 per cent and 40 per cent, but it may be only 5 per cent or less. In July it is usually between 20 per cent and 80 per cent, but 10 per cent is not uncommon. By comparison, at Yuma, Arizona, humidity ranges from 15 per cent in May and June to 65 per cent in August and September, and the central Sahara averages even drier than that.

The Arabian Desert is the exception which makes generalizations impossible. It is bounded by the Persian Gulf and the Red Sea, two of the hottest bodies of water on earth. They give up considerable moisture to the air, and at Kuwait, on the eastern edge of the desert and near the head of the Persian Gulf, humidity readings in August range from 27 per cent to 94 per cent, and in January from 70 per cent to 100 per cent. These high readings do not mean rain, however, because the air is so hot that it can hold its moisture. In fact, Kuwait is a city with a climate so dry that even drinking water had to be imported by boat from across the Persian Gulf before an oil company built a plant to distill sea water for domestic use. Farther south along the coast at Dhahran relative humidity over the years has, at some time, reached 100 per cent in each month of the year; but in the summer months 4, 5 or 6 per cent readings are not uncommon, and the winter range is often from 10 per cent to 39 per cent. High humidity at Kuwait and Dhahran often produces heavy fog which may extend as far as 200 miles inland. Nevertheless, the area is desert and precipitation—less than three inches a year at Dhahran and under six inches at Kuwait—is scanty despite the high humidity.

Fog occurs over other deserts, too. I once saw fog at Tripoli, in Libya, so thick that airplanes had to land forty miles back from the coast. Of course, it was one of those unusual phenomena, for no one had ever seen or heard of fog there in mid-June before. Desert fog is burned away in an hour or two after sunrise, but this one hung around till nearly noon.

When dew-point temperature is used to describe the amount of moisture in the air, variations between regions show up just the same. For example, the mean dew point at Yuma, Arizona, in July is 59°F., while on the Persian Gulf shore of the Arabian Desert it is 67°F. and on the Red Sea side of the peninsula it is 79°F. The range at Yuma may be from 32°F. in January to 64°F. in August. In the High Desert at Burns, Oregon, the range is from 9°F. in December to 42°F. in June and July. The Central Sahara has a low in February of 20°F., and even in the summer this only goes to 41°F.; but

on the northern edge of the Gobi the dew point has dropped to
−15°F. in January.

In deserts where high humidity occurs, as it often does when
deserts are near the sea, dew is not uncommon because temperature
often gets down to the dew point. Dew may collect on stones or on
exposed metal such as the wings of airplanes or house roofs; but if
you want to collect the droplets for your morning drink, you will
have to get up at dawn. Dew forms just before sunrise and dries
away in less than an hour.

Dew may have been important to the ancient vinedressers who
lived in the Negev Desert of Israel, for some years ago archeologists
noticed small heaps of stones placed in regular rows but could find
no explanation for their use. They were obviously placed in position
by man—even prehistoric people didn't heap up stones just for the
fun of it—and eventually someone discovered old grapevine stumps
in some of these stone piles. It has been suggested, and it may well
be true, that the loose stones were placed around the growing grape-
vines to catch the morning dew and so give the vines a little more
water in a land where water is scarce.

Moisture in the air acts as a filter to sunlight and strains out some
of the sun's rays. The relative absence of moisture over deserts
allows more sunlight and heat to reach the ground than is possible
in humid regions. The rocks, the gravel, and the sand of the desert
are also unprotected by vegetation so that they absorb great quantities of the sun's heat. During the day much of that heat is radiated
and reflected back into the air. This is why deserts have much higher
daytime temperatures than other parts of the world. When the sun
sets, heat from the bare ground radiates rapidly and is soon lost
to the upper air.

Accordingly, deserts are best known for their hot summer days
and cool, even cold, nights. In the morning at about sunrise you
will find the thermometer registering in the sixties in the Sahara or
the American Southwest. By one o'clock in the afternoon it will be
well over 105°F. or 110°F. "in the shade"—and no shade available!
Then, when the sun dips down below the horizon again, the desert
cools off fast. This quick cooling always reminds me of the poet

who was going to be true to his sweetheart "until the sands of the desert grow cold." Smart lover, he was, for he could keep his word and still change sweethearts at seven o'clock every evening!

The daily range of 45°F. or 50°F. between early morning and early afternoon holds throughout the year. During a winter in the Sahara I dressed in woolen underwear, heavy riding breeches, wool shirt, and sheepskin overcoat when I got up in the morning. By ten o'clock I had shed the coat, and by noon my shirt was open and my sleeves rolled up. At one thirty I would wish that I could shed the winter woolies, but an hour later the shirt was buttoned up and by five o'clock I was glad to put on the sheepskin again.

In summer we followed the native custom and stopped all outdoor activity about ten in the morning. By that time it was just too hot to be comfortable, even driving an automobile in the desert, and not until five or six in the afternoon did we leave the comfort of thick-walled adobe buildings.

The Sahara is generally hotter than the American southwestern deserts and has a wider daily range between maximum and minimum temperatures. In fact, the world record for heat is held by El Azizia in Libya, where the thermometer officially reached 136.4°F. on September 13, 1922. Death Valley holds second place with 134°F. in July, 1913. Other Sahara stations with long temperature observation records have recorded 133°F. The Arabian Desert is almost as hot as the Sahara, with daily high temperatures up around 110° and 120°F., but the record highs are ten to fifteen degrees lower than those of the Sahara.

In the Kalahari, which is south of the equator, the summer heat comes in December, January, and February, and it rises well over 100°F., with a record high of 115°F.

We have been quoting official temperatures. They are taken in well-ventilated shelters four or five feet above the ground. No one has found a better way to take air temperature for comparisons in all parts of the world, but those who travel in the desert will not be in "well-ventilated shade."

Temperatures on the desert floor may be 50°F. higher than the official free-air reading. Even an inch from the ground it is cooler than on the desert surface, and it is 30°F. cooler a foot above ground. Good black shade, such as that under heavy black cloth which shuts out all sunlight, can make it another 30°F. cooler. When you hear your friends talk about the heat they experienced during their summer on the desert, don't let them give you any new records by recording the heat of sun-baked rocks or the temperature of mercury in the sun. Insist on a free-air temperature in the shade.

The rapid change in air temperature above the desert floor is responsible for another characteristic of the desert climate. As early as nine o'clock on a summer morning you can see the still air over a desert plain shimmering with rising heat waves. These heat waves indicate sharp differences in the temperature of air layers and equally sharp variations in the density of those layers. Variation in air density is the cause of the desert mirage. When you travel along a flat plain and see a beautiful lake with islands a half-mile ahead, do not be surprised. Your eyes are not deceiving you in spite of the fact that there is no water anywhere around. The mirage is so real-looking that newcomers to the desert will refuse to believe there is no lake in front of them—until the car ahead stirs up a cloud of dust where the water seemed to be. Although there is really only flat, black plain where the lake seems to be, it is worth a fast exposure with a camera. The camera eye will see the same lake with islands that your eyes see, because the mirage is simply produced by light rays bent as they pass through air layers of differing densities between a distant object and your eye. Light rays, of course, will register on the photographic film and give a picture. The "water" in the mirage is really a mirror image of distant sky, though not the sky directly above the apparent location of the lake. The "islands" which appear to be reflected in the lake are pebbles or other irregularities on the plain projecting into the air layers which form the mirror.

Another common type of mirage is the appearance of a mountain or other distant object in the clear morning air, just as if it were only a little distance away instead of far off. This desert phenomenon is also due to a distortion of light rays, which seems to bring the object closer just as do the lenses in a pair of field glasses.

The most romantic mirage is the "city in the clouds." This phenomenon is caused when lower air is chilled and made more dense as over a cold ocean instead of heated and thinned as on the desert. In this case, since the density of the layers is reversed, the image appears above the observer.

The intense heat of desert sun which makes the lake-with-islands mirage also causes the air above the desert to rise. Frequent little dust devils whirling across the gravel plain are evidence that rapidly rising air is being replaced by air from the immediate vicinity of the tiny storm. When the heat persists over great expanses of the desert for weeks, it sometimes is responsible, in a similar manner, for the desert winds which blow from directions other than those of the prevailing winds.

Throughout the desert world the prevailing westerly winds are evident the year round. They are responsible for the formation and direction of the sand dunes; they prevent moist air above the warm seas around the Arabian Peninsula from losing that moisture as precipitation on the Arabian Desert; and they keep the Gobi intensely cold in winter. Winds are certainly characteristic of the broad pattern of desert climate (only four days out of ten in the Gobi, for instance, can be called calm), but they are also characteristic of the day-to-day changes and they will be more fully described when we discuss desert weather.

Precipitation, humidity, daytime heat, nighttime cold, and desert winds—every characteristic of desert climate changes with the parade of the seasons. But in the desert world, the seasons, like all other desert features, differ from one arid region to another. The Gobi, which lies at the eastern end of what geographers call the Eurasian Continental Climatic Area, is a good example of seasonal change. A similar climatic area is found in the Great Plains region of North America. Both regions occupy about the same spread of latitude, roughly between 35° and 50° north of the equator. Because the Eurasian area is larger and the continent bigger than the American counterpart, the continental characteristics of climate extremes in east central Asia are even more pronounced than those in the American west.

Four seasons are characteristic of the Gobi: spring, summer, fall, and winter, with usually a false spring at the end of winter. These seasons are distinct, with very pronounced extremes of temperature, as much as 150°F. between the hottest day in summer and the coldest day in winter.

Spring in the Gobi usually begins about the second week in April. For two or three weeks there is a period of delightful weather, with warm, sunny days and not too much wind. But these are the deceptively pleasant days of false spring. About the first of May, the tail end of winter returns, and cold, blustery days of dust-laden winds are the rule then, until early or middle June. Some rain and even snow may vary the monotony of wind and dust. The latter part of June, for two or three weeks after the blustering end of winter, is the real spring. It spreads its rather comfortable warmth over the desert, and occasional light rains help the desert grasses to come along nicely, furnishing pasture for flocks and herds. Oxcart caravans from the south plod northward with their freight. The wind has not stopped entirely, but it has ceased to dominate the landscape and man's thinking.

July, or sometimes mid-June to mid-August, is summer. Hot days —some very hot days—are the rule, but the nights are cool. Wind and dust again dominate the landscape, but this is the season when hard rains, if they come at all, are most likely to dump water on the plains. Hailstones sometimes pelt the earth. Mostly it is just hot and dry during the daytime; dry and cool at night.

Fall usually may be recognized by the invigorating, bright clear days beginning in mid-August and lasting until mid-September or the first of October. This is the time of year when both men and beasts feel best in the Gobi. Summer pastures have restored the winter loss of energy to the animals. Fat meat and abundant milk build strength in man. The clear air, bright sun, and crisp temperature make you glad to be alive.

Winter comes in with a rush anytime after the middle of September. One day you may be enjoying a pleasant temperature near the eighties. But suddenly the air cools. In a few hours the thermometer has skidded below 50°F.; and a little later cold rain changes to snow and blasting wind. Winter has arrived to hold Mongolia in its below-freezing grip for the next six months.

Gobi seasons, however, do not always run on schedule. The above description is only an approximate picture, for changes may come a week or a month off schedule and they can be just as far out of character. A section of the Gobi may be without precipitation for ten months, as actually happened at Ula Usa in 1923, or a cloudburst may sweep the pastures in a torrential flood, drowning flocks and herds, men, women, and children. A dry continental climate replete with sudden changes and complete surprises—this is the Gobi climate.

The parade of seasons in more southern deserts follows a similar pattern but with different emphasis. In the Sahara, winter grades more gradually into spring. Summer heat there is usually strong by May and intense from June to October; then it grades off into autumn. I have gone swimming in the Sahara during early November and been quite comfortable in light pajamas as I rode to and from the swimming hole. But winter will come just as suddenly there around the first of December as it comes in the Gobi a few months earlier. Sahara winters are neither as severe nor as long as those in the Gobi, but the seasonal range in temperature is just as great, because the summers are 30° to 40°F. hotter in the Sahara. The chances of rain in the northern Sahara are better in the winter months, but on the southern edge of that desert rain is more apt to come in summer, if at all.

Once I was in the southwestern United States in early December. For a week we had beautiful weather; then, one afternoon at about four o'clock, the wind changed. The thermometer dropped way below freezing and a howling snowstorm rushed in on violent winds. The newspapers next day reported that four hunters, caught in the storm with only light clothing, had been found frozen to death. That year winter came to our southwestern desert with the same violence and the same suddeness of its arrival in the Gobi.

In most of the southwestern deserts winter rains produce whatever moisture can be expected; but in southern Arizona, southern California, and northern Mexico both summer and winter rains may occur, and summer precipitation may be even greater than the winter totals.

The Arabian Desert has only two pronounced seasons: summer and winter. No one questions that April to September is summer—the heat and dryness are too pronounced to leave room for doubt. What precipitation there is comes in December and January, but old-timers say that it has rained in February and March. Summer is such a pronounced season in contrast to the rest of the year that travelers call Arabia a "two season area." They do enjoy a few weeks of the pleasant in-between weather of fall and spring, however.

In the days before air-conditioned trucks came into being, explorers and others who had business in the desert world selected the most favorable season for their work. In northern deserts, like the Gobi, that season is from April to September. In the Sahara the best season is from October to May. Nowadays, explorers in the Arabian Desert travel and live in modern trucks and are more independent of the seasons, but in the Sahara the buses and many of the truck lines still suspend operations from June to September. The climate is just too rugged—not only for man but also for his gas- and diesel-powered machines.

It seems to be a custom, when writing about deserts, to state that they were not always the barren wastelands they are today; to assume that once they enjoyed abundant precipitation. In support of such statements, extensive dry river beds and deep canyons are pointed out. Some writers go so far as to state that the deserts supported much denser populations in the past than they now do and refer to "vast accumulations of prehistoric camp refuse and Stone Age tools." I wonder who started those fallacies and half-truths, and why they are perpetuated from one generation of writers to the next?

There are dry river systems in deserts, and there are deep canyons cut by rivers which once carried large volumes of water. This doesn't mean, however, that the whole drainage basin or the land between those river systems received any quantity of rain—any more, say, than Egypt and the Nile Valley do today. The water which filled ancient river systems and cut deep canyons fell on the highlands in prehistoric times, just as it does today. The desert rivers, which are now dry stream beds, received the volume of water necessary to make them permanent streams from the mountains surrounding the desert, or from those ranges (like the Hoggar and Tibesti of the central Sahara) which extend high enough into the upper air to catch moisture-laden winds and wring the water from them.

Erratic storms in those prehistoric days of the glacial periods were more numerous than they are today. The seasonal precipitation on the edges of the desert regions was a little more frequent, perhaps even a little more reliable than today; but the non-desert areas also received many times their present rainfall. During the Stone Age, deserts were areas of little rainfall in comparison with the surrounding areas, just as they are now. There was more vegetation along the river bottoms, and some of the dune lands held larger patches of green, but there were still vast areas of true desert.

The evidence for "dense populations" in prehistoric times in a climate "where no one can live today" is found at prehistoric camp-sites. I have collected artifacts on hundreds of such sites in the Sahara, in the Gobi, and on the arid plateaus north of the Sahara, and these sites are all located on the banks of the dry rivers or in the dune areas. Some of them had apparently been occupied time and time again, but none of them showed accumulations of refuse large enough to indicate the existence of populations comparable to those of the Sahara today. Some of the desert oases now have a population density of one or two thousand inhabitants per square mile, and many of these oases are located within a mile or two of the old campsites. In the desert today people live where the water is, just as they did in the neolithic age. Even the large, well-preserved sites north of the desert can be measured only in hundreds of square feet, and were made by small parties of campers, returning often, over many years, to the same spot on a stream bank.

The same is true in the Gobi. Refuse on prehistoric campsites indicates that only small groups occupied them at any one time. Present-day Mongol herdsmen often camp in groups as large, or even larger, than those of their Stone Age ancestors.

When historic records left by ancient Romans are compared with present rainfall records, it is clear that it rains now just as much and just as often in the Sahara or the Negev of Israel as it did in those regions a couple of thousand years ago when Rome ruled the world. The same is true for other parts of the desert world where records can be compared. This does not mean that vegetation and animal life are the same in the deserts as they were a few millennia ago. Wild animals have been hunted out of the desert, just as the buffalo were driven from our western plains, and domestic cattle now overgraze the arid lands where once the deer and the antelope played. But the big difference is that in the bad years of that pre-agricultural period the deer and the antelope died off; in good years, the wild herds multiplied. A balance was thus maintained between the vegetation which the desert climate could support and the population of animals and men which that vegetation could maintain. Very few corners of the desert world are left where such a balance exists today. But the climate, that generalized summary of yearly average wind, rain, relative humidity and temperature, has not changed since the glaciers left Chicago and "the mammoth and the reindeer roared where Paris roars tonight." Desert weather is something different. It is the day-to-day manifestation of climate. Daily temperature, wind, humidity, and lack of rain in the desert may be as constant as the movements of the planets for weeks and months; then change with a suddenness that destroys anyone who is unprepared. Desert weather is the climate of the desert in action.

VI

Desert Weather

THERE IS ONE CERTAIN FACT ABOUT THE WEATHER: IT IS UN-predictable. When I first went to Monument Valley, the desert of northern Arizona, I was told not to bring tent, sleeping bag, or raincoat. "It never rains there in July or August." Maybe it doesn't rain, but I got soaked every afternoon at four o'clock by water that fell from the sky, no matter what it was called. I spent one afternoon on top of Navajo Mountain, a 10,000-foot peak rising above the canyon-slashed plateau, and saw four rainstorms at once, all dropping their moisture on different parts of the nearby desert.

When the U.S. Air Force planned to make the motion picture, *Sun, Sand, and Survival* in the Sahara, I picked the best time as late May or early June, because "the winter rains in Libya will be long past and the intense heat will be just coming in to give us realism." We arrived in late May. The weather was so cold that those who had relied on my advice went out and bought sweaters to keep warm. Drizzly rain and overcast skies twice kept the cameras at the hotel instead of on location.

One August morning after arriving in Kuwait in the Arabian Desert, the fog was so thick that we could just recognize the outlines of buildings a block away; and in the Gobi I have scooped up hailstones by the bucketful after a July thunderstorm. They averaged one and a quarter inches in diameter eighteen hours after the storm.

But I know that any statements I make from first-hand knowledge of the subject will be contradicted by the next observer, for desert weather may be as predictable as the sunrise for twenty years, and then, without warning, produce the unexpected.

Those who meet desert weather eventually discover that it is intolerant of carelessness and merciless in punishment for mistakes. There are many records of instances where the desert has demanded payment of a life for lessons learned too late. Experienced desert fliers, explorers who chart the graceful dunes and gravel plains, even those who regularly cross the desert in air-conditioned automobiles go prepared for weather of every kind and description. Those who go unprepared are quite likely not to come back in good health—if they come back at all.

Each year the desert world claims some victims from among the careless and the unprepared. Sooner or later every desert traveler finds that he is confronted with everything that the weatherman sees in his nightmares as well as in his pleasant dreams. Hailstones and cloudbursts, polar cold and tropic heat, sandstorms, snowstorms, thunderstorms, and windstorms are frequent enough to prevent the weather from becoming monotonous; rare enough to guarantee that it is always "most unusual weather this year."

Experienced travelers find that the "normal" weather consists of contrasting extremes. Sudden changes are the rule, and they are particularly characteristic of desert temperature. The Chinese have a bit of doggerel which emphasizes this phase of desert weather for many deserts when they say that in Mongolia:

> Fur clothes are worn in early morn,
> But linen things at noon,
> And men in droves surround the stoves
> While eating watermelon.

In general, temperature follows latitude in Mongolia, and it is always colder in the north than in the south. Temperature charts show a continuous cold area west and southwest of Lake Baikal.

That area, northwest of Mongolia, appears to be colder than any other section every month of the year. This cold spot does shift somewhat in relation to Lake Baikal, but its influence on Mongolia and the Gobi is always from the northwest. Probably this south-to-north gradient in temperature is due to the influence of the cold air mass in the northwest as much as, or possibly more than, to latitude.

In 1931 the Hedin Expedition made hourly temperature readings from March to October at Chadain Sume. Their records show how erratic and variable the daily temperature is in the Gobi. The

SAMPLES OF ERRATIC TEMPERATURE AT CHADAIN
SUME 1931

Date	Low	Hour	High	Hour	Range
MARCH					
25....	21.4	6 a.m.	37.2	1 p.m.	15.8
26....	10.4	6 a.m.	42.4	3 p.m.	32.0
27....	25.0	5 a.m.	43.2	4 p.m.	18.2
28....	28.6	4 a.m.	55.8	4 p.m.	27.2
JUNE					
15....	50.9	6 a.m.	68.9	4 p.m.	18.0
16....	58.8	3 a.m.	88.7	4 p.m.	29.9
17....	71.2	4 a.m.	90.1	3 p.m.	18.9
JULY					
6....	64.2	6 a.m.	72.5	11 a.m.	8.3
7....	57.2	4 a.m.	62.4	3 p.m.	5.2
8....	55.8	5 a.m.	69.6	5 p.m.	13.8
22....	68.0	5 a.m.	87.6	4 p.m.	19.6
23....	64.8	5 a.m.	87.6	4 p.m.	22.8
28....	73.4	3 a.m.	95.9	1 p.m.	22.5
AUGUST					
9....	64.0	5 a.m.	90.0	3 p.m.	26.0
10....	70.7	6 a.m.	92.3	4 p.m.	21.6
11....	68.9	5 a.m.	89.6	2 p.m.	20.7
12....	68.4	6 a.m.	77.9	10 a.m.	9.5
SEPT					
1....	55.8	5 a.m.	78.8	1 p.m.	23.0
2....	55.8	4 a.m.	59.9	2 p.m.	4.1
3....	44.6	7 a.m.	58.1	4 p.m.	13.5
20....	56.3	4 a.m.	77.4	5 p.m.	21.1
OCT					
3....	51.8	7 a.m.	73.8	4 p.m.	22.0
7....	26.8	7 a.m.	37.4	1 p.m.	10.6
8....	26.2	6 a.m.	40.1	3 p.m.	13.9
15....	51.6	5 a.m.	64.2	11 a.m.	12.6
16....	25.0	7 a.m.	38.3	3 p.m.	13.3

extremes of difference between morning cold and afternoon heat range from two-tenths of a degree one day in April to 32°F. in March but during the eight-month record the usual difference was ten to twenty degrees.

The difficulty of understanding Gobi weather from monthly averages or annual means can best be shown by some actual readings on selected days at Chadain Sume (see chart on p. 86).

The lowest temperature occurred usually around six o'clock in the morning, but it came at five o'clock or at seven o'clock almost as often. Even those generalities had exceptions, for the low also occurred anytime from one in the morning to noon. The daily high was usually around three or four in the afternoon, but it was also reached at all hours from ten in the morning to six in the evening.

At Edsin Gol, farther south in the Ala Shan Desert, the Hedin Expedition recorded daily observations from September 1931 to March 1932. In that area the daily variation was greater and more consistent than at the Gobi station. The difference between maximum and minimum daily temperature was usually 27°F., but occasionally it was as little as 20°F. and as much as 44°F. The disconcerting fact is that the whole range might occur within a few days. This is why it is unsound to generalize about desert weather. For example, take four successive days in November as shown below:

SAMPLES OF ERRATIC TEMPERATURE AT EDSIN GOL
1931-1932

Date	Low	Hour	High	Hour	Range
NOV					
1..	24.6	4 a.m.	48.6	3 p.m.	24.0
2..	35.2	8 a.m.	39.0	2 p.m.	3.8
3..	19.0	6 a.m.	41.9	3 p.m.	22.9
4..	15.4	6 a.m.	51.6	3 p.m.	36.2

The daily range for these four consecutive days is 24°, 38°, 22.9°, and 36.2°F. What clothing will you bring for days like these?

Excessive summer heat for the Gobi is in the vicinity of 100°F. and lasts only a few days at a time. By contrast, winter cold is severe and long-lasting, and even during July and August the nights are cool and a warm sleeping bag is appreciated. During four months I spent in that desert there were only a few nights when it was hot enough to sleep "on the leather," or outside the fur. Regardless of how hot the days, it was necessary to have warm clothes readily available. In the Gobi there is more danger of freezing to death than of getting heatstroke.

North American deserts cover such a range of latitude—from eastern Washington to Lower California in Mexico—that here, too, generalizations about temperature are impossible. One cannot even say that temperature follows latitude as it does in the Gobi, because American desert areas are influenced by so many local conditions. High mountains, cold ocean currents, desert plateau altitudes, and plains open to cold north winds all influence the temperature more than degrees of latitude. For instance, Death Valley is hotter than the Sonoran Desert in Mexico from April through September, although it is nearly 500 miles farther north. But during the winter Death Valley is colder, as one would expect from its latitude. At Yuma, Arizona, it is also colder than in Death Valley, except in December and January, although Yuma is four degrees farther south and according to its latitude should be hotter.

Regardless of these generalities, the difference between maximum and minimum temperature, each day, in American deserts or in any other part of the desert world, is extremely wide and the change is also very abrupt. It takes a rugged constitution to adjust to such daily differences in temperature even when suitable clothing is available.

Next to hot days and cool nights, the most characteristic feature of desert weather is persistent wind. I noticed it particularly in Mongolia where it blows long and often, although not always from the same direction. Wind in the Gobi is as sure as death and taxes. It is almost as characteristic of that desert as the undulating plain itself. It blows so constantly that a traveler from beyond the desert finds it dominating his very thoughts. Fifteen to twenty-five miles per hour winds persist day after day. From April to late August, the wind was sufficiently important to rate twenty-six special references in my diary.

In general, wind died about sundown for an hour or two, and there was also a calm before sunrise. Those periods were in such pronounced contrast to the usual wind that we felt distinct relief. If we were near the mountains, the day and night wind shifts changed direction—one from the highlands, the other toward them.

The limited number of weather observations on record indicates that the Gobi winds are generally westerlies as in most parts of the desert world. Sometimes they are northwest, sometimes southwest; but prevailing westerlies dominate the Gobi. There are times in spring and summer, however, when the wind shifts to the east or southeast, and these are the winds most likely to bring moisture and rain. They account for the greater amount of precipitation in the eastern Gobi and for progressive drying to the west.

During the latter part of June, July, and early August, wind is less continuous, or rather less noticeable, than in April and May. Even in those months when winds are most constant, violent exceptions occur. I remember that the night of May 28–29, 1928, was unusually hot and that there was a light breeze. It was so drying that I got up during the night to drink water. The wind continued all day on the 29th. Dust and heat hindered our field work so that we stayed in camp all day and groused about the dust on our books and anything else we touched. It was so fine that it penetrated cameras, watches, clothes, and our sleeping bags. That night we checked the tent stakes before going to bed, but the heat and dust kept us from sleep for several hours. Finally I dozed off but the wind kept us conscious of its presence.

At five o'clock I was startled by a shout from my tentmate, Mackenzie Young. "Hold the tent," he ordered. "Grab it and hold it while I stake it down."

Half-awake, I automatically grabbed a piece of flapping cloth and heard Mac outside driving stakes. In a moment I was fully awake and climbed off my cot to join him. We drove the tent stakes deeper. We threw extra ropes over the tent and lashed them down.

Every few minutes an extra gust of wind lifted my pajamas and pelted my bare skin with stinging sand. Sandburs added no comfort to my bare feet. Eventually we got our tent firmly anchored, but the cook tent was completely down. I never saw such a disconsolate crew as our Chinese cooks huddled on the ground with the flapping tent cloth all about them.

Mac and I went back to our cots, but twice again we had to rush out. The wind tore loose the front pole, but we caught it in time so that I could hold it while Mac got it reanchored. Fine sand covered everything. It was in our ears and eyes, too. By one o'clock the wind had died down enough for us to get a scanty breakfast, but not until two that afternoon did the storm stop and we could begin to clean up our gear.

Wind in the Gobi is not only a physical force which carries dust into sealed mechanical parts and makes the cold more penetrating, it sometimes becomes a psychological hazard as well. It keeps up so long and so continuously that nerves become taut and edgy from the strain. The letdown that comes with the calm surprises you with the realization that the wind has stopped.

Strong winds are most dangerous to travelers when they first begin, because then they are true sandstorms and blot everything from sight. In 1955 an oil driller in Algeria was lost while trying to walk 300 yards to camp, and a few hours later his body was found five miles away. Two men who crossed the Sahara on a motor scooter got lost between two road markers which are only 100 meters apart. Luckily they took stock of their situation and began a systematic search for the road, using their compass to guide them on each sally from a fixed point. Even so, they were a full hour in getting back on the trail.

Not only do sandstorms blind travelers, but the hot, dry wind quickly dehydrates man and beast. This is the chief danger, for a man wandering on the desert during a hot wind can live only a few hours without drinking great quantities of water.

Desert winds are not just inanimate molecules of air in motion. The exceptional winds are animate creatures with names and personalities readily recognized by desert people everywhere.

In Libya it is the *ghibli,* a hot blast of dust-laden air rushing up from the south in the spring. The desert natives say that the *ghibli* starts with a weird, clear yellow light and an unnaturally calm atmosphere at sunset. Then, during the night, the wind comes and continues into the following day. It reaches its peak about noon. If there is no change at noon, the *ghibli* will go on for another day. It may last only a few hours, or it may blow its searing, hot dry breath across the land for three days. This is the sandstorm wind of the eastern Sahara. Coming up from the south with high temperature and low humidity, it has such strong velocity that caravans and motorcars are halted—unable to see through the cloud "which is night at noon."

Many people are physiologically affected by the *ghibli,* as if the wind were an evil thing. Women and children are particularly affected and quite frequently are prostrated by its effect, especially when the *ghibli* falls and its hot, dry air is suddenly replaced with the high humidity of a sea breeze. In spite of its evil nature, some of the desert Arabs say that the *ghibli* purifies the air and kills off the current supply of germs.

Over in the Arabian Desert it is the *shamal* which has personality. This is popularly considered an early summer wind from the north-by-west (north 20° west) that blows for days and is strong enough to keep sand in the air. Forty miles per hour is typical of a *shamal,* but they also hit fifty miles per hour. One cannot hold a camera on a tripod in that wind and anyway, it will fill the shutter with dust as it will your watch. The popular belief in Arabia is that most of the heavy winds come during the *shamal* season of May, June, and July; but actual records show that the northerly wind, or *shamal,* is a year-round feature and often blows in December, January, and February, as well as during the so-called "*shamal* season." These winds attract less attention in winter, however, because they carry very little sand. Damp sand is not picked up by the wind. When the *shamal* hits in the summer, geologist explorers in Arabia's Empty Quarter sit it out in their tents, and housewives in Dhahran go around the house with dust cloths in both hands. Make no mistake about the *shamal,* it is no local breeze but a continual movement of air from a barometric high-pressure area to a low-pressure region.

Those winds in the desert world which are personalized by proper names are all heavy dust-carriers, whether they are local in origin or continental in sweep. In the Sahara the *ghibli* is only one of several. In Egypt the *haboob* is a local wind that carries dust to great heights and moves on a ten-to-twenty-mile front at thirty miles per hour. The Egyptian name for a whirlwind pillar of sand speeding across the desert is *zoboa*. Egypt, also, has the *khamsin* which blows across the Red Sea and up into Palestine. I saw a sample of its work at Beersheba one morning. Dust nearly obscured the swaying trees around our hotel at seven o'clock in the morning, but in less than two hours the storm had died and our sight-seeing wasn't even interrupted. A *khamsin,* which means "fifty," should last fifty days or fifty hours to keep its reputation as a desert personality.

The *sirocco* is another Sahara wind of continental, even intercontinental scope, for it crosses the Mediterranean to southwestern Europe. It blows from the southeast and over most of North Africa which makes it a hot, dry wind loaded with dust. It hides the sun as effectively as a heavy overcast in temperate regions. My first experience with the *sirocco* was at Tebessa, Algeria, in early September. At that location, northwest of the Gulf of Gabès, the *sirocco* carried plenty of moisture as well as dust. Heat, humidity, dust, and wind dominated our lives for nearly three weeks; and I have a personal resentment against that particular *sirocco,* because the photographer who developed my photographic films tried to do it at that time. The humidity and heat were so high that the films wouldn't dry. Even with careful handling, chunks of the emulsion came off and dust grains stuck until the negatives felt like sandpaper. In southern Europe the *sirocco* is always a wind of high humidity because it crosses the warm water of the Mediterranean. In Africa it is supposed to be a dry wind—except northwest of Gabès.

Some people claim that the *sirocco* has a distinctive odor and in some cases a toxic effect on humans. A depressing effect is quite common on women, children and animals. I expect that native men are less affected because they curl up and sleep it out. However, the wind is supposed to have caused "cerebral excitement" in soldiers at lonely outposts and to have been responsible for outbreaks of suicide in the Foreign Legion.

The *simoon* is another desert wind that stops Sahara caravans with its dust clouds. It is a hot, south wind, which is also recognized on the Arabian peninsula and in Palestine and Syria; but over there it is called the *khamsin* rather than the *simoon* and natives boast about it to impress strangers in their desert.

In West Africa the *harmattan,* also called the *doctor,* is the dust-carrier. It has been known to carry the dust out over the Atlantic and impede navigation.

Australia's desert wind is the *brick-fielder.* Hot, dry and dusty, it blows from the interior of the continent to annoy the good housekeepers on the desert edge.

We have similar desert winds in North America. In the northwest, that is, in Washington, Oregon, and Idaho, it is the *palouser,* a dust wind that also brings light rain and leaves a muddy smear on furniture and floors.

The *Santa Ana* of California, a northwest gale which sweeps down on Los Angeles from over the cold deserts of Utah and Nevada, is better known than the *palouser.* It sometimes carries dust out into the coastal waters of the Pacific.

During the drought years of 1930–39 the "dusters" of the Great Plains were well known. These were called "black blizzards" when the dust load was unusually heavy, but they were not true-named winds with specific personalities, because the duster or black blizzard might blow from the west or southwest and it might be a dry northwester or a north wind. Improved soil conservation has made these winds less spectacular.

Desert winds are not all dust-carriers, by any means, because the prevailing winds, with their steady strength, soon sweep the desert clean and stabilize the up-wind supply of movable soil. The dust-carriers attack the stabilized supplies from a new direction and with increased strength, so that huge quantities of fine material are carried aloft and coarse grains are swept along closer to the desert floor. In the desert world it is always the exceptional wind which is personalized and which gives the desert its reputation for terrible sandstorms.

The desert traveler may stay many weeks in arid lands without experiencing a sandstorm, but his chances of seeing a good hard one are much better than the chances of rain, although it does rain in every desert—sometime.

On the edges of most oasis towns that I have visited in the Sahara there are ruined houses. These are in areas where current climate maps and statistics give the annual rainfall as four inches or less. When I asked how the adobe houses were destroyed, I always got the same answer, "It rained here, ten years ago," or "fifteen years ago," or simply, "It rained here, once." It takes quite a lot of rain to wash away foot-thick walls of sun-dried brick that have been baking in the desert sun for years, but storms of that magnitude go into the statistical averages for climatic studies of the desert world.

Once in the Sahara I experienced three rains in a few days, but none of them was heavy enough to let me wring water out of my shirt. Such rains in the course of a year may perhaps add up to a couple of inches, but when a torrential rain once in five or ten years is added, it brings up the statistical average to four inches per year.

Nowadays, with improved communication services and reporters located everywhere, even desert rains make headlines in American papers. Rain at Tamanrasset a few years ago made the news. Buildings were washed away and some people drowned. The Oued Tamanrasset, a waterless bed of gravel that had been dry for two decades, became a raging torrent for a few hours. In Egypt a twelve-mile piece of railroad was once washed out in a sheet flood at a point where there were no signs of a river bed. These are not river floods such as we read about every spring in temperate climates. These are single, local storms, dumping tons of water in an hour or so where no rain has fallen for years.

Some deserts get a little rain every year, although the quantity may be so trifling that it takes an exceptional storm to keep up the average for the region. This happens periodically in our own southwestern deserts when the big irrigation reservoirs become almost dry and then fill up in a few months.

Over the years most parts of Mongolia expect eight to ten inches of rain a year, but in the Central Gobi and the far west of the Mongolian plateau the average is only two inches.

A steady drizzle may last all day. A Gobi shower may be short and very wet, followed by a double rainbow. In early spring, rain turning to snow is not uncommon. A hard rain with thunder and lightning is also part of Gobi weather. But the real exceptions to desert dryness are the torrential downpours or cloudbursts. Every traveler who stays in Mongolia for a few months in summer and gets around at all comes back with the story of a real rainstorm.

Frans Larson states that a storm on July 5, 1929, drowned people, horses, sheep and cattle. It created a flood that swept all before it in a region so long under drought that the Mongols were on the point of moving their herds to the mountains.

"A few hours after the storm," says Larson, "the Gobi burst into bloom like a magic garden—green grass made a velvet carpet under the warm sun where, only a few hours before, dry, burned grass and dust covered the landscape."

The year before, the Central Asiatic Expedition was halted on the edge of such a storm in a more remote part of the Gobi. We moved on when the rain stopped and soon reached the center of the storm area. Ponds stood all over the landscape. Every hollow was a fresh-water pool. A well near the trail was completely drowned out, and many of the new lakes were deep enough to make good swimming holes. Hailstones were piled in windrows at the foot of hills.

Such storms, of course, do not strike the same locality every year, but if you cover a few thousand miles of the Gobi trails during a summer you are quite likely to have first-hand evidence of a desert storm.

In four months we encountered thirteen rainy days, but only the one described above did more than settle the dust for a day or two.

Even clouds are rare in the desert, and on only two or three days were there picturesque billowy clouds to add beauty to our photographs.

June, July, and August are the months which produce 70 per cent of the Gobi moisture. Snow may fall about once a month from September to April, and often weeks will pass without any precipitation.

Desert storms should never be treated lightly. Twice in the desert of northern Arizona I saw how swiftly they can bring danger far from the site of the rain. On the first occasion, I had a group of students, the Rainbow Bridge Expedition, out in Monument Valley. Some of the men were on a side trip and we expected them to return to our main camp soon. We knew they would have to cross a threadlike creek. Old-timers warned me that they could see a storm gathering over the mountains and said, "The creek will be dangerous in a few minutes."

I took one of the boys and drove to the crossing. Already the creek was a foot deep and swift as a millrace. We decided to leave a note on the other side to warn the truck driver that the creek was dangerous, and the boy with me stripped ready to wade the stream. We tied a rope around his waist in case he should slip. Even in the few minutes it took to make those simple preparations the creek rose ten inches. He waded across, left the note, and got back safely. When we untied his safety line the creek was nearly four feet deep and rolling stones along the bottom. Uprooted trees came tumbling down on the flood and plunged over big drops. Two hours later the field party came in. Yes, they had found our note, but the creek was back to normal and they forded it as usual.

My other experience was on the San Juan River near where it joins the Colorado River. We camped there on a big sand bar at the mouth of a side canyon. Precipitous walls hemmed us in on one side; the river on the other. During the night we were awakened by thunder high up on the desert plateau.

"Better be ready to climb the cliff," our guide said.

Some of us did climb to a little shelf, but one lad was so sound asleep that we could not wake him. Then the canyon back of us began to roar. The water started cutting away at the sand bar. We rolled the sleeper to safety just as his sand bed was washed away. Bushes, which at sunset had seemed as fixed a part of the scenery as the shrubbery on a lawn, were undercut and washed away. We saved the boats only by shifting them to a rock-protected pool.

Since these experiences I take no chances. If I do have to camp in a dry stream bed, I plan my exit to make sure no desert storm can trap me. Desert weather may generally be as monotonous and unspectacular as the flat plains over which it rules, but the spectacular exceptions come with the suddenness of a surprise attack and can be disastrous to those who are unprepared.

More than any other single feature, desert weather makes the desert different from the rest of the world. Its violence has sculptured the rocks, destroyed river banks, and blocked the course of drainage systems. It has shaped the landscape and completely altered the face of the desert.

VII

Desert Plants

THE DESERT IS A DEAD WORLD FOR MONTHS AT A TIME. SOME sections are barren for years. There are parts of the desert world known as five-to-ten-year deserts—and there are even thirty-to-fifty-year drought areas where no rain falls during those long periods—but sooner or later the water comes. When this happens plants take advantage of the event and the desert comes alive like a garden in the springtime. Brown barrens change to green carpets. Dark gravels are spread with colored flowers as varied and as brilliant as any that ever graced a dooryard garden.

This sudden change from somber wilderness to green meadows bright with blossoms is possible because root, branch, and seed of desert plants are always ready. The rains are like a starter's gun that sets the desert flora racing towards the goal of a bumper crop of seeds.

Both plants and animals have found ways to survive the absence or scarcity of water for long periods. Both have adapted to living where the sun beats down on the land unhindered by clouds, unfiltered by air moisture, and scarcely checked by any shade. The animals have an advantage over the plants, for they can move from shade to shade as the angle of the sunlight shifts throughout the day, but the plants have met the challenge in other ways.

Root systems are developed to get water when and where it is available. Stem, branch, and leaves adjust to do their job in air that is hot and dry. Even seeds are equipped to germinate only when temperature and moisture are suitable for allowing them to sprout and grow and flower and seed again.

In the American southwest there is a lag of three or four months between the starting-gun rains and the desert in bloom. If the floor of Death Valley is to be carpeted in the spring with millions of yellow sunflowers, white evening primroses, and pink desert five-spot blossoms, there must be much more than an inch of rain the November or December before. A quarter-inch rainfall will not affect the dormant seeds. Neither will an inch or more of rain in August or January. One of the wettest years in Death Valley's recorded history was 1941, but there was no burst of mass flowering because the rainfall timing did not suit the dormant seeds. How can seeds lying just below the surface of the desert tell the difference between a late summer cloudburst and a December rain? How can the seed measure the difference between a quarter-inch rain and one-and-a-quarter-inch precipitation, when sand at the seed's shallow depth is just as wet after one as after the other?

Botanists explain that soil temperature at the time the rains come and the leaching action of a heavy rain, as well as hours of daylight and temperature of the air at night, all play a part in controlling the germination of desert-adapted seeds.

Except for the way their seeds have adjusted to sprouting only when there is enough moisture to last through the growing season and let them reach maturity, these desert plants are like their relatives in more temperate climates. Sometimes a small percentage of seeds is fooled by early or late rains or by scanty showers, although most of the seeds lie dormant for four or five years before they sprout. Of course, the few seeds which are fooled by the weather never reach maturity.

The seeds of desert plants are also adapted to meet distribution problems of their area. For example, in the northern Sahara, R. A. Bagnold noted that many plants were of the tumbleweed variety and were scattered by the wind, but on the south edge there were more of the stick-tight seeds which could be carried against the wind by animals and so kept in the desert instead of being carried into more humid environments. Frits W. Went has noted that in our American deserts the smoke tree seedlings, which grow in dry washes, are always found 150 to 300 feet downstream from the parent trees but not 50 feet nor 400 feet. How do such seeds "know" when they have been carried far enough from their parent tree and yet not too far? It's so simple. The seeds are hard-coated to protect them against a long drought, and this hard coat must be mechanically broken before the seed will grow. Grinding and battering by sand or gravel in the torrential flood of a wash will do the trick. A flood which carries the seed 150 to 300 feet will break the shell and also leave enough moisture in the area for the tree to grow. Seeds carried farther will be ground to pieces.

The smoke tree and the crucifixion thorn have further adapted to the desert by giving up leaves almost entirely in order to prevent loss of moisture. They depend on their stems to carry on the manufacture of necessary food.

Even more remarkable than plants whose seeds "measure" rainfall and distance traveled, and distinguish between August and December storms, are the "quickies" of the Sahara; the botanists call them ephemerals. In one study of fifty species, many of them (14 per cent) sprouted the first day after a heavy rain. In forty-eight hours 62 per cent of them had germinated, and in three days sprouts were showing on 88 per cent.

In Arizona many plants are green in January, in flower by February, and bear ripe fruit in March and April. Then the plant dies down. But in middle Asia the cycle is usually complete in two or two and a half months, although the earliest shoots don't appear until March. Those plants seed in May.

The south Sahara quickies, however, break all speed records for the cycle from dormant seed to flowering plant to seed again. In the late 1920's at Timbuktu, O. Hagerup, the Danish botanist, says he saw *Boerhavia repens* scatter seeds eight to ten days after the parent plant had sprouted. Two weeks after the rain most other species in the area had flowers, and some were already bearing fruit.

These fast-growing plants have made no change in their roots or stems or leaves to meet desert conditions. Those collected in Arabia or Central Asia look just like dwarf copies of other grasses and showy flowering plants from temperate climates. Only by shortening their life cycle from months to weeks are they adjusted to an arid world. These plants survive by avoiding heat and dryness and "living" only in the short period when the desert meets their requirements.

Sometimes a patch of the Sahara will be as bare as a concrete pavement for years. Then, only a few days after a hard rain, it is purple with mustard flowers. Once I rode my camel into one of these colorful pastures. The ungainly beast made a fantastic picture as he wandered about with purple blossoms dangling from his ugly mouth.

Most of the so-called ephemeral desert species are annuals, but a few true perennials show similar characteristics in their stems and other parts above ground. They put out leaves, then flower and seed quickly, but they are more truly adjusted to life in the desert and survive the long drought between rains as thick roots or bulbs. The thick, below-ground parts of the plant are protected from the heat and high evaporation, and their stored moisture keeps the plant alive until the next rains. One such bulb, *Leontice eversmanni*, about the size of a potato was collected in Turkestan. It was kept exposed for about three years, during which time it lost very little weight by evaporated moisture. Even after that long, dry period the bulb was able to sprout.

Not all desert plants have thick water-storing roots. I remember once in 1925 when we met our soldier escort on the desert plain north of Tesnou in Central Sahara, and they invited us to tea. Teapots, glasses, tea leaves and sugar were produced from their camel saddlebags and water from a goatskin, but I saw nothing to fuel a fire. When one of the soldiers walked out over the plain a few yards and started digging with a knife, I joined him. He had found a finger-thick stick showing not over two inches above the gravel. In a few minutes he dug out a mass of roots that had spread over nearly a square yard of desert but only a few inches below the surface. That single stub protruding above the desert floor was the clue to enough fuel to boil a quart of water. I don't know what species of plant it was, but it had solved its water problem with its extensive root system close to the desert surface. When any rain comes these far-reaching shallow roots are ready to get a maximum share before it is lost by evaporation.

Tamarisk, or salt cedar, eucalyptus and mesquite have solved the problem another way. They get water in desert areas in much the same way that man does—by going down to ground water level. Man digs wells, while the plants send down deep taproots. When the Suez Canal was dug, the workers there found tamarisk roots one hundred feet below the surface. In the American deserts the same plant is called salt cedar and is a good water indicator. You can also find water where the mesquite grows if you dig, but you may have to dig down thirty to sixty feet!

Mesquite has been invading the grazing lands of the southwestern United States and northern Mexico for many years. In Texas alone it is estimated that it is costing the ranchers $30,000,000 a year in lost income. These trees and large shrubs may be an expensive nuisance to Texas ranchers, but they were a blessing to the Papago Indians before the white man brought in cattle.

In April, after the winter rains have ceased, and again in June and July, when summer rains occur, the mesquite blossoms scent the desert air with a fragrance which attracts the honeybees. Mesquite honey is clear amber in color and enjoyed by the Indians. Upright poles for the Papago house were forked posts of mesquite, and mesquite poles were used for stringer and siding. A snag, or crooked piece of mesquite tree, was often sharpened at one end and used as a plow, and the roots were made into cradle boards on which to carry the little papooses.

The fruit of mesquite is a pod much like a locust pod and was eaten raw, boiled, or fermented for a drink. The pods could also be stored in the ground for later use. They contain 25 per cent to 30 per cent of grape sugar and are richer in sucrose than sugar beets. The Papago chewed mesquite gum and used it as the Europeans once used gum arabic to cover flesh wounds. As long ago as 1871, 12,000 pounds of mesquite gum was produced in one county of Texas for the market in eastern United States, where it is used in making gumdrops and mucilage. Hundreds of pounds have also been shipped to Australia.

Mesquite wood is hard and beautifully colored like mahogany. It takes a high polish and makes beautiful souvenirs, but unfortunately the trees are not large enough to make good lumber for other uses. The pioneers in the southwest found the wood excellent for the hubs and spokes of their wagon wheels; and it also makes good fuel because it gives a very hot, long-lasting fire. None of these uses, however, is now as important economically as the grass for range cattle which the mesquite is replacing, so perhaps in spite of its excellent adaptation to the desert environment mesquite is doomed.

In parts of the Libyan Desert there are trees growing where it rains only once in fifteen years. Drainage from these rare storms is trapped in local catchment basins where shade and local rock formations protect it from evaporation and keep it from filtering deep into the earth. The tree whose roots reach such a hidden pool will survive on its secret well even in a ten or fifteen year desert.

When you reach a well four or five days' journey from the nearest water, and find it has been dug down 100 or 200 feet, the natural question is, who dug the well? How did he get water enough to live while he sweated at his digging? The same question applies to the mesquite bush with its roots thirty to sixty feet below the desert floor. How does the tiny mesquite seedling get enough moisture to live while it sends its roots to water level? That, I believe, is still one of the desert mysteries.

In the American desert the creosote bush has an interesting adaptation in a "keep-your-distance" root system. These evergreen bushes make an even pattern on the desert floor. In Death Valley where moisture is very limited there are wide bare spaces between the plants. On other deserts where rains wet the earth a little better the bushes are closer together, but the spacing is just as regular.

Creosote bush roots are wide ranging so that each plant gathers water from a large surface. They also excrete a toxic material which kills off any seedling starting too near established bushes. This system ensures plenty of elbowroom for the olive-green bushes and guarantees that living plants shall continue to have the water they need. The distance over which the toxic material is effective seems to be controlled by the amount of rain in the area. Wherever they grow, creosote bushes are evenly spaced, but the distances of this even spacing are greater where water is scarce and smaller where the rains are more frequent.

This interesting shrub goes even further in its desert adaptation. If a drought is long continued the plants lose their olive-green leaves and keep only the brownish-green ones; but if it lasts too long —say, five years or more—even the brownish-green leaves will fall and the plants die. Such long dry periods result in wholesale killing of creosote bushes. Because of the keep-your-distance root system, new seedlings can get their start only after the wholesale killing of old plants, although a season of heavy rains while old plants are still alive may reduce the effective range of their root inhibitors and allow new seedlings to start. That is why a stand of creosote bush is characterized by only a few age groups—groups of plants, all of which are five, ten, or fifteen years old, for example, but none of in-between ages.

In the American southwest there are about thirty-five million acres of creosote bush cover, and the pungent odor of its small leaves is particularly noticeable there after a rain. The plant is the source of an antioxidant chemical (nordihydroguaiaretic acid) which sells for about $35.00 a pound. If properly harvested, creosote bush could produce about a million tons of stock feed and two hundred million pounds of resin every two years.

Water is so essential to the life of plants that some desert seedlings send up only one or two leaves and then devote the rest of the growing season to the production of their root systems. *Pistscia vera* in Central Asia will develop a root nearly five feet long in one summer, and *Aristida pennala* has three to five roots as much as forty inches long three weeks after germination, although only a tiny blade of grass will show above ground. In general, the roots of desert plants are ten to fifteen times the length of the plant stem above ground.

The roots may do their job well and supply the plant with water, but the rest of the plant must also be adapted to desert conditions if it is to live and reproduce.

The date palm is often pictured as a typical desert tree; but it is an oasis dweller, and, like the oasis people who tend it, the date palm is not found except where it can be watered regularly. In the course of 365 days, the date palm in the Sahara desert loses twenty times (42,268 gallons) as much water as an apple tree in New York. It is often planted in water-bearing sands at the base of mountains bordering the desert. At Negrine, south of Tebessa, Algeria, on the northern edge of the Sahara, date trees are planted three feet deep, for that layer of sand is constantly supplied with water from the Aures Mountains. There the date tree's "feet" are truly in the water, but if planted above the water table it must be watered every few days throughout the year. It is a sunshine tree but it is not adapted to the drought of the desert world.

Intense heat, absence of shade, and dry air, all speed the evaporation of water from plants, and unless a plant can keep in water balance under these conditions, its desert days are numbered. Some botanists claim that there are few, if any, desert plants which can withstand wilting without injury, but D. N. Kackarov and E. P. Korovini say that in the Kara-Koum Desert of western Asia they found plants like *Scaligeria, Eremostachys,* and some others which had wilted leaves all day, showing that "the bulbs of these plants were incapable of maintaining the plants in water balance." They also found that the *Armoise* lose part of their leaves in summer and those which remain on the plant "roll up and so reduce the surface exposed to evaporation."

Many desert plants like *Lachnophyllum gossypium* have the stems and leaves covered with tiny hairs which protect the surfaces from evaporation as well as catch and hold any atmospheric moisture which might condense as dew. Even the breathing pores of some desert plants (*Altriplex cana,* for example) are only on the underside of the leaf and have valves that close during the day. Others, like the acacias, cut down the loss of water by shedding some of their leaves when the summer heat is on. Other plants, such as *Zygopbyllum dumosum* drop their leaves but keep the green leaf-stem which remains active through the hot season. Still another group, the Artemisias, let the large winter leaves at the base of the plant die off in summer but produce tiny summer leaves on the flowering shoots. *Reaumuria* produce small budlike branches between the winter leaf and the main stem. When the winter leaves are gone, these tiny parts carry on the plant's activity.

Some desert plants go even further, and whole branches of last-year's growth are allowed to die and fall in order to reduce the evaporation surface. Anyone who is unfamiliar with desert adaptation of plants would naturally assume when he sees the dead branches of *Calligonum comosum* that the plant is dying instead of merely adjusting its evaporation surface to the hot dry season so that it can be ready to continue its growth in the following favorable season. If whole branches are not lost, the green skin of some of last-year's growth will split and fall away, as in the case of *Anabasis articulata*.

In northern Mexico and southwestern Texas, the Jumete, or Candelilla, grows as bunches of reedlike stems with gray leaflets. The stems, as much as four feet tall and a quarter-inch in diameter are coated with wax. Without the wax coating such tall stems would evaporate more moisture than the roots could supply in that arid environment. The wax is collected in commercial quantities in the American deserts and used to harden other waxes. It takes a high polish, making it useful in shoe polish and floor waxes, but it is also used in sealing wax, candles, electrical insulators, and waterproof boxes.

Besides the Candelilla, there are evergreen plants which keep their leaves, but they are so thick and leathery or wax-coated that very little moisture leaves the plant from their surfaces. Still other plants have tiny, hard spines instead of leaves, but these do the work of leaves and keep down the water consumption.

It seems as if every one of the possible solutions to surviving in the desert has been found by some plant. As Kipling might have said, there are nine-and-sixty ways of meeting desert days, and every-single-one-of-them-is-right.

Apparently *all* the ways are utilized by the strangest group of plants in the desert world. These are the American cactuses—or cacti, if you remember your Latin. There are 1,700 species of these exotic plants known to the desert botanists and every one of them is native to America. Their history goes back 50,000,000 years to wet tropic species which existed before our western mountains were raised to act as barriers against moisture-laden prevailing westerlies. Every step in their adaptation from that humid past to the arid present can be illustrated by species still living in America. Some of them, like the prickly pear, have done quite well when carried to arid lands across the sea, and they will probably be ready to take over the moon should a few seeds drop from the trouser cuffs of the first man to stride across the lunar landscape.

The cacti are engineered to meet every phase of desert conditions. From the tiny, inch-diameter ball of the Arizona Pincushion in the Grand Canyon to the big, thirty-branched, twenty-foot-high Organ Pipe Cactus in Organ Pipe National Monument, they have used every conceivable method of desert adaptation.

The below-ground part of the plant is like the pipeline gathering system used in the desert oil fields. Roots and tiny rootlets are spread out in every direction near the surface of the desert, ready to carry all available moisture to the main stem whenever a shower dampens the ground. In addition, large cacti, such as the Giant Saguaro, have a taproot that anchors them against the strongest desert winds.

Aboveground most of the species are cylindrical, but they are fluted and carved to present concave or convex surfaces and oblique angles to the sunlight as the direction of that light changes minute by minute throughout the day. Smooth-stemmed cacti grow only in the shade of other plants.

It was once customary to say that cacti were covered with spines as protection against being eaten by animals. Botanists now give another explanation. It is known that there are more spines on the plants growing in the hottest sunlight. Studies of micro-climate have shown that it is much cooler in the shade than in direct sunlight. The conclusion is that cactus spines make a "lattice shade house" over the green parts of the plant so that they keep the "body temperature" of the cactus 20°F. cooler than would be possible for a naked cactus in its desert habitat. The curves and angles of the plant's body and the shade of its spines combine to reduce to a minimum the radiant heat striking the plant. Still, these do not prevent hot, dry air from surrounding the plant, and such air can evaporate moisture so rapidly that it could kill the plant. But cacti are protected against this, too. The spines and outer walls of the plant are resin-covered to prevent evaporation. Even the little areoles from which spines and flowers grow are pads with fuzzy centers to keep the heat out and the moisture in. All in all, the cactus has an air-conditioning system par excellence.

Nevertheless this "All-American" plant operates on a water economy system which assumes that there is never a surplus to be wasted and that the budget must stay in balance with adequate reserves to cover several successive bad years. It has no leaves because it has no surplus water to get rid of. A cactus does not receive as much moisture in an average year as a big tropical fern will receive in a single day. Compared to a corn stalk, whose leaves lose four quarts of water a day, or an apple tree in New York, which loses 2,166 gallons in 188 days of its growing season, a fifty-foot cactus loses about a thimbleful each day. Most assuredly the cactus plants operate on a budget which assumes that there will be years of low income; but regardless of those bad years the plant must continue to grow, to flower, and to fruit on schedule every year. That it does, year after year, in as rugged an environment as any in the world.

To maintain adequate water the cactus stores it behind evaporation-resistant walls. These walls expand and contract as the stored volume rises and falls. The fluted walls act like those of an accordion, allowing the pleats to fill out when there is a large volume of water and shrink into deep grooves as the volume shrinks. On my desk, as I write, is a cactus (a species of *Echinocactus*) which I water very rarely. I can tell when it needs moisture because the grooves are deep valleys, the ridges thin and sharp-edged. Then I flood the roots, and in less than a day the plant swells into a tight ball. The ridges and valleys almost disappear. It will be many months before it looks peaked enough to warrant another torrential rain.

Cacti are even able to repair leaks in their moisture-resistant walls when occasion demands. Desert woodpeckers drill holes in the Giant Saguaros for their annual nesting, but the Saguaro coats over the inside of the hole with a resin and suffers little moisture loss. When the woodpeckers leave, the elf owl takes over. The Papago Indians use the watertight linings of the woodpecker holes as water sacs. Healed scars on the large Barrel Cacti also testify to that plant's efficient repair system.

When you realize how completely and efficiently cactus plants have adapted to desert conditions, it is little wonder that artists consider it symbolic of the arid lands and often picture it even in other than its native American deserts.

VIII

. . . .

. . . .

. . . .

. . . .

. . . . .

Animals of the Desert

THE CENTRAL ASIATIC EXPEDITION WAS MOVING TO A NEW LOCA-
tion in the Gobi of Mongolia when a rainstorm caught us. We
crawled under our trucks for protection until the storm passed,
then continued on our way. Our route crossed a valley near a well,
then turned on the ridge and paralleled the valley. Soon after we
had turned, I noticed that the valley was filled with animals. The
flocks kept getting thicker until I turned to the Chinese cook beside
me and said, "I'd sure hate to draw water at the well for all those
sheep."

"Not sheep," the cook answered. "Antelope."

I did a double-take then and almost rammed the car ahead! The
cook was right; there were no sheep in the valley! Our leader, Roy
Andrews, called a halt just then and signaled us to get out and
look at the herd. The valley, perhaps a quarter-mile wide, was a
solid mass of antelope. They moved in an unhurried stream as we
studied them through our field glasses. Where they came from or
where they were going no one knew, but that river of antelope
was three miles long and a quarter-mile wide. We estimated
there were 25,000 head in the herd and nearly all females or
young.

As Roy said afterwards, "Probably that sight could not be duplicated anywhere else in the world, unless possibly in the African veldt."

Desert antelope were no novelty to us. We had been eating antelope meat twice a day for nearly three months. We had seen them in small groups of a half-dozen or so and in bands of fifty or a hundred individuals. We had hunted them from our trucks and knew their habit of racing along on a course almost parallel to our motors, then suddenly turning "to cross our bows" about seventy-five yards ahead.

Once I was able to maneuver my truck fast enough to get close to a buck and follow him. The speedometer needle swung up to forty-five miles per hour, and the animal was able to hold his distance ahead of me. We raced along for a couple of miles. When I was satisfied that he was going at top speed and just couldn't dodge out of my path, I dropped back and let him go.

There are no records that the two species (goitered gazelle, *Procapra gutterosa,* and desert gazelle, *Gazella sub gutterosa, hilleriana*) of antelope in the Gobi, or their near relatives, the gazelle of the Sahara and Arabian deserts, drink water in their wild state. In all three deserts they are found where no open water exists. They do have to eat, however, and you will not find them where vegetation is lacking. Apparently they can get all the moisture necessary for their physiological needs from the vegetation.

Their ability to move from one desert pasture to another, to exist without water to drink, to outrun their enemies and "get into high gear" from a standing start are all adaptations enabling these graceful creatures to live in the desert. They do not like the midday heat of the desert, and even good hunters cannot find them when they lie quiet in the shade of rocks or handy vegetation.

The Gobi storm which halted us just before the valley of the antelopes was much more severe nearer the head of the valley where we made camp late that afternoon. At that camp our zoologists had the easiest collecting they experienced all summer. The storm had killed scores of small birds and animals. Some had been drowned by the downpour and others had been killed by hailstones. All the collectors had to do was pick up the bodies and prepare the skins.

An inventory of the fauna collected in any desert will read like
a naturalist's sight record for more temperate regions. That is because animals can go wherever the environment temporarily meets
their needs, and many of them move into the edges of the desert
for short periods when their favorite food is found there. This is
why records of desert animals include many which are not especially adapted to arid lands. Some snakes and predatory birds have
been found living far out in the Libyan Sahara, so far from other
forms of life that their observers have concluded that they depend
on luckless migrants for their food.

Among the birds recorded from various deserts, the spring and
fall migrations of geese, ducks, cranes, etc., swell the list of species.
Grasslands bordering the desert are the habitat for many nesting
species. Some birds, like the sand grouse, fly great distances to get
water night and morning. We used to see them come whirling in at
dusk to one water point in a section of the Gobi where the only
vegetation was scanty bunches of grass.

Eagles, ravens, hawks, owls, falcons were all found nesting in
the Gobi badlands and made good pets for the expedition. But their
keeper used chopsticks to feed them chunks of meat; otherwise the
sharp beaks would have pinched his fingers in lightening-quick
grabs.

Wolves, foxes, marmots, gophers, desert hares—all are fairly
common in the desert near the mountains and in badland basins.

Out in the far western Gobi, the wild ass, or kulon, ranges in
small herds of one stallion with from four to nine or ten mares and
young. They go to water at least once a day about sunset and
will trot twenty-five or thirty miles. A Russian expedition during
1942–45 reported that the kulon's favorite range is small valleys
between mountains, the lake basins, and lower foothills. Dr.
Andrews noted that the mares herd in the summer and drop their
young on the plains well away from "ravines, gullies, or wolf cover."
The stallions stay near-by, but they do not mingle in the herd. The
little colts can do twenty-five miles an hour, as well as twist and
dodge, by the time they are a week old.

This Mongolian wild ass is a beautiful creature. Their fawn-yellow upper parts shade into pure white on the belly and rump spot. The mane is short and dark brown. A chocolate-brown band with white margins extends down the back from mane to tufted tail. The ears are longer than those of the Mongol pony but not so long as donkey ears. All in all, they are shaped much like a fine-bodied mule.

The kulon is not quite as fast as the antelope, but he can hold an average of thirty miles per hour for half an hour. This is as fast as his enemy, the wolf, can go. On short runs the kulon can do thirty-six miles per hour, and even forty to outdistance the wolf, but those speeds are in spurts, not long stretches.

The wild ass feeds on camel sage, onion grass, Gobi feather grass, and several other grasses of the desert plain. In the mountain valleys they have been seen grazing on wild alfalfa, along with both types of Gobi antelope and the hare, but if feed is available they seem to prefer grazing out on the plain a couple of miles from the mountains. They will race off the plain into a sand dune area if pressed too hard by hunters.

Many of the animals, birds, reptiles and insects found in deserts are not much different from their relatives in more humid areas. They are able to get along in the desert during months of favorable weather, but retreat to the borders of the arid land or to tolerable "islands" when heat and dryness become too severe. As long as they can find food and shelter from the midday heat, many creatures can live in desert areas without special adaptation. Most of them can avoid the intense heat by going underground in burrows or rock dens. Snakes, lizards, and various insects have little trouble keeping out of the heat, even though the desert floor can get so hot that it will cook them alive in a few minutes if they are forced out of their midday shelter. Desert rock temperatures may be 170°F., but a foot or eighteen inches below the surface it may be 100°F. cooler—a very comfortable 68° or 70°F.

Birds, of course, can avoid the heat by perching in any bush or shrub, for it is 40° cooler a foot above the ground. If there are a few leaves to cast a shadow, the bird can benefit by another 30° of "coolness." Desert creatures all learn the value of shade when the sun is high. I've seen donkeys crowd themselves against an oasis building to get the advantage of a ten-inch shadow cast by short, overhanging eaves.

Many, if not most, birds and some animals living in the desert practice birth control. They have smaller families than the same species living outside the hot deserts. The scarcity of food means that birds have to hunt over a greater range of territory to get the food they need for themselves and their nestlings. The greater distances which they must travel, of course, take more time than the short food forays of their non-desert relatives. They are further limited by the short working hours, which a long, but necessary, noon-hour rest enforces. Even if the birds could stand the temperature and did waste their energy by hunting through the heat of the day, it would do them no good, for the insects on which they live are in hiding then from the heat.

The "planned family" of desert fauna is not limited to controlling the number of offspring. It includes timing their arrival as well. Desert birds nest and start their families to coincide with the maximum growing season of the vegetation. In the Negev, that season is in March, but the same species would not nest before late April or May in non-desert Mediterranean areas.

On the southern edge of the Sahara the birds extend their breeding range into the savannah to take advantage of a larger food supply. In that same area the little lizard or chameleon does not reproduce until late autumn when the sycamore and charob trees blossom and attract the insect food they like.

Baby gazelle are born about a month after the peak of the rainy season, that is, during the climatic spring. In the northern Sahara this is April and May; farther north, in the Gobi and other Asian deserts, it is as late as June. In the southern hemisphere the climatic spring is, of course, in October and November.

Gazelle, deer, and sheep, if moved from the north to the southern hemisphere, adjust to the changed calendar in a year or two and have their young when vegetation is most luxuriant. Camels, however, are just as stubborn in their sex habits as in everything else. When moved from north to south they not only will not change their timing, they will not reproduce at all!

Some animals have made even more remarkable adaptations to desert conditions. The gazelles or antelope, which do not drink water, and the camels, which can go months without drinking, are true desert creatures. The Gila monster of American deserts, like the fat-tailed sheep, can live off its thick tail when food is scarce— just as the camel can use the fat in its hump when food is lacking. One lizard, the horrible moloch, found in western and southern Australia, is said to absorb water through its skin after a rain, and another Australian amphibian, the flat-headed frog or chiroleptes, apparently can absorb water through its skin, too, although it also drinks in a normal manner. It survives long periods of drought by resting in a burrow and storing water in its body. This is an adaptation few, if any, other animals have achieved. The flat-headed frog fills its urinary bladder, its subcutaneous tissues, and its peritoneal cavity with water. When filled to capacity it looks more like a rubber ball than an animal. Filled with water and buried in the soil a foot below the surface, it can withstand the dry season, even though the soil above it is baked by the sun; and native Australians in the desert sometimes use these buried frogs as a source of drinking water. The creatures must be exposed to periodic dehydration to keep in good health, and a dry chiroleptes will swell into a knobby round ball in two minuites if placed in a couple of inches of water.

Plants and most animals have solved the problems of desert living in much the same way. They get water from their surroundings one way or another, and they then conserve the water they get by preventing loss through evaporation. Some plants store water for drought just as the Australian amphibians, but there are a few animals whose adaptation to the desert surpasses that of both the plants and amphibians. These are the kangaroo rats, pocket mice, and jerboas.

These desert rodents have developed similar characteristics in different parts of the world, but they are not all the same species and even belong to different families. In the African-Arabian-Gobi deserts there are a half-dozen species, at least one in South Africa, two in the American deserts, and two in Australia. All have elongated hind legs enabling them to make long jumps. In the Gobi the kangaroo rats cover six or eight feet at a single jump although they are not much larger than a house mouse. Their long hind legs and very long tail make them look somewhat like the kangaroo, and when they get into a fight they use those powerful legs like their namesake. There, however, the likeness ends. They do not have pouches on the abdomen to carry babies in, but they do have either cheek pouches or gullar pouches to carry seeds back to their burrows.

The jerboas have gone all the way in desert adaptation. They can avoid their enemies by quick starts and spurts of speed. Their long tail is a rudder which enables them to dodge by turning at a right angle in mid-flight of a jump. They conserve moisture by spending hot desert days in underground burrows where the air is cool and moist, so there is even little loss of moisture from their lungs. When their burrows warm up, the little animals go out into the cool desert night to look for food, and they do not return until their shelter has cooled off. Their fur enables them to maintain a relatively even body temperature by insulating them against the air temperature changes they encounter.

Their kidneys can eliminate body waste of urea and salt in a solution almost four times as concentrated as that of man. Even the feces are much drier than those of similar non-desert rodents. It seems as if these jumping animals of the desert have used all the possible tricks for water conservation.

However, jerboas not only use every possible means of conserving water, they even manufacture what they need from the dry food they eat. These thoroughly adapted little animals have been found living in the Libyan Sahara fifty miles downwind from reliable vegetation. Apparently they depend on the prevailing wind to bring the seeds they need for food. Even in captivity they live for years on dry grain and continually maintain normal water balance in their bodies. Some other desert animals can live without drinking water if they can get succulent vegetation or dew-covered plants to eat. The predators, of course, can get considerable moisture from the animals they eat, and perhaps the little jumpers of the arid wastes supply a swallow or two of moisture to a thirsty carnivore who is quick enough to catch them.

There are a few corners of the desert world where you can catch a string of fish for dinner but their number and their size will not warrant an extended fishing trip. The few places in the deserts of Asia and Africa where fish are found are all hundreds of miles from normal, fish-inhabited waters. Their great distance from any natural open water makes their presence in the desert a real mystery.

At the oasis of Tamentit, in the Algerian Sahara, I photographed a school of minnows swimming in the waters of an irrigation ditch. This may not seem strange to those who do not know the desert, but in that oasis all the water comes from seepage-accumulation tunnels, or *foggara,* which have no connection with a true stream or lake and which are several hundred miles from natural open water.

I have seen French soldiers in the Sahara walking back to their quarters with large strings of fish from the irrigation ditches. They told me that they thought the fish tasted as good as the little ones they caught in France, but the natives of the oasis would not touch them. The natives gave no special reason; they just "don't eat fish."

Dr. E. F. Gautier, who probably knows more about the Sahara than anyone else, shows drawings of desert fish which look like our catfish, but those I photographed at Tamentit had more pointed heads than catfish. I am inclined to believe that there are several different species found in the Sahara. Some fish have been found in the permanent water holes of Tibesti in the Libyan Sahara, but I have never seen pictures of them. Blind fish have also been reported from Sahara irrigation tunnels. Those I saw appeared to be normal, but if there are blind fish in the desert they could have come through underground streams flowing in caves or cracks in the limestone. This explanation cannot apply when the fish are found in water which has seeped through miles of sand or sandstone. There is no doubt about the presence of fish in the Sahara, but how they got there is still a mystery.

One of the most interesting accounts of fish in the desert was reported by Dr. Roy Chapman Andrews in 1925. At Tsagan Nor, in the Gobi, his expedition camped on the east bank of a shallow lake. A strong west wind piled the water toward the camp, but at two o'clock in the morning the wind ceased and the waters rushed back into the shallow basin, leaving a mud bank three feet wide. Stranded on the mud were thousands of fish. Their flapping struggle to get back to the lake water, Andrews said, "sounded like the ripple of applause from a large audience." In the moonlight their wet bodies glittered like silver spangles.

There were fried fish for breakfast that morning but the sophisticated palates of the Americans found them "muddy" tasting. The Chinese members of the party liked them, however. They salted many and dried them in the sun.

The fish of Tsagan Nor were about eight inches long. They were a different species from those collected at Orok Nor, about thirty-five miles to the east, and though the lakes are not connected now they are in the same drainage system and must have been connected at one time.

Two theories are commonly given as explanations for the presence of fish in the isolated waters of desert basins. Some claim that the lakes in the Gobi are stocked by birds carrying the fish eggs from permanent streams. It is a possible explanation, except that it doesn't account for the fact that each lake has a single species and that near-by lakes have different species.

The favored theory in the Sahara is that the fish are survivors of more humid ages when their present habitats were connected with permanent streams of the prehistoric drainage system.

Whether the desert fish are survivors from geologic ages or hitch-hikers on migrating birds is still an unsolved problem of the desert. In the Gobi they must be able to bury themselves in lake-bottom mud to survive periods when the lakes dry up and the basins bake hard. In the Sahara this problem has not appeared, for the fish have only been reported in water that is now permanent.

The list of desert fauna makes an impressive showing on the printed page, but in the desert all species are rare. I once needed a gazelle from the Sahara for a museum study in comparative anatomy. Every morning we drove to some settlement on the northern edge of the desert and sent out native hunters. Every night they came back without the game. I traveled hundreds of miles in the desert on one trip and saw only three gazelle. It is true that we lived on antelope meat in the Gobi, but our cars ranged through more than 4,000 miles of the desert country. If there were no animals in one area, someone would find them elsewhere. Our zoologists put out their traps regularly, but often we were camped in an area where even their skill produced nothing.

There are many desert animals you can eat providing your food prejudices are neither too all-inclusive nor so strongly fixed that you will refuse to try an unfamiliar dish. The most palatable animal food in deserts is gazelle or antelope. The meat is better than mutton and as good as baby beef. The animals are pretty well hunted out in most deserts, especially where modern firearms are in use by the natives or where soldiers keep the peace and practice marksmanship. The kulon is sometimes eaten by Mongols in the Gobi, and various mountain sheep are found in higher altitudes on the borders of desert areas, but they are not as truly desert creatures as is the gazelle.

The marmots in the Gobi are eaten by the Mongols sometimes. Their flesh tastes like rabbit. Other rodents, including the kangaroo rats and jerboas, are also food for the starving but they are not standard items on many menus.

All birds are edible, but those which feed on carrion and even those which catch live prey are pretty strong meat. If the situation is desperate enough, many people will eat crow or eagle or any other tough bird they can get. The migrating birds are as good to eat if taken in the desert as they would be elsewhere.

All the snakes are edible, and there are some desert-living gourmets who claim that the thick tail of a big lizard is an appetizing meal when properly skinned and roasted.

Insects may be classed as desert food, and some species are recognized as tasty and nourishing by desert peoples. The desert locust is fried or roasted when in season and dried for future use. It has considerable food value and when a swarm is located the supply is abundant. R. M. Elton states that in Africa and Australia he has eaten forty-three species of insects, including the witchetty grub. This grub is so rich in food value that Australian natives are able to travel long distances in the desert with no other nourishment.

The list of desert creatures, of course, includes some undesirables —at least they are undesirable from the traveler's point of view. These are not numerous and they are far less vicious than desert fiction would make us believe. In all my travels I have never once found a scorpion in my shoes. The poisonous snakes I have seen (and half of these were dead) could be counted on my fingers. The desert commands respect in many ways, but I just cannot get excited about its dangerous and poisonous inhabitants. They are there, to be sure, but apparently they are more afraid of me than I am of them, for they are always hard to find.

Fear of a poisonous creature can cause as much damage as the creature's poison. Once in the American desert country we had a young biologist who loved a practical joke. He caught a scorpion and, holding it between thumb and forefinger, showed it to several of the boys. When one timid soul came toward the group, the biologist pretended to throw the insect at his face. The lad fainted. We got him to a hospital shortly, where a diagnosis showed that he had a weak heart and fear of being bitten by the scorpion had caused his collapse.

In contrast, we had another individual on the same party who was bitten by a small rattlesnake. At least he could show two tiny punctures on his arms where the fangs had struck. That chap was as calm as could be. We gave him emergency treatment with the snake-bite kit and he had no ill effects at all.

In the American deserts scorpions have statistics on their side to prove that they are the deadliest creatures. At least in Arizona the sting of a scorpion has caused more deaths than the bite or sting from all other poisonous creatures combined. Most of the victims have been very young children—because a single injection of the deadly poison can be fatal to a four-year-old, whereas an adult in good health will recover.

There are twenty-one species of scorpions in Arizona, but only two are deadly. These are found across the southern part of the state and in the bottom of the Grand Canyon. There are others, however, in Mexico.

The two deadly species of our southwest are streamlined as compared with the non-deadly species. The deadly creatures are about two inches long and straw-colored. Everything about them is slender—their bodies, their tails, even the pincers and joints of the legs. In contrast the non-deadly scorpions are thick and chubby.

The sting is a sharp, curved tip on the end of the tail. The quick flick of a scorpion's tail, like a suddenly released spring, drives the sting into the victim. When the sting has punctured the flesh, poison is squeezed into the wound from a sack at the base of the sting.

Favorite haunts of these little murderers are the dark corners of buildings, old stumps and lumber piles, and civilized places such as linen closets and drawers. Probably that is why I've seen so few of them. My desert wanderings have been too far away from the dark corners of civilization. Those I have seen were in oases or exhibited by Arabs in desert towns.

Non-deadly scorpions can also sting, but their poison acts locally to cause only swelling and discoloration. The poison from the two deadly species affects the whole body of the victim.

The tarantulas or bird spiders are large, hairy "monsters" which look ferocious and dangerous. Actually they are quite docile and nearsighted creatures. They can inflict a painful bite which, if not treated with iodine or some other good antiseptic, can become infected. Otherwise there is little danger from their bite and, anyway, they are more interested in eating insects than in attacking people.

The giant desert centipede, a creature six or eight inches long, has glands at the base of his jaws which produce poison. The jaws are strong enough to make a painful bite, and the poison will cause the area to swell, become painful, and get feverish. The spot may stay sore for weeks, and the bite is slow to heal, but it is not serious.

The rattlesnakes are not limited to deserts, but in the American deserts they are most active during the summer nights. It is too hot for them on the desert floor in the daytime. They cannot get along without water and most of their prey also needs water, so if you go to a desert water hole at night take a flashlight and watch your step. The rattlers will get out of your way if they can, but if you step on them or annoy them unduly they can strike back suddenly and effectively.

Snakes are not common in the drier deserts like the deep Sahara, for there is no water for them outside the oases. Even there they are not numerous, because oases are so densely populated and so intensively cultivated that the natives keep them hunted out. You are more likely to find them in the mountains bordering the desert, where food, water, and rocky hideouts are well suited to their needs.

In the Gobi of Mongolia, the Central Asiatic Expedition collected only one poisonous snake, a pit viper, and one non-poisonous species.

The pit vipers made life interesting one night. Camp had been made on a rock-bordered bluff to work the near-by fossil beds. During the night the temperature dropped suddenly. It was warmer in the tents than outside, and snakes sensed the greater comfort of the tents. One member of the party saw a snake cross a moonlit patch on the tent floor and reached for his collector's ax—only to discover other vipers near his bed. His shouts startled the rest of the tent's occupants. In the resulting melee more than two-score pit vipers were killed.

The spot was a sacred preserve for the Mongols and they would not kill any living thing on that bluff, which accounts for the unusual concentration of snakes. Three years later I visited the spot with two of the expedition members. We hunted the bluff carefully, turning over rocks and making a thorough search for vipers, but we could not find a trace of them.

In New Mexico and Arizona, one who is skilled at finding snakes may locate a Sonoran coral snake. They are not often seen because they are so very timid, but their beauty makes them a favorite subject for color photographs used to illustrate magazine articles on desert life. Narrow bands of cream color encircle the snake's body and alternate with similar bands of red and black. The sequence of black, cream, red, cream, black, cream, etc., of the Sonoran coral snake distinguishes it from other banded-color snakes. It is only about two feet long, and it has such short, verticle fangs that it requires a full bite to inject its poison. These pretty reptiles are often so sluggish that some people who have handled them claim it is difficult to make them bite. Others have been surprised at their agility when teasing was carried too far.

One of the ugliest creatures I have ever seen in the desert is the Gila monster. He was resting in the shade of a bush when I stooped under its branches in passing. He just looked at me, and I was in no mood to disturb him. He is a most unpleasant-looking fellow and all sorts of legends are circulated about him.

No doubt his best friends have not told him that he needs a new mouth wash, but his bad breath is not the gas of the death chamber as his enemies claim. Neither is his body a living septic tank. He has a normal body opening for the removal of fecal matter like all other animals. He *does* possess poison glands, but they are so far back in the Gila's mouth that he has to chew his victim in order to make it effective. If you can break away from the first bite before he gets to chewing your flesh, the poison will not affect you. If the poison does get into your system, it acts in much the same way as rattlesnake venom.

Ordinarily, the Gila monster prefers to get away from a person, but he can be cornered and teased into biting a stick. When he gets hold with his jaws he has bulldog tenacity and chews vigorously.

Deserts are generally quite free of disease, because the hot, dry air hampers germs as it does all other forms of life. Conditions in oases, however, are not as rugged as life on the open desert, and malaria has been reported in some Sahara oases near the Mediterranean coast. Malaria means mosquitoes. Ordinarily the little pests travel only short distances from their home, and a mile or two from their breeding place you would be safe. The desert, of course, is an exception for mosquitoes as for almost everything else.

During World War II sentries in Libya once saw "a cloud of vapor coming from the north which looked like a dust storm in the moonlight." This cloud turned out to be a swarm of mosquitoes. There were two breeding places from which they could have come. One was eighteen miles away; the other twenty-eight miles. The entomologists say that under ideal (for the mosquitoes) conditions and favorable winds the little pests might make a 200-mile journey into the desert.

Not all mosquitoes carry malaria; only the female Anopheles. They are the strong, silent type. They don't sing like the culicine mosquitoes which are not considered disease carriers. The Anopheles lands with its body at a 45° angle to its landing field; the Culex stands with its body nearly parallel with its resting place. If a strong, silent mosquito drills you at a 45° angle, play safe and reach for the chloroquine.

Probably among the scores of thousands who visit the deserts of the world not a handful will even see a snake or Gila monster; fewer still will be bitten by a poisonous creature; and none will get malaria from a cloud of mosquitoes carried into the arid lands from a swamp many miles away. Probably more children are drowned in desert wells in Libya than die of scorpion bites in Arizona. But the scorpion looks so terrifying that he is more newsworthy.

Desert animals, with the exception of Gobi antelope, never dominate the landscape. The traveler who honestly can report many species must be either a most alert observer or a very lucky person, for each creature sighted and identified marks a red-letter day of a desert journey.

IX

. . . .

. . . .

. . . .

. . . .

. . . . .

Nobody Loves a Camel

The 'orse 'e knows above a bit, the bullock's but a fool,
The elephant's a gentleman, the battery-mule's a mule;
But the commissariat cam-u-el, when all is said and done,
'E's a devil an' a ostrich an' a orphan-child in one.
    O the oont, O the oont, O the Gawd-forsaken oont!
      The lumpy-'umpy 'umin-bird a singin' where 'e lies,
    'E's blocked the whole division from the rear-guard to
    the front,
    An' when we get him up again——the beggar goes an'
    dies!

'E'll gall an' chafe an' lame an' fight——'e smells most
    awful vile;
'E'll lose 'isself for ever if you let 'im stray a mile;
'E's game to graze the 'ole day long an' 'owl the 'ole night
    through,
An' when he comes to greasy ground 'e splits 'isself in two.
    O the oont, O the oont, O the floppin' droppin' oont!
      When 'is long legs give from under an' 'is meltin'
    eye is dim,

The tribes is up be'ind us, and the tribes is out in front—
It ain't no jam for Tommy, but it's kites an' crows
　　for 'im.
　　　　　　　From "Oonts" by Rudyard Kipling.

Kipling really knew his camels. No one has given a better account of the creatures than that in his two stanzas quoted above, although there is a vast literature on the subject, full of conflicting statements, some romantic fancy, and, in recent years, a few facts. The facts about camels are stranger than the legends they shatter.

Camels seem to have been known in Iraq about 6,000 years ago and in Egypt for half as long. Apparently it was early in the sixth century B.C. that they plodded into a permanent historic position on the freight line between the Nile and the Red Sea. Their seniority still entitles them to that run, as well as to the feeder lines for freight trucks, railroads and airlines, but they are fast being pushed off the trunk-line routes across the desert world.

Fossil hunters every now and then dig up camel bones in various parts of Africa, but he disappeared from there long before he was brought back as a domestic animal. In fact, the paleontologists insist he is a hang-over. He looks like one, of course, and he belongs to the Pleistocene period of the earth's history but was too ornery to become extinct with the other unprogressive creatures like the wooly mammoth. He'll probably also survive the age of trucks and airplanes that are now replacing him in freight service, because camel breeders of the Chamba tribe continue to raise the beast and have been offering him for sale in the meat markets of Algeria. Instead of carrying freight for six months and loafing in pasture for the next six months, he will now loaf all the time and fatten up for not-so-juicy steaks.

My intimate acquaintance with the camel began at In Salah, Algeria. The evening of our arrival there, the army physician, a Dr. Nicole, suggested a swim for the next afternoon. This amused all of our party. Every civilized American knows that you don't go for a swim in the middle of the Sahara, but the doctor tolerated our kidding.

"We'll ride out on camels," he said. "We'll start about two o'clock, so you better wear pajamas. It is still warm here in October and light pajamas will be more comfortable than what you are wearing this evening. Sandals are better than shoes, too."

The next afternoon the younger members of our party gathered outside the Officers' Mess. The pebbled plain near the adobe building was dotted with strange-looking humps. They resembled poorly piled stacks of brown wool, but each had a thick protrusion at one end which bent and twisted like an animated stovepipe. The most ridiculous little whisk broom waved occasionally back and forth at the other end of the wool stack.

"These are the riding camels," said the doctor. "I see they have a real Tuareg saddle for you; the one with the cross in front."

"You call that leather-covered piece of board a saddle?" I asked. "Where are the stirrups?"

"A proper camel saddle doesn't have stirrups," the doctor assured me, as we walked over to the animated wool stacks.

"It is easy to mount the camel, Tuareg fashion," he added. "Take the reins in your left hand; kick off your sandals; place your left foot on the left knee of the camel, then swing your right leg over the back of the saddle and get comfortably seated."

Gingerly, I followed instructions. I hung my sandals on the cross of the saddle and put my bare foot on the camel's wooly front leg. The wool tickled my tender foot. The camel wiggled his leg. I stepped back onto the gravel.

"That's all right," called Dr. Nicole. "Don't be afraid. Just put your foot firmly on his leg and swing into the saddle."

I stepped firmly on the wooly leg; swung my right leg over the back of the saddle, like a ballet dancer doing the splits—but I never got comfortably seated.

Perhaps you know, but I didn't, that the ship of the desert launches *stern first*. Before my pajama-clad anatomy crashed onto that board seat, the hind-end of the camel went skyward. I pitched forward and bashed my chest against the front of the saddle. Before I could catch my breath the other end of the creature came up. There I was, eight feet above the desert, with no place to put my feet. Doc saw them dangling. "Can't you see that neck out in front of the saddle?" he asked. "Put your foot on that and balance yourself."

I looked at the wool-covered, two-by-four-set-on-edge which held the pinhead to the camel's shoulders. My feet were not intended to rest comfortably on any such narrow rail but I tried. First the foot slid off on one side; then it slid the other way.

"No! no! Not that way," shouted Doc. "You're supposed to grasp the skin of the camel's neck between your big toe and the next one to it. Use your toes for pinchers and your foot will balance on the ridge. That's why camel riders are barefoot. Shoes would wear the skin off the animal's neck and make him sick."

There came a day, weeks later, when I could hold one foot on the camel's neck with my toes, but I never did learn what to do with the other foot. Mounting is only a small part of camel riding, but, at least, I was sitting high and could watch the others.

Little Massaouda, the doctor's pretty Arab wife, was last to mount. Swathed from head to foot in white silk veils and shawls, she floated unassisted into her saddle. While I watched her, my foot moved a little on the camel's neck. That means "giddap" to a camel and the brute started to walk away. I grabbed for the saddle cross. Soon I was righted again and rode over the desert with exactly the same motion as grandma used in her little old rocking chair on our side porch at home.

In slow motion a rocking chair eight feet above the ground isn't bad transportation on a warm October afternoon, and the Sahara seemed a restful, romantic vacation land. But my pajama-clad comfort was doomed.

Massaouda was an outdoor girl. She didn't wear jodhpurs and sweaters, like the Wild West girls, but she could ride! Shawls and veils were no handicap when she decided on action. Her little brown foot began to tickle her camel's neck, and he began to trot. This was all right for Massaouda. She understood the rhythm of a camel, but it wasn't all right for me.

When her camel swung into action, my stupid animal did the same. Massaouda flew across the desert like a cloud of streamers.

Mongol lamas in the Gobi.

A group of Mongol women.

A Mongol boy mounting a camel.

Tuareg nobles—veiled men of the Sahara.

A group of young Tuareg women.

The goatskin tent with matting walls used as a "palace" by the King of the Tuaregs.

Navajo women at their looms.

An artesian well in the northern Sahara.

The oasis of El Kantara in the northern Sahara is irrigated from a river.

The central square in the oasis of Oued Djellal near Biskra.

Small irrigation ditches raised on adobe walls carry water long distances
to storage basins in Sahara oases.

Gathering dates from a date palm.

Water from a *foggara* flowing into an oasis garden. The stone across the irrigation ditch serves as a "water meter," and the garden owner buys the water flowing between one or more "teeth."

Aerial photograph showing walled garden plots in the Sahara along the Algerian-Moroccan border.

Negro water carriers at In Salah.

The garden around the muddy spring at Tadjemont.

The water hole at Tigelmimi in the Algerian Sahara—a natural cistern.

At an ancient well in Saudi Arabia donkeys are used as a source of power to pull up goatskins of water.

A section of the Arabian pipeline system, carrying crude oil from the eastern Saudi Arabian fields to the Mediterranean port of Sidon.

Pretty, no doubt, if I could have watched her ride, but my camel was trotting, too. I began to go up and down.

Observers of that ride have reported that I was suspended in mid-air for the duration of the trot. The statement is untrue. I hit the board saddle at every jump, and thin summer pajama pants have no padding where I needed it. However, the leather on the saddle kept the slivers out of me.

When we reached the edge of a palm grove, our native escort signaled a halt. They made strange gutteral trills and my ship began to founder. The front end plummeted earthward and I almost sailed over the bow, but the saddle horn caught me. Then the stern fell from the sky in an elevator drop, and my ship of the desert settled onto the plain like a freighter that has gone aground on a mud bank.

Yes, we had our swim in the desert, for just beyond the fringe of palm trees was a pool of fresh water. A springboard at one end made it an ideal swimming hole. The heat and dust were forgotten as we swam in that oversized irrigation basin on the edge of the desert oasis. We stayed there till sundown, then started the long ride back to our quarters. While we rode a big, yellow harvest moon swung up through the palm trees, and frogs began their evening chorus. Moonlight made romantic, slender shadows of our little fleet; shadows that bobbed and swayed like rowboats on an evening lake.

Since that first ride on camel back, I have learned that the camel really is a strange creature. He is so docile that a little child can lead a string of six or eight individuals; so vicious that he will bite a man or shower his master with evil-smelling spit. He is so timid that the Arab phrase for a shy little girl is "bashful as a camel," but Arabs also swear that there are 11,000 devils in the head of every camel. He has been domesticated for thousands of years, long enough for legends about him to be accepted as fact. He carried the commerce of Asia, Africa, and Arabia for centuries before sailing ships rounded South Africa to bring spices and rare silks from the fabled East. He has been almost as necessary to man in the desert world as the water holes. In spite of his long association with man and his essential contributions to ancient, medieval and modern civilizations, there is probably less factual information known about the camel than about any other domestic animal. Even first-hand information about him differs with each informant.

We were making one of the first motorcar crossings of the Sahara when the camel most impressed me. The cars were stopped on the northern rim of the desert, when a caravan came up out of the south and plodded by with slow, majestic strides. Those camels looked so haughty and sagacious that I remembered the remark of a literary friend who called them "the Ben Franklins of the animal kingdom." They seemed to embody the storied wisdom of the East, and they really made me apprehensive about attempting the desert crossing with gasoline-powered machines instead of intelligent animals who knew the desert and could meet its terrors unafraid.

At that time I believed all the legends I had heard about the camel. He had tremendous powers of endurance and could travel great distances without food. He could always go ten days without water because he had storage tanks in his stomach and in the hump on his back. His terrific speed was proverbial. His foot was broad and had a "sponge-rubber-like" construction that enabled him to walk over loose sand without sinking. Most important of all, he knew his way about the desert, and if his master got lost in a sand-storm the trusty mount would lead him first to water and then to the home camp.

But, one by one, I have found my camel legends shattered and replaced by stranger facts. There is no question about a camel's spongelike foot. Every time he puts it down you can see it spread and flatten like a soft automobile tire. It does not feel soft, however, when one of the brutes steps on your bare foot and rests at least half of his 990 pounds on it. When they were developing special truck tires for off-road travel in the sand desert of Arabia, the Arabian-American Oil Company's engineers considered the anatomy of the camel's foot and built tires on the same principle. The strange fact is that a camel has to learn to use those especially-adapted-to-sand-travel feet when he gets into the dunes, just as a truck driver has to learn sand-driving tricks.

The white *mehari* I rode for several months was brought up on the desert plain. When we got into the sand dunes that animal floundered and sank into the sand like a horse in a snowdrift, but the hard-hoofed little horses ridden by our escort had no problem at all. They just trotted over the dunes or walked along without trouble. Other camels in our caravan had less difficulty than my mount, but they had been in sand before. On rock or gravel plains the camel's feet are often badly cut. In the Gobi we used to patch the cut feet by sewing pieces of leather or auto tires to the live hide. The needle didn't hurt the camel and the patch protected the foot.

Once as we neared an oasis in Sahara, our trail disappeared in the sand. It was after dark so we decided to wait until morning to search out the route. However, a young lieutenant at the military post was anxious about his replacement, who was with us, and led a search party which soon located us. Our rescuers all rode horses!

"Why didn't you come on camels?" I asked.

"Because we were afraid we'd get lost, too," was the answer. "Horses, you know, can travel faster over the sand dunes than camels anyway, but if we got lost we could let the horses take us home. Camels haven't that much sense."

Years later I learned that camels are far more apt to get lost themselves than they are to rescue a lost master. In the Syrian Desert where there are great herds of camels, the Bedouins say that a camel will often stop in an attractive piece of pasture, or loiter over a favorite fodder plant and let the rest of the herd graze on without noticing. By night the herd has disappeared and the lone camel is lost. He runs around moaning and is unable to find his companions. Observers say the camel seems to lack the sense of smell or any instinct which will help him find the herd. Maybe he is too stupid to use the senses he has.

The herdsmen must stay with the large herds or many more of their charges would stray and get lost. This is why they do not search for strays until the return to camp at night. Then a man who has lost a camel will stroll through the camp singing his herd song. If the lost camel hears the song, he may walk toward the herder. Other camel men may recognize the stray and return him to his proper herd. In any case, if a lost camel is found, it is the result of the herdsman's search, not any sixth sense belonging to the camel.

A good riding camel usually walks with a long, regular step which is a very comfortable rhythm for a rider. Some say that the rhythm of Arab music is patterned after that of the camel, and it may well be, for caravan men often sing on the trail and it would seem easier to follow the metronome of the camel rather than to sing on an offbeat.

When prodded, a camel will trot, but riders, at least in the Sahara, do not keep that pace very long at a time. In Arabia, riders also make their mounts gallop on occasions like a surprise attack. How a man can stay up on a galloping camel, I don't know. The only time I ever saw them use that pace was once when our motorcars frightened a caravan. The galloping runaways scattered boxes and bales all over the desert. Each camel looked like a pair of circus clowns on stilts under a canvas animal trying to imitate a galloping horse. Stilt-legged creatures like the camel just do not seem made for graceful gallops. For fast movement, camels do best at an un- hampered full swinging trot at around sunset.

Unfortunately, there are no sports statisticians to compile accu- rate records and settle arguments on camel speeds, loads, and dis- tances covered; but there are numerous stories about how fast and how far camels can travel. Most stories, however, do not give the other details necessary for comparison.

Sahara military men will argue that in a race between a horse and a camel, the camel wins if the distance is long enough; on a short course the horse wins. Personally, I think it depends also on the individual horse and camel. Still, when the Bedouins of the Syrian Desert went on raids, they held the camels in reserve and used horses for the initial surprise. This seems to indicate agreement with the Saharan belief that horses are faster on a short course.

There are records of Sahara camel riders who covered fifty miles in a day, and even 250 miles in five days in emergencies. Dr. L. Cabot Briggs, quoting Monod, reports a ride of 370 miles in six days, which tops anything I have ever heard of. These are exceptional cases and usually represent winter journeys in Africa, but there is one account in Egypt of 281 miles ridden in ten days in May.

In Arabia both speeds and distances covered seem to be greater than in the Sahara. This may be on account of better food, milder climate, and a greater interest in camel breeding. The Rwala consider that a good camel can travel 125 miles in twelve hours, and forty miles is counted a short day's ride. One rider, fleeing for his life, covered 166 miles between sunup and sunset. Another rider covered 312 miles on a round trip in "two daylights." After such forced marches, the camel must rest in pasture for at least three months.

Miles per hour, total elapsed time, and distance covered are only part of the story. It should also include maximum temperature during the movement, weight of the "jockey," size of the camel, elapsed time since its last drink, and its condition at the end of the journey. Most camel men are very reluctant to push their animals anywhere near their capacity, because it takes them so long to recuperate from hard work. Five miles an hour is a good pace for a riding camel in the Sahara. Caravans travel only about two and a half miles an hour, and a five- or six-hour day is usual. Twelve or thirteen miles a day is a short journey, but it is usual for migrating tribes in Arabia, because it gives the animals time to rest and forage. There is one Arab story which claims that the Creator forgot to give the camel a brain and tried to make up for it by giving him extra stomachs. Accordingly, the camel's idea of heaven is a great stretch of pasture where thorny plants are far apart so that he strolls leisurely from one bite to the next, with plenty of time to enjoy each individual mouthful.

In many respects the camel is a fragile beast. He can take water and food at irregular intervals, but he demands compensatory leisure to recuperate after any excessive effort. If he is kept too long in an oasis where the only food is good green fodder that a horse would relish, the camel goes on a hunger strike. When this happens, his master force-feeds him with a mash of crushed date stones and water. With one hand the camel's mouth is held open, and a handful of mash is thrust arm's length down his throat. He is a temperamental creature who must have six month's vacation every year in pasture to his liking. If he doesn't get exactly what he wants, he will die—just to be spiteful! Officers of the Sahara Camel Corps know this, but such unreasonable demands on the part of a government servant cause consternation in the ranks of those concerned with paper work. Nevertheless, the camel insists, so each soldier of the Corps owns two camels. One is in pasture while the other is used on patrol.

There are those who claim the Tuareg camels are bred for speed. Equally good authorities say the Tuaregs keep no "stud book" and that the *mehari*, or fast riding camel, is of the same lowly origin as the pack camel. The difference is that a given camel looked promising in his youth, so the Tuareg master gave him a little better food and better training than the other calves. This makes the *mehari* just a likely youngster who was subsidized in a college education and was graduated into an aristocratic job instead of plodding along with less athletic members of his generation.

In Arabia a fifth-generation female and a ninth-generation male are recognized as thoroughbred if the ancestral dam was a well-formed animal mated to a thoroughbred male and each succeeding generation of dams covered by thoroughbreds. Such matings must be certified by reliable witnesses. Different breeds are named for the district to which the original dam belonged, as the Oman, Sararat, etc.

Whether the Tuaregs keep a stud book or not, they are past masters of the art of training camels. Those freighters of the arid sea are the greatest grumblers in the animal kingdom. They complain with a loud voice when you make them kneel to put a load on their backs; and they complain with equal anguish when you make them kneel to take it off. But not the Tuareg camel. He kneels in silence.

There is good reason for this silence. In the days before the French occupation of the desert, the Tuaregs enjoyed a reputation as the Apaches of the Sahara. Noisy camels could easily give away a secret hiding place before a raid and destroy the advantage of surprise attack. This is why Tuareg-trained camels are as silent as a desert night.

A camel will not stand without hitching like a well-trained horse. If you let him out of your sight for a few moments and expect to find him when you return, you must hobble him, for you won't find hitching posts in the desert. His legs resemble stilts with hinges. One hinge lets the leg bend forward. The one at the knee bends back. When the camel is settled on the ground with all four stilts neatly folded in place like the blades of a Boy Scout jackknife, you wrap a rope around the left front knee. He can still do a creditable three-legged race, but not for long. If you hobble him at night in scanty pasture, he won't be more than five miles away by daylight, but it may take hours to find him. Sometimes we used to hobble our riding camels by tying the two front feet so that they could not move more than eight or ten inches at a stride. This was only done on short journeys when grazing was not essential to the beasts' health.

The best riding camels are females. They have a reputation for greater endurance than the males and can travel longer without water or good pasture. They also endure heat better, according to the Bedouins of Arabia. During the rutting season, in February, the males are easily exhausted, sometimes they can't even get off the ground.

When a calf is taken away from its mother, the latter will moan for days. But if the calf has died, the owner may cover a healthy calf with the skin. Then the bereaved mother will accept the foster child and stay "fresh" so that she can be milked. Otherwise she would dry up and the owner lose both the camel and the fresh milk. Sometimes the bereaved camel will moan until it gets to be a habit. If a cord tied around her mouth doesn't cure the moaning, natives advise "either butcher the brute or sell her and let a new owner be annoyed."

There are several other bad habits that are serious. Some riding camels will shy at anything and even start to run away the moment a rider dismounts. It is customary for a rider to guide the mount by striking her shoulder with his heel, tapping with a stick, or with pressure on the sides of her face with the reins. Occasionally a camel will get "notional" and refuse to be so guided. Another bad habit when on the march is to run from plant to plant sniffing each one but not eating any of them. Probably the worst habit of all is sudden kneeling. This corresponds to bucking in a horse and is likely to produce the same headlong flight of the rider.

The Bedouins say that camels with these bad habits are "guilty of death," because in the desert they could easily cause the death of a rider. If a purchaser of a camel in Arabia discovers any one of these habits within twenty days of the purchase, he can return the animal and his money must be returned.

How big a load a camel carries will depend on many things. If you are new to the desert, the size of the load may depend on how good a bargain you make. This is why scientific expeditions buy camels instead of renting them. An owner will vary the load according to the length of journey, time of year, temperature conditions, distance between water holes, available pasture, and, above all, the condition of the camels. After all, they represent a capital investment comparable to horses, and no owner likes to jeopardize his investment.

Accordingly, loads vary from 200 pounds per camel to 1,200 pounds. The camels introduced into the United States in 1856 could carry 1,000-pound loads and travel thirty to forty miles per day without water for six to ten days in winter. On July 16, 1856, the U.S. Government report states that "Yesterday the camels drank water for the first time in 26 hours. Although the day had been excessively hot they seemed to care little for it." The report compares this performance with mules "which would have been set wild in such weather and become useless, if not break down entirely." Daily distances at that time were twenty-four to thirty miles compared to forty miles in cooler weather.

Those camels were not average, however. They were the biggest and strongest animals that could be found in the eastern Mediterranean. Then, too, the vegetation in the southwestern United States, although useless as feed for horses or mules, was luxuriant camel fodder. On the Central Asiatic Expeditions of the American

Museum the normal load was 400 pounds per camel in the Gobi. The caravan traveled twelve to fifteen miles a day in June and July. Even under those circumstances, two or three camels, about 2 per cent of our caravan, were lost each season. They had been on the trail since March and in unknown territory, so all travel was in daylight. On the well-known trails, camel men would only move at night so that the animals could feed during daylight.

The importance of the camel to the desert nomad can hardly be overemphasized. Even the Arabic language confirms this importance, for there are hundreds of words to describe the animal. A single word for camel will convey the beast's age, sex, color, size, state of health, and defects. Other words will convey the idea of a group of camels—whether a small group, a large group, running free in pasture or in organized caravan, etc. A word for watering camels will explain that the animals leave pasture, water, and return in one day; that they reach water one day, spend the night, and return the next day; or indicate the various stops on a four-day round trip. In other words, the Arabic vocabulary on the subject of camels is rich, varied, and explicit in detail—far beyond the comprehension of a Westerner.

The camel's place in the Arabic language is no more important than in the daily life of the nomad. In the desert the camel is transportation. Without the beast, the nomads could not move their possessions as the seasons dictate their living areas. Next to its importance as transportation is the camel's use as food. Its milk is drunk by all people who raise the camel. In winter pastures it is sometimes the only drink the herdsmen get for weeks. Although it contains no fat, and so cannot be used to make butter, it is used for cheese. Whenever we entered an oasis in the Sahara the local sheik always sent a bowl of camel's milk for us to drink. I never refused it. To do so would have been discourteous, of course, but I fortunately rather liked it, even though it tasted much like watered milk.

Although camel's milk will not make butter, the camel is said to have been the cause of the discovery of that delicacy. The legend is that rich milk from goats carried in goatskins slung on camels' backs was churned to butter by the rhythmic movement of the animals' stride. Whether the story is fact or fiction, it *is* true that desert people churn butter by shaking the cream in a goatskin.

Camel meat is eaten by all camel-raising people, although where the need for transportation is great, only old, sick, or dying animals are butchered. Camel meat has long been available in the city markets of Iraq and Egypt and, more recently, in Algeria. The camel steaks I have eaten in the Sahara tasted like beef, except that the meat was dry and coarse. A really important banquet in Arabia will include roast camel. The animal is roasted whole and stuffed with a whole sheep, which is in turn stuffed with a fowl stuffed with boiled eggs stuffed with rice! Nomad epicures claim that the hump of a young camel is a really delicate and tasty morsel.

Wool from the camel is spun and woven into clothing or tent cloth. If the animals are on the march when they start shedding their winter coats, the caravan men collect the wool as it falls, or they may pull off loose patches. Each animal will produce six or eight pounds of wool a year, but the men are careful to take only the wool that is falling naturally, because they claim the animal will catch cold if deprived of his coat too fast. In the Gobi the caravan boys spend their evenings in a camp carding the wool and next day spin it into yarn as they walk beside their charges. The yarn is easier to carry than the raw wool, and it brings a better price in the market at the end of the journey.

Leather made from camel hides is used for many household and personal items by camel people. We have camel-hide trinket boxes, bags for storing clothing, and sandals made by Sahara nomads. Like the pig at the Chicago stockyards, every part of the animal is used except its squeal.

The most widely accepted legend about the camel is the one most recently shattered. This concerns his drinking habits, and it has at last fallen before the attack of carefully conducted scientific investigation. Most travelers have accepted it as fact that a camel drinks less than other animals in the first place and, more important still, that he can store up enough water to last for ten days without drinking. Once when I had to take my young son to the circus I asked the camel men what their experience was with the camel's drinking habits.

"They drink about as much as a horse of equal weight," was the answer, "and we water them every day."

In the Sahara I learned that they start training camels to go without water while they are calves. When they are trained to abstain for four days regularly, they have no difficulty, as adults, on a journey for six or eight days—and ten-day intervals are possible. "But you have to give them enough to make up for it after such abstinence, and she'll collapse if forced to endure more than two or three such intervals in succession." In less arid areas regular watering periods are every two or three days; and in some parts of Arabia they prefer to water every day, but two- or three-day intervals do no harm.

Lieutenant Colonel N. Prejevalsky reported that his camels drank six gallons of water a day on hot days in the Gobi. Some travelers from Egypt say that a camel takes five gallons the first drink and ten gallons the next one. Another authority says that "a camel working in moderate weather requires nine to twelve gallons of water" and that "they drink every four or five days."

There is so much variation in eye-witness accounts of the camel's drinking habits that one needs an electronic brain to compile statistics on his past performances. However, Drs. Knut and Bodil Schmidt-Nielsen have shattered the legend that a camel can fill up "storage tanks" with water for a long, dry spell. They have produced facts to show how the animals endure long desert marches without water. Their studies, conducted at Beni Abbes Research Station, Algeria, for UNESCO show that the adaptation of the camel to life in an arid world is far more elaborate than the simple addition of water storage tanks to his anatomy.

The camel, like the sheep and cow, has a stomach divided into four sections. The first and largest is called the "rumen." In the camel there are little sacs in the rumen wall which are not found in other animals. They are called water sacs and were supposed to be the water storage tanks. The Schmidt-Nielsens discovered that all the sacs in a camel had no more than five to seven liters capacity, which, if filled with water, would be of little use to an animal the size of a camel. However, the sacs did not contain liquid. They were filled with food and not much liquid. The rumen contains a smelly, green substance, which, when analyzed, proved to be coarse vegetation and digestive juices. Its salt content was nearly the same as that of camel's blood, which is a long way from being water.

Many desert people and a few Western travelers have used the vile-smelling liquid of the camel's first stomach when their water supply has run out. The Bedouins of Arabia on occasion have strained out the more solid material and used the remaining liquid as an emergency drink. There is no doubt that it has saved the lives of dehydrated men by restoring their energy, but the stomach contains digestive juices and not stored water.

After determining that the contents of the camel's multiple stomach and misnamed water sacs do not include water, the scientists turned their attention to the water needs of the camel. They found that animals which had been weeks in green winter pasture would not drink when water was offered. If the pasture is succulent enough, or if the plants are often dew-covered, the camels will go three or four months in winter without drinking. Even on dry food in January, the experimental camels suffered no great inconvenience after sixteen days without water. They were thirsty, however, and drank when water was offered, in contrast to the camels which had been on green pasture.

In late June, when the Sahara heat was on, a camel was kept without water for eight days. At the end of that time it had lost about 220 pounds of its original 990 pounds and was in sorry condition. In ten minutes, however, it drank twenty-seven gallons of water, which was just about enough to restore its usual weight. The studies show that a water loss of 30 per cent of normal weight can be endured. Other camels were weighed before water privation of various periods and their intake measured at the end of the period. Always the camel drank just enough to replace the lost weight. In forty-eight hours the water was completely distributed throughout the body. Blood, body fluids, cells, etc., were all back to their normal concentrations. When a camel takes a big, long drink, it is not tanking up for an expected dry spell; it is just paying the water debt its body has contracted.

The ability to tolerate a water debt equal to about one-third of its body weight is only one of the camel's secret weapons against the desert. Another is its wide daily range in body temperature. In man, body temperature is normally about 98.6°F. It may be a little lower in the early morning, a little higher late in the day, but the range is only a degree or so. More than that indicates trouble for man, but the camel has a daily range of 12°F. in summer. This means that its body temperature can be down to about 94°F. in the morning and climb to 106°F. in the afternoon before the camel would need to start sweating and reduce his body heat.

Heat, like water, moves faster on a steep gradient than on a lesser slope; and it is a steeper slope from 120° to 90° F. than from 120° to 110° F. This means that the camel gets less heat from the air about him when desert temperatures are 115° to 130°F. than man will get. Accordingly, there is less to get rid of by sweating; also his wool coat is good insulation against heat coming directly from the sun, or reflected from the gravel, rock, or sand of the desert. When the camel sheds, the wool on his back which protects his body from the sun is the last to come free. It does not loosen until there is a reliable new growth ready to keep out the sun's rays. Finally, the wool lets his sweat evaporate slowly and gives maximum cooling effect to the camel's body.

When it comes to heat regulation, the camel has been doing for thousands of years what man is just beginning to accomplish in the new solar-heated houses. He stores heat in his body during the daytime to give off at night, and he is well insulated against both excessive heat and cold.

Many travelers have supposed that the camel does not sweat. This is because the wool absorbs moisture and evaporates it gradually. The beast sweats all right, but it does not show as it does on other animals. I have noticed a couple of wet spots on the back of my riding camel's head a few times which I supposed was sweat. However, the Schmidt-Nielsens found sweat glands all over the camel's body.

Like other animals, the camel uses water for the elimination of body wastes in urine and feces; but when the animal is deprived of drinking water and kept on a dry diet the urine flow is as little as a half liter (0.5283 quarts) per day. This is in sharp contrast to seven liters (7.3969 quarts) per day for an animal feeding in pasture.

The camel's hump is not water but fat. Like the fat in the hump of Brahma cattle, now so common in the southern United States, and in the tail of fat-tailed sheep, it is stored energy which can be used when the feed bag goes empty. Some travelers have suggested that the hump is indirect water storage, because when the animal burns the fat for energy it produces more water than is used in eliminating the waste products. The Schmidt-Nielsens have emphasized that it takes more oxygen to convert the fat to energy; and more oxygen means more breathing. This, in turn, evaporates more moisture from the lungs, so there is no gain in water for heat regulation.

Slow motion is a pronounced characteristic of the camel, and slow motion generates less heat than high speeds. Perhaps, after all, the camel is not really lazy, as we Westerners think. He is just well adapted to his environment. If he were a fast operator, he would use more energy for each job, which would generate more body heat to be dissipated and require more water for sweat.

There is still another advantage which the dromedary, or African and Arabian camel, has which I have never seen mentioned in print. His long, stiltlike legs carry his body mass well above the desert floor, where the desert air is cooler than close to the ground. In contrast, the Bactrian camel of eastern Asia is shorter legged, of stockier build, and lives in a colder part of the desert world. Actually the range of the two species overlaps almost 50 per cent; but the Bactrian never goes into the hot country of India, while the dromedary is common as far south as the equator. It can also develop a thick coat of wool to protect it against the cold, but it cannot endure the extreme cold of Central Asian winters. Both species are intolerant of humid climates where insects and fungus parasites attack them.

Biologists recognize the one-humped dromedary and the two-humped Bactrian camels as separate species, but they believe that the dromedary is derived from the Bactrian because the dromedary embryo at one stage in its development has two humps. The skeletons of the two species are so much alike that it is almost impossible to distinguish the dromedary from the Bactrian on the basis of bones alone. This makes it difficult to trace the creatures back to the point at which they were first domesticated. So far, no records have been found to indicate where domestication first occurred, and there are no historic accounts of wild camels to hint at a possible locality. The wild camels of Asia are descendants of those which have been lost from caravans, like those which roamed the southwestern United States in the late nineteenth century.

The camel has taught me the basic principles of desert living, but I still do not like the beasts. Their stare is haughty; their manner insolent. They complain constantly; they don't know their way home; and their breath smells from gas on the stomach—but they do get a lot of mileage on a gallon of water and have a most efficient heat-control system.

All in all, the camel is a case of certain virtues being overshadowed by a bad disposition: good merchandise, poorly packaged and very badly advertised. If he didn't look like a stilt-legged, giraffe-necked, ostrich-faced pinhead, people might overlook his stupidity. Then, perhaps, someone might love him.

X

· ·
· ·
· ·
· · · · · · · · · · · · ·
· · · · ·

Desert Trails and Caravan Tales

DESERT TRAILS ARE DIRECT PATHWAYS TO POINTS OF IMPORtance in the desert world. Sometimes those points seem unimportant to the Western traveler when he visits them, but a dot with a printed name looks as significant, on a map, as the mark for a town or city, even though the spot on the desert may be only a hole in the ground five or six feet across. No house, no shed, sometimes not even a wall of stone; a spot so inconspicuous on the flat, empty plain that a man on foot could easily miss it. However, the traveler who *does* miss that dot may wander to his death, for the hard-to-see hole is a desert well, perhaps the only source of water the traveler can expect to find within a two- or three-days' journey.

All trails lead to water, but they also lead to other important points. Trails connect oases with one another and with distant market centers. They are the lines of communication between the desert world and non-desert centers. Along some of these trails cultures have grown to civilizations, flourished, and been destroyed. Some of the famous ancient "ports," such as Carthage, Heliopolis, and Leptis Magna, are today only heaps of stones. Others, like Baghdad or Damascus, still hear the swish of camels' feet along their streets, but the loads they carry today are prosaic firewood rather than glamorous silks from distant lands. Cities on the edge of China, like Kalgan, are still connected by caravan with seemingly romantic centers of Asia. Camel loads of furs and hides and bales of wool stacked on the edge of town remind one of the docks at seaports, although their "points of origin" are landlocked Uliassutai and Urumchi, or far-off Kobdo. Some of those centers, like Ulan Bator, once were commercially and politically oriented toward China and maintained all their contacts by camel or ox-cart caravan. Now they are Russian dominated, and motorcars or truck lines carry all but the most bulky and least expensive cargoes.

Generally, desert trails are distinct paths swept free of broken rock and gravel by the feet of camels traveling the same routes for centuries, even millennia. Where the land is flat and bare, the trail may consist of three or four almost parallel paths so straight that an automobile can use them for a bouelvard. If the route leads through a land of scanty vegetation, the trail becomes a lacy network like the cowpaths on a pasture hillside. In the mountains and on steep or rocky edges of a mesa, the trail becomes a single thread that twists and curves and doubles back upon itself to climb the heights or keep direction on a narrow shelf. But when the route leads through abundant pasture, the paths sometimes become so scattered and so faint that only one who knows the route well can find his way.

The same is true in sandy deserts and in the great dune lands. Where the winds can wipe away the footprints of a caravan and where there are no markers for the route, the leader must trust his memory or navigate by sun and moon and stars. Some say that the science of astronomy was born on desert trails, where men had time to watch the movement of the planets and depended on the certainty of their hour-by-hour positions to guide them to their journey's end. When we crossed the Sahara's western *erg,* our guide was much more earthy in selecting signs for our route across the dunes. He kept us on the dune crests where the sand was hard and walking not too difficult, but he held direction by looking for camel droppings which had rolled down into the cups and hollows of the sand hills.

In the Gobi and Central Asian Deserts where the religion of the people is Lamaism, caravan trails are often well marked by *obos*. These are really religious monuments built of heaps of stones. Generally they are well laid up without mortar, the stones fitted together into very substantial structures. Sometimes though they are loose piles of rock to which each passing traveler adds a stone. Many of the substantial *obos* have small holes in which the Mongols place food for the spirits of the region. They are also decorated with pieces of ceremonial cloth each year at a festival. Gobi winds eventually whip the streamers to shreds, but they are replaced at the next festival if the *obo* is in an area frequented by the nomads or more sedentary groups.

Although the purpose is primarily religious, the prominent location of an *obo* on a high point in the vicinity of caravan trails also makes it an excellent trail marker. Each has its own name, and a distinct shape, which prevents any confusion with other *obos*.

Except for the *obos* in the lands of Lamaism, I know of no regular marking system used by desert peoples along the caravan trails. Desert areas under political administration by European peoples have trail markers of various sorts. The motor routes followed in the Algerian Sahara are marked now every 100 meters with oil drums. I have seen wooden direction signs on posts at trail junctions, and sometimes even concrete posts are used. Over most of the desert world the trails are old and well established and usually followed by leaders who know the route, so that markers are not needed. There are many tales of men who have successfully led caravans over routes they had not trod since they made the journey as young lads with their fathers. Even though the first and only journey was perhaps twenty years in the past, the native desert man remembers each hill and valley, where the wells are located, where pasture will be found for the camels, and how many days each march between the wells will be.

Since the advent of automobiles and trucks in desert lands, the trail systems have been augmented. Ancient trails made for travel by oxen or camel caravans are routed to pass wells and water holes as often as possible, and to give the animals adequate pasture during the journey. Such routes are not always the shortest distance between two points, but they are the shortest distance between water points. Auto routes, on the other hand, must avoid sand dunes and rocky or mountainous terrain, and their greater speed makes them more independent of water holes.

Native desert peoples are not much interested in miles or kilometers as measures of distance, because they think of travel in terms of days, long days or short days, between water points. Their attitude confuses us Westerners, accustomed as we are to measured miles. I recall that one time in the Sahara we asked a sheik how many kilometers it was to a nearby well.

"Twenty kilometers," he replied. The country was pretty rugged, and we thought we might have to take a longer route with our cars, so we reminded the sheik that we had automobiles.

"Oh, then it's only five kilometers for you," he said. The kilometer was not a measured 1,000 paces to him. It was just another kind of time measurement. He knew that it was a good half-day's journey to the well for a riding camel, but less than an hour for the automobile. That is why the actual twenty kilometers distance became only a fourth as far.

The desert retains evidence of a trail long after it has ceased to be used. I have photographed automobile tracks on a desert plain seven years after the car had passed. When we conducted a survival test in the Sahara for the U.S. Air Force, we picked two wells on a map. Each was on a north-south trail, but there was no east-west trail between them. Our ground survey party visited only the first well. However, we flew over the route to the second well before we turned the men loose on a compass course. While we did not see the second well from the air, we did see a distinct trail, so we felt certain the "survivors" could not miss it.

The "survivors" did find the well. It was probably 130 feet deep, completely filled with sand, and the north-south trail we had seen from the air was barely distinguishable on the ground. The desert police at the station only thirty miles away had no knowledge of either the well or the trail to it. In their opinion the route had not been used for more than a century. Our modern map makers had taken their data from other maps which, in turn, had been taken from still older charts, and so on back; but from the air that north-south trail showed just as distinctly as its line on the latest map.

In the Syrian and Arabian deserts the airplane has revealed scores of forgotten trails and lost cities. Even camps and stopping points on those ancient caravan routes are clearly outlined from the air, but to the man on the ground there is often not a trace until hard work with pick and shovel confirms the air photograph and vindicates the writers of ancient manuscripts.

Western travelers like to speculate on lost cities and forgotten caravan routes, but there is seldom much mystery about them. Generally there is either a political reason or an economic one to account for their disuse. Towns and desert cities in the center of irrigated agricultural regions become ghost towns when the land is salted-up from inadequate drainage and thus becomes unproductive. Ancient mining centers were abandoned for the same reasons as more modern ones are: the ore played out or a better supply was discovered closer to the market. When the important terminal point of a trail was abandoned, the intermediate police posts and administrative centers were also no longer needed. The scorched earth policy of Genghis Khan and his Mongol hordes destroyed the irrigation systems of large areas in the desert world and slaughtered so many of the inhabitants that none were left to repair the damage and get the region back into production. The breakup of the Roman Empire, like the later withdrawal of the Italians from their conquered lands in the Sahara, left the region without technicians and managers. Accordingly, dams went unrepaired, cisterns and reservoirs silted up, and the "shifting, whispering sand" smothered plantings and young orchards left untended.

In our own time, political changes and bandit activity have caused significant re-routing of the caravan trade in Central Asia. In 1926–27 Chinese bandits became so numerous on Gobi trails that merchants could not afford the risks, and for nearly two years no caravans left Kalgan in North China. Eventually the local Chamber of Commerce negotiated with the bandits, and certain leaders were allowed to enter the city to negotiate protection fees with the merchants. Finally, 13,000 camels left Kalgan to fan out on the Gobi trails for distant centers long starved for the goods of China.

Russian control of Outer Mongolia brought about official harassment of caravans using certain trails which crossed a corner of Mongolia en route to distant points, and unreasonable taxes were levied on goods in transit. As a result it became cheaper for caravans to travel west by longer and more arid trails than to risk an encounter with the Russian-inspired Outer Mongolian government officials. One of our attempts to explore to the west was blocked because a trail which might have been used by our motorcars led into the forbidden land. "Don't go that way," a group of caravan men advised. "That way lies official trouble."

Most desert habitation centers have been occupied for centuries, and the trails connecting them are maintained by those who use the routes. After all, there is little deterioration to a camel trail. A rare flood, an even rarer landslide, may destroy a section of a route; but the next caravan to pass that way immediately picks a new path either through or around the obstacle. Those who come later follow in the footsteps of this new route, and soon the trail is well established. At times I have carried rocks and used a shovel to make a road passable for my own car in desert country. In some areas the local inhabitants keep up the trails, and even build new ones if the need exists. And so it was in ancient times. Governments and rulers who needed commerce or communication with distant points established routes and sent out details of workers to keep up trails and dig the needed wells.

Wells, too, are kept in repair by those who use them. In Central Asia there is a very long, dry stage between wells on one caravan trail. It was a route which could only be used in years of unusual rains. A bandit, or robber baron, at his own expense, dug new wells to make the route more tempting. Then, acting like more conventionally established governments, he exacted tribute from those who came that way.

All sorts of traffic follows the desert trails. In the Gobi we watched heavy-wheeled oxcarts plod north from China to the capital of Outer Mongolia with heavy freight, and gold miners

from China pushed wheelbarrows loaded with their personal possessions along the desert routes. There is an account of one thrifty
miner who hid the gold dust and nuggets collected during his summer's digging in the hollowed planks of his wheelbarrow as a protection from bandits and unscrupulous officials. I do not recall
now whether the heavy weight wrecked the vehicle, or whether the
officials became suspicious at the weight. Whichever it was, the rich
man suddenly became a poor man again. In many parts of the
desert world, law and order are just words. Each individual must
enforce his own meaning of the terms. Likewise it is often difficult
to distinguish between bandit and government official, or between
soldier and highwayman.

Once in the western Gobi some of our party met a small, swift-
moving caravan. Their camels were big and well cared for, and the
caravan men were as hard-looking characters as one would expect
to find in a Wild West movie.

"Smugglers," our own caravan men insisted. That night our
party mounted guard with loaded rifles, but the smugglers broke
camp early and hurried on their way without bothering us. We
never learned whether they were smuggling opium or not, but they
did not come to our campfire, which is an almost certain sign that
they were on business "not quite ethical."

We found that most caravan men, however, were friendly and
more carefree than either wealthy merchants or smugglers. Each
man has his string of six or eight camels tied nose to tail by a thin
cord. Generally the men walk at the head of their string, although
sometimes they will climb atop a lightly loaded animal for an hour
or so. Ambitious camel boys pass the time as they walk by spinning
camel wool. They use the simplest of spindles, a round stick on
which the yarn is wound as fast as a length of it is spun. Other
camel men sing as they move across the desert. A truck driver in
Saudi Arabia, who used to be a caravan man, sings as he drives—
"a song about the winds on the desert. I used to sing it to my
camels. It kept them awake," he says. Sometimes it is rather
startling when a caravan man you have known as a hard-limbed,
stolid sort of fellow in an oasis suddenly bursts into a lusty song

out on the open plain. The true caravan man can walk day after day for two or three months at a time, but he is never bored for "only men who are not happy and free get bored."

In Arabia they say that the merchant caravans are always in a hurry. They never have time to stop, and they seldom even wave as they pass. That is not true of family caravans on the march from one pasture to another. When they meet out on the desert, they stop and spend hours over their coffee cups; but they keep the camels and the flocks well separated so that there will be no extra work in sorting them out when the parties move on again.

When the weather is hot, caravans start early in the morning, even before dawn, and plod across the desert for four or five hours, then make camp for the day. In late afternoon, if there will be no moon, they break camp; otherwise they wait until evening and travel by moonlight. Then the sands are cool, the sun is dimmed, and moonlight makes the desert soft and beautiful.

Caravan people generally have their big meal of the day after sunset. When the meal is finished, if they are in a region where there is enough fuel, they sit on the ground around the fire and tell the stories of their people. Old men, of course, are the favorite story-tellers for they know the tales of olden days and desert heroes.

In Arabia these stories include the tale of the horse that galloped to Damascus and back in one night, and the twenty adversaries who attacked Aby Zaid and were all slain by his mighty sword. Exploits of the late Ibn Saud and of his son, the present king of Saudi Arabia, who in their younger days brought the tribes together through the tactics of traditional desert warfare, are told along with more ancient tales.

Among the Tuaregs of Sahara the tales are often of the *jinns*. I particularly remember the one related about the Gorge d'Arak. There, straight-walled cliffs tower up from the canyon floor—the sort of walls a "human fly" might climb but impossible for men accustomed to the flatness of the desert. According to this tale, the Tuareg men went off on a long caravan journey and were gone for several weeks. When they returned they were unable to find their women. Finally one of the men saw the girls on the cliff top.

"How did you get up there?" he called.

"The *jinn* carried us up," the girls answered. And, as every Tuareg always believes what his womenfolk tell him, the Tuareg men know that the Gorge d'Arak is inhabited by *jinn*.

Caravans vary in size from less than half a dozen camels to several thousand. Water and pasture are the most important governing factors, and these differ with the season of the year and the location of the trail. Danger of the bandit menace, and consequent need for armed protection, often determines the size of a caravan. I once saw an oxcart caravan in the Gobi in which there were two hundred carts. Our expedition supply camels numbered 125, and we sometimes saw passing caravans with twice that number. Along the Avenue of Palms in the western Sahara, where the oases are so close together that one can travel for two or three hundred miles in the shade of the date palms, I have also seen a hundred or two hundred camels moving together. But farther east, where the trail led over plateaus and plains bare of vegetation, we seldom saw strings of as many as fifty animals.

One military expedition in the Sahara back in the early days of European occupation started out with 10,000 camels. The first arrivals at the first well drank it dry. Those behind them were forced to the next water point, and in their turn drank that well dry. The result was that before many days half of the 10,000 camels died of thirst.

Travelers still tell of big salt caravans in the southern Sahara numbering several hundred camels. It is a rugged march from Timbuktu to the salt mines; one on which men and camels die each year. In the old days, when much of the salt for the people of the desert and of Central Africa passed through Timbuktu, there were thousands of camels where now they are counted in hundreds. Perhaps the day is not too distant when salt from other sources will completely replace that from the desert mines.

I have never been on a salt caravan, but from the accounts of the few Westerners who have made the journey one gets the impression that it is a brutal ordeal for man and beast, perhaps unequaled in modern times except by pioneer crossings through the Sonoran Desert and Death Valley in America, or by some journeys in Central Asia.

On the northern edge of the Sahara and in Arabia, the caravans of the nomads move at a leisurely pace from one seasonal pasture to another. These caravans include men, women, and children; camels, sheep, goats, and dogs. Sometimes a couple of chickens are tied by the legs to a camel pack. In the Sahara they bring dates from the oases to markets beyond the desert; and in the north they help harvest wheat and carry back their share to the oases unable to supply their own needs. In the Arabian desert small tribes of only a few families will travel in a caravan of twenty camels, together with their flocks of sheep and goats. A big caravan of a hundred camels probably represents twenty families. When they move, all of their possessions are in the camel packs. Tents, poles, pots and pans, bedding, clothing—everything they own—is loaded on the camels, for to the true Bedouin "home is where he is."

Unlike the merchant caravans, the Bedouin caravans do not always follow the same pathways, but they do have their objectives of greener pastures and precious water holes. Occasionally they must go to the cities to dispose of their surplus and to obtain supplies they cannot produce themselves. They trade sheep's wool for dates, goat's milk for rice, and camel's hair for pots and pans. On such journeys they pitch their black tents outside the city walls and stay no longer than is absolutely necessary. The Bedouin has no love for towns, and only when desert drought reduces him to near starvation will he leave the freedom of the desert for the cooped-up city.

It is only a generation or two since stable government in both the Sahara and Arabian Deserts has policed the caravan trails and effectively discouraged raids and plundering of unprotected strings of camel transport. But the desert patrols are few and often far away, so that a small caravan, especially if its loads are valuable, can never be quite certain that the trail is safe. I still remember a fright I received in the western Sahara many years ago when I was traveling with a M. Reygasse, a Frenchman whose interest in archaeology had brought us together for Stone Age research in the desert.

Reygasse surprised me one day on the trail by asking if I had heard what Ahmet said. Actually, he knew that all I could understand of Ahmet's chatter was his Arabic for "somebody welcomes you."

Ahmet was half of our military escort, a native soldier who rode the prettiest little bay mare I ever saw. He and his companion were assigned by the Commandant to see that we did not lose our way and would arrive safely at Beni Ounif de Figuig. Reygasse was a moody one, not given to much talking on the trail; and since he had raised the question, I knew that whatever Ahmet had said it was now a worry in his mind. I decided to make conversation and help him to get it out of his system.

"No, I didn't pay any attention," I said. "What was he talking about?"

"Ahmet says we are the ones who opened the tomb of Tin Hinane," replied Reygasse. "Worse than that, he says, we have forty-eight cases of jewels from the tomb, besides lots of gold and silver."

The idea was absurd, of course. All that we had found had been sent north by motor weeks before. It was now five months since we had started into the Sahara for science and adventure. Armed with rifles as insurance against the bandits, we had met only friends. The fierce and treacherous Tuaregs of fiction had turned out to be fine fellows who sat beneath their goatskin tents to swap stories with us. We almost forgot our guns. There wasn't even any game on which to use them.

It was true that deep in the Hoggar Mountains we had opened the tomb of Tin Hinane, legendary mother of all the Tuaregs. Near the skeleton we had found two hundred carnelian beads and a tiny column-like ornament of gold. On the arm bones were fifteen bracelets of silver. Those few trinkets were sent back to civilization with other members of the party. Reygasse and I had stayed on in the Sahara.

For months we collected flint tools left by prehistoric peoples along the banks of streams long dead and waterless. Now, as we plodded on into the western Sahara, our pack camels were loaded with barrels and boxes of those crude stone implements. Heavy loads they were, but valuable only to science.

The monotone of desert plain gave way to a new monotony of sand dunes and palm trees. The ceaseless wind, which on the plains had blotted out all other sound, was gone. In its stead there was now the silence of the dune land—a hushed silence that shrouded even the footsteps of our camels.

As I chuckled at the absurdity of Ahmet's report on the treasure, Reygasse frowned. It was no laughing matter to him. He was certain that if our soldiers knew we had been at the tomb, then every native in the area knew it, and, of course, they could surprise us anywhere in the dunes. Reygasse didn't like the situation at all.

"But how could any of them get the news?" I asked. "We're two thousand kilometers from the tomb!"

"How did that reception committee at Tit know we were coming?" countered my companion. "There was no word sent ahead! How did Sergeant Leman know in time to meet us five kilometers out of Aoulef? The natives told him. Those same natives told him he was going to be transferred . . . told him twelve hours before the special messenger arrived with sealed orders. And you ask me, how would the natives get the news of anything as important as treasure from a Tuareg tomb?"

This sobered me. The desert does have its mystery of communication, and perhaps we were more important to these desert people than I realized.

That night we stayed at the *bordj*, or guest house, of a little oasis. As usual I ate my fill of fresh dates and drank a bowl of sheep's milk to acknowledge the hospitality of the local Caid. Reygasse would have none of the native food, but he ate a good meal from our supply of canned goods. I could see that he remembered how desert natives had poisoned the food of the Flatters expedition and was taking no chances on meeting a like fate. His attitude was getting on my nerves, too, and I began to lose patience with him when he said, "I don't trust this military escort, either. Both of those native soldiers have fast horses. They can run circles around our so-called swift-riding camels."

"All right," I admitted. "Our companions can outrun us. They can outshoot us, too. So what? We haven't anything valuable with us and we aren't important enough for either murder or ransom." I pushed my camel up to the head of the caravan and left Reygasse to his gloomy thoughts.

The next day was like the first. Our slow-moving caravan went on and on. The soldiers trotted ahead around a dune, then rode back to chat with Reygasse or help our cook boy urge on the pack camels. Late in the afternoon I rode with Reygasse.

"I wish I had Ahmet's little bay mare back home," I said, just to make conversation. But at the mention of Ahmet, Reygasse's face darkened.

"That soldier's no good," he said. "He's been asking more about the jewels."

"Well, we haven't any worry on that score," I insisted. "We haven't any jewels."

"True! But the natives don't know that," said my gloomy companion. "What native will believe that our heavy boxes are loaded with flints? Jewels and gold make sense to the natives, prehistoric flints make only nonsense."

When a trail-mate talks like that there is not much use in trying to answer him, so we rode on in silence. That night, again, Reygasse refused the dates and sheep's milk. He even refused to sleep in the *bordj.* I kept him company in the walled courtyard, but I didn't sleep. Dogs howled. Wind stirred dry palm leaves. The night fairly reeked with sound after the silence of the daytime. By morning I was tired and jittery.

That third wintry dawn was dull and gray. The wind died. Sand around the *bordj* muffled sounds of breaking camp. Desert silence again pressed against us. As soon as we were on the trail, Reygasse began his gloomy talk again.

"What were those people saying last night?" he asked.

"I heard no people," I answered. "There was wind in the palms."

"You're too new in the desert," Reygasse continued. "It was people. They talked. When I crept over to the gate they slipped away into the night."

I was certain that he had heard only the wind, but I couldn't convince him at all. He was just as certain that he had heard people and that they were planning something.

We left the oasis and plodded over the desert, a silent, cold, gray desert, too monotonous even for thinking. By mid-afternoon I was slumped in my saddle half-asleep. Ahmet on his bay mare rode a hundred yards ahead. We swayed on into a little valley. Dunes towered high on either side, shutting us in between walls of yellow silence.

A blood-curdling yell split that silence! I jerked up, fully awake. Six wildly yelling horsemen dashed out from behind the dune ahead. Straight toward our caravan they rode. Robes flying, guns blazing, they came on!

Ahmet yanked the bay mare back on her haunches. As she pawed the air with her front feet, I glanced toward the dune on my right. Over the top of that yellow hill came six gleaming, black giants. Yelling, leaping through the sand, those demons cut off our only escape. I fumbled for my gun.

"Reygasse was right," I thought as I saw Ahmet whirl the little mare around and lash her toward me. Not fifty yards behind him raced the yelling horsemen. Ahmet leaned far over the bay's neck, urging her on with his heels, but the six horsemen were gaining.

"Blast your soul!" I shouted at him. "Why don't you cut through those black devils?" He just kept coming toward us as hard as he could ride.

Finally I got hold of my rifle, but it caught under my saddle bag. Before I could free it, Ahmet reined back right under my camel's nose. Behind him the horsemen were so close I could see the gold embroidery on the gorgeous red cape of the leader. His purple velvet trousers and red leather boots splashed brilliantly against the glossy white of the wild-eyed stallion he rode.

The half-naked black giants converged on Ahmet. The horsemen whirled their mounts, surrounding us in a cloud of sand. Their guns blazed again, straight at us, as they leaped to the ground. Ahmet threw his right arm high in the air. I held my breath in terror.

"Caid of Salah welcomes you!" he shouted.

The black giants, like medieval slaves, took their masters' horses. The Caid and his lieutenants advanced on foot with outstretched hands. "In the name of Allah, you are welcome to my village," the leader said.

I breathed again, as I realized that we were important visitors welcomed with a real desert fantasia.

Reygasse and I leaned down from our high mounts and shook hands with each of the oasis dignitaries. Then they mounted their beautifully saddled horses and led our little caravan to the guest house in the village. That evening Reygasse did not refuse the bowl of milk and basket of dates. He, too, had been impressed by the splendor of our official welcome to that oasis.

At night the caravan camps are romantic and mysterious. Camels *barracked* by their loads become vague shadows instead of the ungainly heaps of wool they are in the glare of the desert sun. The stars seem far away in the Sahara, like little candles that flicker and almost go out but never quite disappear. Perhaps one of the smaller shadows over beyond the camels stirs, then moves upright. A match flares up and dies. In another moment a little blaze outlines the form of one of the camel men who has awakened to brew a pot of tea. His fire dies down. His silhouette against the distant sky bows and bends as he goes through the ritual of his early morning prayers. Then he rolls up in his woolen cape for another nap.

Once my wife, Dorothy, and I camped for a few days in the little patch of dunes outside the oasis of Biskra. The first night there was a white moon in a black-velvet sky. Deep purple shadows lay on the silver-crested sand dunes. A string of camels plodded across the desert; now stately, silhouetted against the sky; now vanished in the valley; then once again they rose above the dune tops—

silent, plodding shadows against the back-drop of a stage. From our tent came the rhythm and the melody of the "Desert Song" blending with the magic of the Sahara night.

Suddenly, as out of nowhere, two men with packs appeared from the largest dune.

"Bon soir, monsieur, madame," they said. "You will see our wares? In the moonlight of the Sahara they will weave a spell."

Then, tossed carelessly before us on the sands, there were Mecca veils of black net with countless silver knots that sparkled in the moonlight, and gorgeous Chinese silks of red and black with gold-embroidered dragons. We wondered if this was young Marco Polo and his father returned from the palaces of Kublai Khan. A silver-handled dagger gleamed and glistened at our feet. "Who knows" these strangers asked, "what Arab prince once used it quietly on his rival sleeping in the shadow of oasis palms? Then, perhaps, before the camp was aroused, he dashed away across the sands on a swift, white stallion. In his arms he held his black-eyed beauty firmly against his breast. Her soft, white form quivered, half thrilled with joy, half terrified."

Even as we touched the mysterious dagger, long strings of amber, round and limpid in the moonlight, dropped into our laps. "From the throat of China's youngest princess," said the merchant. Then silver bracelets glistened and the soft voice added, "Once the pride of graceful Massouda, the dancing girl and favorite of the Bey of Tunis."

At last the younger merchant began to reroll the packs. "You will buy no more, Monsieur, Madame? Then we must go," he said. "Yes, Madame, danger lurks in Biskra's streets at night. Many there are who love the dancing girls. Only last night a Caid from the south was stabbed by a——ah, well, who knows by whom? It is not safe when caravans come from the oasis in the south."

Silently the lovely silks and jewels were packed away in bags. The merchants disappeared beyond the shadow of a desert dune. A cloud floated across the moon and dropped a curtain on the desert.

My wife and I blinked our eyes. Had someone rubbed Aladdin's lamp for us? Had we been dreaming of Arabian nights? Again the big, round moon flooded our desert camp with silver. There, still before us on the sand, lay the gossamer veil of Mecca, the silver-handled dagger, and the limpid amber beads. The magic of the desert had been real. Then, while we marveled at the skill with which the Biskra merchants had handled their sales pitch, and displayed their goods, a shot rang out across the dunes. Then, a second shot was fired! Perhaps it was just an added touch of realism, but in the silence of the desert night we couldn't quite be sure.

XI

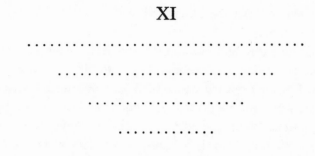

Desert Wells and Secret Water Holes

THREE THINGS THERE ARE WHICH EASE THE HEART FROM SORrow," states an Arab proverb, "Water, green grass and the beauty of women." A song in India personalizes the five "elements" as Mother Earth, Father Sky, Brother Wind, Friend Light, and Sweetheart Water. Kipling is more brutal on the subject, for he says,

> But when it comes to slaughter,
> You'll do your work on water.

Finally there is the blunt comment of Major General Collins, speaking of the Libyan Campaign in 1941: "Water has been and may be again the crux of the whole show."

Those who know the desert, whether poet, philosopher, or military leader, agree on the importance of water. All have discovered the one great truth about the arid wastes: "Where there is water there is life." Without it the desert is a dead world.

Step to the edge of every oasis and you see the truth of this statement. As water becomes available through new wells or irrigating projects, date groves and garden patches spread into oncebarren desert. If the wells go dry the desert reclaims the area. If you fly over the desert, you can look down on the sharp lines between the watered and the unwatered land like green ink on yellow drafting paper.

Mountain streams and transient rivers have been diverted to water oases in all deserts since man began to plant seeds and harvest crops. But far from the banks of those few streams, water for the gardens, water for man, for sheep, goats, and camels—all must come from wells. Wells are also the reliable source of water on desert trails. Without them there would be no commercial caravans, and the range of nomads would be severely shortened. The desert would be a more formidable barrier to the movements of man than the ocean.

Desert wells were dug by hand until rather recent times when Europeans and Americans brought in modern drilling equipment, which can cut deeper into the earth in one hour than the hand labor could dig in days. Some of the machine-dug wells spout thousands of gallons of water a minute and irrigate thousands of date palms. In the northern Sahara, however, there were artesian wells long before the advent of Europeans and their power-driven well-digging machines.

When I first visited the oasis of Temacine, in the northern Sahara, there were six Negroes of the Ghouara tribe still living who practiced the profession of well-digging. Two of them were at work deepening a well in which the water no longer reached the surface, but which was visible four feet below the desert floor. We arrived at the well while the two men were sitting close to a little fire— "absorbing warmth to last them while they were in the cold water," they said. They wore only short baggy breeches and were positively the skinniest human beings I have ever seen. You could count their bones from any angle as they sat there on the ground, with their heels against their buttocks and their knees against their chins. Instead of greeting us with a handshake as other natives usually did, these Ghouara men simply moved their right hands up and down before them with the palms turned down.

They considered their work extremely dangerous and surrounded it with a great deal of ceremony. They even claimed it was so difficult and fatiguing that a man could make only one dive each half-day.

When one of the men had warmed himself sufficiently, a process at which he took his own good time, he decided to go to work. The well was about thirty inches in diameter and cribbed up with stones. Above this well-curb was a frame of split tree trunks from which hung a pulley and a rope. Another rope was tied to the side of the crib and hung down into the water.

With slow, deliberate movements, the workman climbed into the well. He stepped carefully from stone to stone, always holding onto the fixed rope until he was waist deep in the water. There he paused to put water on his head and chest, just as I used to do at the ol' swimmin' hole in early spring before plunging into the cold water. There was a difference, however, for the man at Temacine accomplished the act with all the solemnity of a religious rite. He even muttered a few words, which Belaid, our interpreter, said was the prayer uttered by all good Moslems in preparation for death. Finally the man took a few deep breaths and exhaled with exaggerated chest contractions which vividly emphasized his lack of fat. At the same time, he placed his thumb against his lips so that the exhaling air whistled softly. Finally, he took hold of the fixed rope and went down out of sight.

We held our watches while the seconds ticked away. We had heard all sorts of stories about the great lengths of time these professional well-divers could stay under water, and we expected the man to be down at least five minutes. However, it was just under three minutes when we saw his head come above water again. His partner climbed to the water's edge and began to rub the diver's shoulders. Then, after several deep breaths, the diver climbed out of the well and crouched once more by the little fire. Other natives hauled on the rope over the pulley and brought up a basket full of sand. It held about two quarts: one-half of a day's work for a professional diver! At that rate, it would take many days to clean the well so that water again could reach the surface. Of course, if the diminished flow was due to a much-lowered water table, which probably was the trouble, the diver's work might be of little value. Even at that time, well-digging machinery had so increased the number of artesian wells that the water table had been lowered and government restrictions on new wells were being imposed.

We asked Belaid to tell the divers that we wanted to photograph them, but he had difficulty in making them understand that we wanted them to pose together. Finally, one of us noticed the trouble. Both men had great lumps of wax in their ears to protect them from the pressure of the water, and perhaps also to impress their public with the dangers of their calling.

Most wells, like the oases they water, are located in low places, or depressions, in the desert. Basins, dry river beds, and hollows among the sand dunes are all possible locations, but some of the wells on desert trails are located out in the middle of arid plains. These are the deep wells dug to break the long marches of the caravans. A true well reaches ground water, in contrast to a cistern which is a storage place for collected drainage. The desert traveler isn't usually very fussy about such distinctions and calls any dug water hole a well.

There are many, many different types of wells in the desert world. There are wide-mouthed wells, which the water-seeker must walk down into if he will fill his water bucket, and which remind one of open pit mines. There are wells in soil so unstable that stone or logs or planks are needed to crib the opening and prevent a cave-in. Other wells are in solid rock, like the cistern at Tesnou on the edge of the Hoggar in the Sahara, which collects drainage from the granite mountain. Some, too, are unprotected holes easily contaminated by surface refuse washed back into the reservoir by water spilled from buckets. More often the well is protected with a curb, and sometimes a well house is built with a doorway on the least windy side.

The water of desert wells differs as much from one location to another as the terrain in which they are located. There are soft-water wells from which the water tastes as flat as rain water. There are hard-water wells, located in limestone, which produce as good a drink as any in the world. There are, also, alkali wells of varying degrees of unpleasantness, depending on the cultivated taste of the individual drinking the water. We encountered one such well in the Gobi which was so strong that none of us Americans could drink from it. Fortunately there was a sweeter well only about fifteen miles farther along the caravan trail, and we filled our water cans there.

In the Sahara there are several wells with water containing magnesium salts. Some of our party were made really ill by the water at In Salah and the military surgeon sent them to bed for a day. His prescription was a most enjoyable cure to take. The patient was given a bottle of champagne with orders to drink a cupful every hour or so.

Some years later, I had a group of American archaeological students with me on the northern edge of the desert. The time was May and summer heat was beginning to bear down. I bought a hundred lemons and told the men to drink all the lemonade they wanted. Every one of us spent more time at the latrine than we did on the job during the few days at that station. I could not understand the trouble because our food was good, and it was not until the last day that I remembered our experience at In Salah. Then I realized that the quantities of lemonade we had been drinking were actually the equivalent of citrate of magnesia.

Bad-tasting water, often the source of stories about poisoned wells, may not be seriously harmful, like the alkali water well-known in the western United States. It is rare that such water is dangerously toxic, but, because of its salt or mineral content, you may have to drink larger quantities to prevent dehydration than are required when fresher water is available. In the Sahara there are said to be only two wells, both in the Erg Esh-Shesh, which are really poisonous. The water of one contains so much chlorine that it will burn clothing, and the other has so much salt-peter that it causes vomiting.

In some of our southwestern deserts there are springs containing arsenic salts. These are easily recognized by the absence of vegetation, which is always abundant around a desert spring of good water. Around these truly poisonous springs there are also the remains of wild and domestic animals killed by drinking the waters. Such dangerous water holes belong in the class of desert curiosities, and they are so uncommon that you probably will never meet one, even in years of desert travel, unless you make a point of searching out the unusual.

There is no rule of thumb to answer the question, "How deep is a desert well?" In the Gobi we found they were generally only ten to fifteen feet to water. In the Sahara I was once told that if I carried a hundred-foot rope I could always reach water. However, our "survivors" in the Libyan Sahara Field Test, which I supervised for the U.S. Air Force, found that the first well they reached, Bir el Chor on Hamada el Hamra, was 130 feet deep. They dipped water from that depth by attaching parachute shroud-lines to a canteen cup weighted with a small stone.

Ordinarily, desert wells are not hidden and are located close to trails, but in rocky deserts and on some gravel plains it is not always easy to find the well, especially if it has no superstructure. When they are located in solid rock or hard-packed soil where paths do not show, the traveler may have to hunt to find the water point. In the Libyan Sahara, doughnut-shaped mounds of camel dung often surround the wells. Unless you recognize the small mound ring, you could easily miss the well.

Secret water holes *do* exist. These are known only to their discoverer or to the select few with whom he shares the discovery. They are not truly permanent as a rule, because they are dependent on rare rains. The first one I encountered was a small pond on the plateau of Algeria. We were looking for a Stone Age campsite which my companion had visited a year before. When he saw a flock of sheep and goats in the vicinity, he followed them over a little rise of ground, below the crest he found a good-sized pond. He could not believe his eyes at first, because he had known the region for ten years and had never seen water in that hollow before. When he asked the shepherd about it, he said that rain had fallen recently in the area and surface drainage had filled the hollow with good, fresh water. A rocky canyon in the Sahara, a full day's auto drive south of In Salah, had a similar pool, but there were no sheep in that barren region to take advantage of the water. We filled our water cans and used the pool as a swimming hole.

One of our guides once took us up onto a mountain ridge and led the way in under a mass of tumbled rocks. There, well-sheltered from the sun, he pointed out a secret water hole discovered on one of his earlier trips. He gave us quite a story about a rival who also claimed to have discovered this sheltered water. At the time of our visit we could have accused both of them of being liars, for the spot was as dry as the open plain. The location was similar to that which the natives at Gara Cheurfa call the Mother of People Spring. It, too, was a dry basin when I saw it, but well-hidden under gigantic blocks of quartzite tumbled from the cap of the butte. There the story was clear. The butte was a flat-topped area, perhaps two acres in extent. When a big rain hit that part of the desert some years before, all the water falling on the butte drained toward the end and collected in the sheltered basin, where it remained for many months or even a year or two. Such secret water holes exist in all deserts, but to find them you must study the local topography and be favored with a recent desert downpour.

In Australian deserts certain water holes are called "soaks." These apparently are points where water seeps out of the ground enough to dampen a small area, but does not flow fast enough to produce a runnel or a pool. When a native or a traveler uses such a soak he scrapes out a little hollow, lets enough water accumulate to supply his needs, and then covers the spot with brush to protect it as much as possible against evaporation. The next traveler must know how to recognize in such brush piles the possible covering of a source of water.

Even more interesting are the "sip-wells" of the Kalahari Bushmen. Livingstone called them "sucking wells." A native, usually an old woman, scoops out a hollow in the sand below a certain type of brush. When she has a small pit about arm's length in depth she wraps a large bunch of dry grass around the end of a hollow reed. The grass bundle, with the reed projecting straight up, is placed in the bottom of the hole. All the sand is then packed back into the pit to cover the grass bundle. In half an hour or so, moisture from the sand collects in the grass-protected cavity around the end of the reed. The old woman next starts sucking hard on the exposed end of the reed to produce a partial vacuum around the buried grass bundle. A skilled operator will suck so hard that "her cheeks almost meet." Eventually the process draws water out of the moist sand up through the reed to the woman's mouth.

Next she puts a shorter reed into one corner of her mouth, the other end leading into an empty ostrich-eggshell. As she sucks water out of the sand into her mouth, she squirts it through the second reed into the ostrich-eggshell. It sounds like a laborious way of getting water, but it is effective. There is a record of one "Bush" MacIntyre and a companion who went into the Kalahari to dig a new well. One Bushman woman with her sip-well supplied the two white men and their four donkeys with the water which kept them alive until their well-digging brought in a plentiful supply.

In some oases there are central wells from which the people get their daily supply. Community wells are also located in the arid lands bordering the true desert. One of these down on the southern edge of the Sahara is as colorful a place as you will ever find. We passed there early one June morning. There were fifteen or twenty women and a few children standing around waiting their turn to fill their jars with water. It would be hard to imagine more brilliantly colored and gorgeously flowered dresses than those girls displayed. All of them were sturdy-limbed and arrow-straight. It was easy to see why, when I observed one of them lean down, grasp a huge pottery jug, which must have held five gallons of water, and lift it to the top of her head. With the more than forty-pound load on her head she walked away, giving me and my movie camera a broad smile.

The scene reminded me of another well some 3,000 miles away on the northern edge of the Sahara. We saw it one day in May when we were looking for a place to lunch. Because there was a bit of grass there, we drove off the road. A half-dozen men in white *gonduras* and twisted cheesecloth turbans were squatted on the ground near-by, but they paid no attention to us; and two women were hauling at a well rope with all their might. The rope passed through a pulley which hung from a cross-piece supported above the well by two upright posts. One woman grasped the rope with both hands, then pulled down with her arms and bending body in one quick swing. When she was bent nearly double, the other woman grabbed the rope as high up as she could reach, and in her turn bent double. So they alternated—with such swift smoothness that the rope seemed to "flow" over the pulley—until a dripping, black goatskin full of water shot up above the stone well-curb on which the women stood.

One of them carried the full skin of water a little way from the well and emptied it into a stone trough which had been salvaged from near-by Roman ruins. Then she laid a white garment on a large, flat stone, threw a pan of water over it, and rubbed it well with a cake of soap. Next she stepped up onto the garment and, bare-footed, began to dance a fantastic jig all over the soapy cloth. Her skirts were tucked up above her knees to give her plenty of freedom. She stamped and struck the garment first with one foot, then the other. With dexterous toes she turned over the garment and tramped vigorously on the other side. Finally, she poured more clear water over the cloth; and when this was tramped out, she attacked another and another until the whole week's washing was dirt-free and spread on the grass to dry.

While we watched the woman dancing the dirt out of her clothes, other women came with donkeys. They filled goatskins with water, tied them to the donkeys' backs with ropes of goat-hair, and went back up the path toward home. Some of them came as much as two or three miles to get the water for the family needs. One old hag in a faded red calico dress and a disheveled turban rode up on a tiny donkey. The little burro was so small that the woman sat way back on his hindquarters, and her feet scraped the ground in long, swinging strides while the tiny hoofs of the little mount gave a quick staccato beat in contrast. Each woman tended to her own business, but conversation flew thick and fast. There is no newspaper in the vicinity of that community well, and all the news that is worth repeating will be heard there and carried back to homes miles away. Once news about my camp traveled nearly 200 miles and was picked up from natives' conversation by an English lady whom we knew.

Desert wells have names which identify them to all travelers— names like Hassi el Hadjar, south of Ouargla, for instance. It sits on the open plain where it gets the full sweep of the wind, but it is protected by a dome-topped little well-house of stones with a pointed, open doorway facing east. A pulley hangs over the mouth of the well, and when we arrived a native was drawing water with a goatskin bag, which he emptied into a metal trough. The night before we had made a dry camp, so we were hot and dusty when we got to Hassi el Hadjar and everyone enjoyed a cold sponge bath.

Then at In Guettara, farther south in the Sahara, there are two water holes in the deep rock canyon below the fort. Three or four scraggly date palms and one or two little desert bushes struggle hard to maintain their hold on life, and they seem especially alone there in the canyon, surrounded by brown, bare rocks and crumbling little hills. Our guide pointed to red stains on the stones above the protected spring at the head of the canyon. They were mute testimony to the fate of three desert soldiers who were surprised by a band of Tuaregs. After that surprise attack, the French army of the desert built a tunnel from the fort to the bottom of the canyon and dug a well at the tunnel mouth.

Americans are fanatics about water supplies, and I remember how shocked we were when we reached Tadjemont. At first view we were delighted with the tiny oasis a native was building at the base of the mountain. His hut had evidently been built by the army, but it was surrounded by a small garden of fresh green vegetables. He even had a little fence of brush which he had collected from scraggly desert trees. This patch of short green vegetation at the base of the slowly crumbling mountains was in sharp contrast to the somber grays and browns of the surrounding desert, and we were quite ready to praise the courage and industry of any human being who dared to make a farm on these crumbling rocks. Then we saw the well! Four or five feet below the surface the gardener had struck water. Instead of building up a stone curb around the well, he had dug an open ditch out toward the garden. Water flowed directly to the irrigation ditches, but the well and main ditch were so filled with mud and trash that only a tiny stream trickled out. It was not even deep enough for us to dip in a cup and get a drink of clean water. Everyone on the expedition set to work with shovels, and in half an hour we had cleaned out the well and main ditch so that when we returned from the south, a month later, we would have water fit to drink at Tadjemont. Times have changed since then. Recently I saw a photograph of a beautiful irrigation basin and a modern-looking building taken at that same water hole in the Sahara.

One year, late in January, we traveled by camel from Timokten to Titaf in the Sahara's western *erg*. There was nothing special about the journey, except that it gave us a glimpse of the Sahara's sternness and showed us what could have happened if we had not carried water enough to be independent of wells. We started at seven o'clock in the morning, and all that first day we traveled across a barren land. At night we camped on the unprotected plain. My diary reads, "Absolute desert. No well." The next day we found a "scant pasture for the camels about two hours from camp but no water." That night we camped again on a sterile, wind-swept plain, as clean of vegetation as a floor. The diary reads, "Still no well," but adds, "we have plenty of water so that we suffer only from the monotony of the scenery which is always empty, level plain." Only once on that long, flat stretch of empty gravel did we pass a well. As we urged our camels close to the two upright palm trunks which supported a heavy cross-piece we realized how much that well might mean in June or July to a weary traveler. Then we looked down inside the walls of the crib and saw, not water, but a heap of sand! The well of Hassi Nous, the half-way well, had been abandoned to Sahara winds.

Desert travelers must carry their own well-rope and their own version of the old oaken bucket. These essential items of desert equipment are not left at trailside wells. I recall a story about one man, an adventurer, who recently hitch-hiked his way about the Sahara with a wire recorder for collecting native songs and stories. He missed a rendezvous at a remote well and was left alone there for several days. He had no rope, and the well was too wide for him to try to "Santa Claus" his way down the hundred-foot shaft. He finally used the wire from his portable wire recorder and saved his life, but he lost all the interesting native songs and stories he had collected over several months.

Desert people seem to have discovered every type of mechanical aid for lifting water from deep or shallow wells except the suction pump. In the Gobi, wells are shallow and the universal method of drawing water is a skin bag lashed to the end of a four- or five-foot stick. A short rope is tied to the other end of the stick. The well man stands on the edge of the well, drops the bag and stick to the water, then pulls them back with the short rope. When he has the stick in his hands again, he lifts the bag of water and pours it into a trough from which his sheep, horses, camels, or goats can drink. For domestic use, the water is poured into wooden casks which are lashed onto a pack camel or other beast of burden and carried back to the *yurt*. In more than 4,000 miles of Gobi travel, I never saw any other method of raising water.

In the Sahara oases, well-sweeps are common. These are long poles swung between two upright posts near the well. The butt end of the pole has a heavy weight such as a box of rocks attached to it. At the tip is a rope with a bucket. The operator pulls down on the rope, which then tips the pole into the well. The bucket fills and the weighted pole helps the man to lift the load to the surface. The squeak and groan of well-sweeps is the eventide chorus, for each little walled garden has its own well and there may be hundreds in one oasis.

Man power applied to a rope over a pulley is common in all oases, but the rope and pulley is also operated by ox power, donkey power, and sometimes by camel power. When such power is used, the water bucket is a much larger bag than a man could lift. These have a long spout, with a second rope attached so that when the skin bag is lowered into the well the flexible spout is folded back and no water can run out. The ox, donkey, or camel is led up a steep path to the well and the heavy bag falls to the water. Then the animal is driven down the path, pulling the bagful of water clear up to the pulley hanging above the well-curb. The short rope straightens out the spout so that the water pours into the catch-basin outside the well-curb. From the catch-basin, the water runs through ditches to storage ponds; and when they are full it is spilled out through other ditches to irrigate the various parts of the garden.

There are several types of windlasses used, and once I saw an endless chain of little cups operated by man power on a large iron wheel. But the well-sweeps or rope-over-pulley systems are preferred wherever Arabs operate the gardens. In Arabia there are some very large wells, with as many as six or eight pulleys hanging on one frame. These are spectacular affairs, but each rope is pulled by one camel or ox or donkey. As each animal reaches the end of his path, the skin bag he has lifted dumps its gallons of water into the irrigation system. The pulleys always have a distinctive squeak, and the well owner knows the tune of each pulley—so he can always tell which one of his gardeners is loafing on the job by listening to the evening symphony.

Back through the centuries there have been some lazy desert peoples. They were so lazy that they did not like the labor of raising water from deep in the earth for irrigation, and eventually they discovered a way to make gravity do the work. I first met this interesting system in the central Sahara where it is called *foggara.* On the desert plain, a *foggara* shows as a long string of wells which may extend several miles from an oasis out into the desert. Below the surface the wells are connected by a continuous tunnel.

When I first saw a *foggara*, it was "common knowledge" among European desert travelers that the system was very, very ancient and that modern natives did not know how to produce it any more. We learned otherwise from a map which gave the location of a Stone Age campsite discovered only two or three years before our visit. Compass directions were given from the "last well of the *foggara*." For two days I hunted that area. I even assumed that the map maker did not know north from south or east from west and used his distances in all directions, but still I could not find the site. Finally, while talking to one of our workmen, I learned that two years before they had extended the *foggara* about a mile. He took me back to the old terminal well, and I found that the map maker had made no errors in direction. Later, the local sheik organized a *twized* or, as colonial Americans might have called it, a "digging bee" to begin the construction of another *foggara*.

About fifty Negro men and as many women assembled for the *twized* organized by the sheik at Aoulef. The men, armed with broad grub hoes, were lined up by a foreman. Several pottery drums and a primitive "clarinet" furnished the inspiration for the labor. When the band started playing, the foreman started singing, "Who's a lusty worker?" The men with the hoes swung them into the ground and answered, "That's us!"

"Who digs the deepest trench?" the leader asked. Again the hoes cut into the sand and the men answered, "That's us!" The hoes swung up and down in time with the song, and every down-beat moved a little sand up the side of the trench and stirred up a cloud of dust. The women filled their water jugs at a near-by well and poured it into the ditch to clear the air a little. With song and rhythmic swinging hoes, the trench was deepened. Eventually it would extend from the edge of the oasis out into the desert—too far to be maintained as an open ditch. Then, well-diggers would put down a shaft about ten yards from the end of the trench. When they reached the trench bottom depth, they would tunnel to the open ditch and tunnel out in the opposite direction as far as they could see by light from the open shaft. Then they would sink another shaft about ten yards beyond the first and tunnel back and forward. Eventually, they will have a long string of wells connected by a tunnel at ground-water level, or at least in a moist stratum of the earth. Water seeps into the tunnel. The floor has a very gradual slope so that the water flows to the open trench and on into the oasis. The wells get deeper and deeper as the chain extends out from the oasis. All the dirt from well and tunnel is piled around the mouth of the shaft. The resulting doughnut-shaped mounds on the surface of the desert mark the line of the *foggara* and serve as guidelines for pilots of desert airlines. Some of the *foggara* reach depths of 120 feet. This means that 120 feet of shaft must be sunk for each thirty-two feet the tunnel advances. Four or five miles of tunnel represent a lot of labor.

The ancient water tunnels were built with slave labor and represented a heavy capital investment. Today the labor is more expensive; and it may take a man several years, hiring a few laborers as he has available funds, before his *foggara* flows enough water to irrigate many palm trees. The water, of course, belongs to him who builds the tunnel. He can use it on his own garden or he can sell it to others.

When the water is sold to others, or shared if several gardeners have divided the expense of construction, an interesting type of water meter is installed where the ditch from the *foggara* enters the oasis. This is a large slab of stone which has been cut into teeth like a comb. The space between any two teeth is a unit. A gardener may buy the water which flows through one or more of the openings. He builds a mud-walled trench from the meter boundaries of his purchase to his storage pond, and all the water flowing through the spaces he has purchased belongs to him. It may take a day or more of flow to fill his storage pond, but whenever it is full he will break the wall and let the water flood out to ditches leading around his palm trees and garden plot.

Officials of the oasis keep a standard measure with which they can determine the actual flow of any part of the channel. This consists of a copper cylinder punched full of uniform holes. At one side on the upper edge of the cylinder is a rectangular notch. This copper cylinder is placed in the channel to be measured in such a manner that the water flows in through the notch. Official witnesses watch the procedure. All the holes in the copper meter are plugged with clay. Then, as the cylinder fills, the holes are opened one at a time until inflow and outflow are exactly balanced.

In the course of years the flow of water may decrease for several reasons. Cave-ins or silting may block the flow in the tunnel. The water level in the area may be lowered. If the aquifer, the water-transporting layer in the earth, is supplied only from desert rains and the rains fail, the flow will eventually cease until a storm replenishes the water source. This is more apt to happen when the tunnels are dug in the beds of ancient rivers.

Several years after I had seen the desert people start digging a new *foggara,* I was explaining the system to Dr. Sven Hedin, the Swedish explorer of Central Asian deserts.

"That's very interesting," he said. "I've seen the same long chains of wells out in Turkestan. Do you suppose the idea spread from one area to another? Or did desert people in different parts of the world hit on the same principle?" Since that time there has been a lot of research by historians, and explorers have published their observations from so many desert regions that we could make out an excellent case for either theory, diffusion or convergent development and independent discovery.

It is now known that some of the *foggara* in the western Sahara were started four centuries ago. In Morocco the tunnels are called *khotteras* or *rheteras.* The first one was built at Marrakech about A.D. 1078 or soon thereafter by Ubayd Allah Ibn Yamus. It is still flowing. The system was also known to the ancient Assyrians and Persians; and, although it has not been proved, it is believed that the Romans built some systems in the Sahara.

In Iran the tunnels are known as *kanats* or *qanats* and are still in use. They are called *karez* in Iraq, and in Palestine they are *fuqara.* It is not difficult to believe that the system spread from the Middle East through North Africa and the Far East, but identical tunnel-connected wells are reported from Rio Salado near Tehuacan in southern Mexico. Whether the idea had a single origin or was discovered in each of the areas in which it has been used makes little difference to oasis dwellers. Wherever it is possible to have perpetually flowing water from a tunnel, the system is preferred to the well-sweep, the rope and pulley, or to simple rope and bucket water-lifting.

Motor trucks, passenger buses, and automobiles have speeded

up desert crossings and have made the desert available to time-conscious travelers. They have not yet made man independent of desert wells and secret water holes. Every year someone has to be rescued on the Sahara caravan trails or the side roads in American deserts because they ignored the one great truth about the desert. "Where there is water there is life."

XII

· ·

· ·

· ·

· · · · · · · · · · · · ·

· · · · ·

Date Palms and Oasis Garden Patches

A GREENSWARD BY A GURGLING BROOK BENEATH A GROVE OF stately palms was my mental picture of an oasis before I knew the arid wastelands. Just once, at El Outayia, on the northern edge of the Sahara, we found such a corner. We stopped there to picnic and take pictures of the leaning trees and narrow streams, but the spot was not typical of Sahara. Water in an oasis is too precious to be wasted on a grassy lawn. It is all needed for more practical crops like wheat, beans and peas, edible fruits, and camel fodder.

Deep in the desert you may first see an oasis by looking down from some high point, because oases are usually located in valleys or basins. There are exceptions, of course. Close to the mountain boundaries of deserts in Africa, Central Asia, or anywhere else, water is only a few feet below the plain, and date palms can be planted right in the moist soil, literally fulfilling the Arab proverb by "having their feet in the water and their head in eternal sunshine."

At Souf, near the Tunisian border of Algeria, date palms are planted on the floor of sand dune hollows; and from the air it is like looking over a field of odd and irregularly shaped bowls filled with feathery green bouquets. The gardener has no irrigation labors in that region, for the water level is at the base of the sand. His problem is to keep the sand walls of his property from tumbling onto his crop, but Souf is a Sahara curiosity, not a typical oasis. Generally, from a distance an oasis is a long, broad, asymmetrical mass of dark green, sprawling over a valley bounded by crumbling, rocky cliffs or graceful dunes of sand. You see only the green mass of feathery tree tops at first. When you get closer, this becomes a green canopy supported by thousands of tall slender columns. Roads through some big gardens look like avenues in a city park with here and there a rectangular reflecting basin which mirrors the long, curving leaves of the tall date palms.

An oasis may be a quarter-mile or a half-mile wide and two to ten miles long. Some are much larger; some are smaller, for there is no fixed size or shape. Both depend on available water and the man power to take advantage of it.

Always at one side of the green mass is the cluster of houses of the oasis dwellers. They are not scattered through the gardens. In some desert towns all of the houses are whitewashed, but in many oases they are all the same dun color as the dirt of which they are built. Except where the oasis is on a flat plain, the village is piled up on the valley slope above the palm trees like a heap of children's play blocks. This enables the gardeners to watch their property from the roof tops of their homes, and it also leaves free all the land that can be irrigated.

Desert buildings are thick-walled, flat-roofed structures built of adobe or sun-baked mud. The flat roofs are surrounded by high walls so that the women can enjoy fresh air, when the sun is low, without being seen by their neighbors. Most houses also have a walled courtyard. When you fly over such a village it resembles a field of rectangular wells packed close together and divided into sections by irregular lines, the streets that lead to the central market square.

In Sahara oases this central square is a huge open space surrounded by buildings, some of which are fronted with broad colonnades. Almost always there is a mosque, the religious edifice of the Moslems, somewhere around the square, even if there are other mosques in various parts of the village. The mosque is easily identified by the many-storied minaret which towers high above the common one- or two-level buildings. From the high balconies of the minaret the musical voice of the muezzin rings out to the farthest corner of the oasis, calling the faithful to prayer five times each day. When the call to prayer breaks the desert silence like a silver trumpet, every faithful Moslem stops whatever he is doing, turns his face to Mecca, and goes through the prescribed movements and set phrases of his prayer. Those who live or work near the mosque may enter the cool, dim sanctuary, remove their sandals, and spend a few minutes or an hour in prayer and contemplation. But the good Moslem need not hurry across the open square to the mosque for prayers. He may kneel, and bow, and sit in reverence beneath the palm tree he is tending, below the scaffold of a new building he is constructing, or wherever the call to prayer may find him.

Some of the buildings around the square, especially those with colonnaded porticoes, may be shops if the human population of the oasis is large, but many small population centers depend entirely on the market held in the square one day each week for all the needs of retail commerce.

Market days are fixed, and each village has its day so that merchants can make the rounds of several oases. Early in the morning of a market day, all roads will be crowded with laden donkeys or camels and men in flowing robes; and by five or six o'clock the great open square will be crowded with people. Heaps of dates, piles of wool, tethered flocks of goats and sheep, vegetables and fruit, old clothes from army surplus, basket trays of brilliantly colored candies, bolts of cloth for dresses, collections of coarse pottery, stacks of aluminum pots and pans—everything and anything an oasis dweller can use—is laid out on the desert floor. Behind each heap of wares a merchant sits or stands to wait a prospective buyer from the milling crowd. The butcher and the silversmith each sets up shop in his particular section of the market square. Each is exposed to the same dust and flies; each ready for the next argument with a customer.

The price of anything is seldom posted in the markets of the desert world, especially where the Arab culture rules. "Fixed price" and "the customer is always right" are concepts hardly dreamed of in a desert market. Each purchase involves a battle of wits, a contest in which the merchant tries to guess how much the customer knows of an item's true value, how badly he wants it, and the maximum he will pay to get it. The buyer aims to guess the lowest price the seller will take. It is a fascinating game which may take five minutes for a ten-cent purchase, or many weeks for the purchase of a large, good-quality rug.

Sometimes the battle of words becomes loud and violent. Spectators join in and take sides in the argument, and everyone has a wonderful time shouting at the top of his voice and displaying his knowledge of quality and price to all within hearing. I recall one transaction between a blanket merchant and a buyer in which the buyer grabbed the disputed blanket, worth probably twenty dollars, and tried to tear it from the merchant's hands. The two men tugged and pulled; they screamed and shouted vituperation at each other until they were separated by one of the officials of the market place. Bargaining is a part of the way of life among the desert people. Those who are merchants like to meet a buyer who knows the value of his purchase, and they really admire one who knows how to get the most for his dollar. They are rarely beaten, of course, because they know what they have paid for their stock.

I recall shopping in the *souks,* or permanent market place of Damascus, that large oasis in the Syrian Desert. I saw some yard goods I thought my wife would like for a dress and began to bargain for a dress length. I got the merchant down quite a bit from his initial asking price, but then I could not bring him down a penny lower. I left his booth and went on to another. Again I got the merchant down, but he would not budge a cent below the lowest price the first seller had asked. I believe I saw the same quality and design of cloth in five or six shops that day, and while the asking price differed at every one, yet every merchant refused to bargain below a certain figure and the bottom price was the same every time. I did not buy the cloth, because the lowest price was still too high for my pocketbook, but it was quite evident that all those merchants in Damascus had bought from the same wholesale place and all had paid the same price and demanded the same minimum profit.

Once in Baghdad I made several trips to a silversmith's in buying some jewelry. After an hour or two we agreed on price, but I did not have the exact change and had to submit a large denomination bill in payment. The merchant counted out the change but tried to include coins which were neither Iraqi nor American currency. The argument started all over again and only ended when I insisted on either correct change or a canceled sale. I got my change and an admiring smile.

"Some day," said the merchant as we shook hands, "you will be a rich man." So far I have seen no sign that his statement was prophetic even though it was made in fabulous Baghdad.

In the market places of oases each merchant pays some sort of rent to the market officials. Sometimes it is a sort of sales tax, for I have watched officials counting the number of sheep a buyer takes out of the market square; but on produce and manufactured articles I think the merchant usually pays rent for the space in the market square, although the procedure varies in different oases.

By ten o'clock in the morning the stocks of perishable merchandise in the market squares of most oases will be gone, and by midday, especially in summer, the big square will be as empty as the desert plain beyond the palm trees. Nomads from the surrounding desert will have sold their surplus sheep, goats, and wool. They have bought the grain, the dates, the tea and sugar needed to supplement their diet of animal products. Camel caravans have disposed of merchandise brought from far places. Itinerant silversmiths, the vendors of pots and pans, and dealers in cloth for women's dresses have moved on to be ready for tomorrow's market in another oasis, but they will be back next week in the same corner of the now-vacant square. The big open space surrounded by scores or hundreds of adobe-walled buildings has served its purpose for the time.

Regardless of how many houses there are at the edge of the oasis, or how many thousands of people they shelter, they are less important in the minds of the desert dwellers than the date trees.

It is the number of date palms that count in the desert, not the number of people. I can remember when Biskra was an oasis of 120,000 trees. There were also 8,500 people living there, but no one, except a European census taker, cared about *them*. Biskra, in the minds of desert dwellers, was a BIG PLACE. A place of 120,000 date trees!

Date palms are planted a rod apart, but over the centuries that some oases have existed, the symmetry has been broken. Bent and leaning trees, shoots sprouting from an ancient favorite, changes in water rights—all contribute to interrupt the straight lines. In some of the large new properties, the trees make broad, majestic avenues; and the square plots between them, planted in wheat or garden vegetables, look as neat as the row crops of market gardens near Western cities. But there are many oases in which each property is surrounded by a high mud wall to keep out wandering animals that have strayed from their herders. In other places, the walls are topped with thorns or broken glass, or even with the flat, thorny leaves of prickly pear cactus. These pointed frostings on the garden walls are wicked-sharp and stern reminders that the fruits behind the walls are forbidden to all except the gardener and the owner.

When the oasis of Aoulef, in the central Algerian Sahara, was being enlarged, the new addition extended into the bed of a dry salt pan, or drainage basin. Through the centuries the basin had collected and evaporated whatever rain had fallen in that area. The soil accordingly was hard and salty, but there was quite as much mud in it as there was salt. This had to be removed before a garden could be planted. A crew of Negroes attacked the land with the same grub hoes which others had used to dig the *foggara* ditch. Some of them tore up hard lumps of salty, sun-baked mud, while others loaded these onto stretcher-like carrying frames. Each frame was carried by two women to the side of the field where the lumps were piled into a wall. It reminded me of stone walls built in New England of the stones cleared from the fields to make more room for the crops.

After the salt earth had been removed, the next layer was broken up with the same grub-hoe technique, rather than with the spade or plow that we would use. Finally, sand swept from the floors of houses and stables of the village was spread over the land as a fertilizer. The sand was carried in large baskets slung like saddle bags over the backs of little donkeys. Small boys drove the donkeys without halter rope or bridle rein. The stiff rib of a palm leaf served each boy as a whip or goad, and the lads seemed to enjoy their work of keeping the donkeys on the job.

Once the land was salt-free and fertilized, it was lined and cross-lined with shallow ditches. Each plot at Aoulef would have a storage basin for the irrigation water because the supply came from wells or *foggara;* but if the source had been a flowing stream or large artesian well, the basins would not be necessary.

When a storage basin is filled, the wall is breached to let the flood run into the ditches which go around each tree. Some of the moisture seeps out through the ground between the trees, and this is absorbed by other crops. Most of the vegetables common in Europe are raised in oases. I have eaten lettuce and tomatoes, as well as carrots and onions; but next to date palms, the most important crop in the Sahara is wheat. Some of the wheat fields are almost as big as a city lot, but more often they are no bigger than the squares between the palm trees. The grain is sowed by hand in these small patches, and the seed scattered so thickly that the sprouting plants look like a well-tended lawn in a city suburb.

In the desert there is more work to raising wheat than in our big grain states, because when the grain begins to form, the crop must be protected from the birds. Oasis dwellers have rigged up all sorts of scarecrows. Often there is the typical old-clothes-on-sticks, so common in cartoons; but I have also seen a dried camel's head on a stick. It was a hideous-looking thing, and I suppose was intended to warn the birds of what their fate would be if they persisted in robbing the wheat field. More effective than old clothes was a network of strings tied over the field. From the strings hung all sorts of old junk and tinware. A main string led off to a shady corner where an old man leaned against a tree in comfort. When he saw birds alight in the grain, he would give the string a tug. This set the hardware all a-jangle and made such a racket that the poor birds were frightened out of their wits. They left for distant parts in panic, and the old man leaned back to his nap until another group arrived. Some watchers did not bother with strings and hardware. They sat in the shade with a pile of hard earth clods. When the birds dropped into the grain, they let go with deadly aim and came close enough to drive the birds away. One gardener in Aoulef arranged an old blunderbuss so that he could fire it from a distance with a string. It frightened the birds all right but, as the field had only about two square rods of grain, the cost of powder must have been more than the value of the crop. However, it gave the old man some fun to make all that noise.

Date palms are by far the most important crop in Sahara oases. Most of us think of dates as a dessert fruit, but among the desert Arabs dates are a basic food for man and beast. Our workmen often had only bread and dates for their meal, and, with sheep's milk, dates were always offered as a sign of hospitality and welcome when we entered an oasis.

There are many kinds of dates just as there are many kinds of apples. I remember that the day we stopped at Charouin, in Sahara's western *erg*, the sheik's welcoming gift was a tray of the most delicious dates I have ever tasted. They were large and soft and sweet as honey, a most welcome change from our diet of canned sardines and potted ham. I am sure I ate two or three pounds of them. When we moved on, a day or two later, I sent the guide into the village to buy ten pounds of those delicious Charouin dates, for at that time I was willing to stake my reputation that they were the finest in the whole Sahara. After a while the guide returned. I eagerly opened the ten-pound package. Inside were the hardest, meanest, most miserable fruits I have ever seen. They resembled peanut shells much more than dates. Patiently I explained that I wanted the same delicious fruit which the sheik had given us when we arrived. The guide was gone for another hour, but this time when he came back he had an explanation. There was just one tree of those choice dates in the oasis of Charouin and that was in the sheik's private garden. The only dates for sale at that late season were the hard camel-food species. I was very disappointed, and the memory of those first Charouin dates still makes my mouth water.

No part of the date palm is wasted. There is even an etiquette for eating the fruit. Although you are outdoors, you do not throw the pits over your left shoulder or in any other direction. It just isn't done. I know, for that was my technique until my host scowled so fiercely that the interpreter explained.

"Put the date pits back on the tray. Don't throw them away," he said. "They'll be saved. Later girls and women will sit in the court-yard with large, flat stones in their laps and crush the pits with smaller hammerstones. The crushed pits will be carried by caravans on long, pastureless trails. When the camels need food, the mashed date stones will be mixed with water to force-feed the animals."

Every winter the dead lower leaves of the trees are cut out. No ladders are used, even though the trees are sometimes forty to sixty feet high. The gardener climbs the tree like a monkey. The trunk is rough from the scars of old leaf cuts which makes it easy for the man to "walk" up the trunk with bare hands and feet. When he gets to the top, he stands on the trunk, leaning his weight against a palm-fiber rope which passes around the tree and around his waist, exactly like a telephone lineman's safety belt. The safety rope leaves both hands free to trim the tree, or, in harvest time, to cut the bunches of dates and lower them to the ground with another rope. Dead palm leaves are good fuel for cooking fires, and the stems are also used in many kinds of construction.

Trunks of old trees make frames for houses. They support the roof, and form the superstructure at wells. They also serve as simple bridges across irrigation ditches. Baskets are woven from the leaf blades. Even the coarse fiber that grows at the base of the leaves is used. It is twisted into a coarse but very strong rope and may be used for almost anything from camel hobbles to the tree-climber's safety belt. The fiber is also woven into coarse cloth, rather like gunny sacking, to cover the carrying-frames used instead of wheel-barrows.

Date trees are sexed, and only the female trees bear fruit. The male trees, which bear the pollen, take just as much water as fruit-bearing trees, so the gardeners keep only enough male trees to meet their needs. The pollen could be carried by winds to the flowers of the female trees but the Arabs recognize this as wasteful. In the spring, when the pollen is ripe, they climb the trees and carefully pick the stems of male flowers. They carry these to the female trees and shake the pollen over their flowers. The blossoms grow on stems three or four feet long and hang in a dense cluster from the crown of the tree. When those stems are loaded with big, ripe dates they make a heavy load.

It takes a lot of faith in the future to start a date grove. After the labor of getting the land ready and bringing to it a constant supply of water, young shoots from choice old trees are planted. The ideal is to plant a camel-load of dung with each shoot. When the tree is about three years old, another load is added around the base of the tree. In the Sahara a few dates may be harvested from five-year-old trees, but the trees are not full-bearing until the eighth year. From then on, the owner will harvest 300 to 500 pounds of dates each year for the next one or two centuries. His heirs, of course, enjoy their inheritance even unto the seventh and the eighth generation, but their shares sometimes get quite involved. Eventually one tree may be owned by a dozen people.

Despite all the stern practicality connected with date palms and garden patches, an oasis is a fascinating place of peace and quiet. It is pleasant to wander down an avenue of palm trees in late afternoon when the shadows stretch out long and straight. You hear the soft murmur of little streams rushing around the roots of century-old trees, and now and then you see the feathered tops mirrored in rectangular pools from which they draw the water that is life. At dusk, weary little donkeys, homeward bound with rustling loads of palm leaves, walk slowly along the sandy roads. There is a different charm about the older oases. There your stroll is along mud-walled alleys, but now and then you can peek through broken doorways into tiny gardens, each corner marked by the trunk of a well-trimmed tree.

Once, at Feriana in Tunisia, my wife, Dorothy, and I went for a walk just before dinner. In the dying half-light that followed the setting of the sun, we strolled along the alleys of the oasis. We had not gone far when an appetizing odor of cooking meat attracted our attention.

"Am I so hungry that I'm smelling things?" said Dorothy. "We're in the gardens. Why would anyone be cooking here?"

We peered between the palings of a fence of palm-leaf stems. There in the corner of the garden was a sugar-loaf-shaped hut of palm leaves. Before it, squatting on the ground, was an old woman cooking *cous-cous,* wheat-flour pellets steamed over boiling meat. An iron pot was suspended from a tripod over an open fire. Now and then she leaned over the kettle, and light from the flames flared on her wrinkled face. In the yellow campfire, her mouth seemed shrunken, toothless, except for one yellow fang that overhung her lip. Her eyes were deep, black pits. Even when she walked a step away for sticks to add to the yellow fire, she did not straighten up.

"It's just like Halloween," said Dorothy. "Is she a witch, a-brewin' potions?"

"Just some poor old woman," I answered. "She's probably lost all her kin and is barely tolerated in this garden." Then I heard a rumbling growl. Curled up beside the hut was a big, black native dog.

We wandered on to the oasis edge and watched the last light fade beyond the silent, barren plain. It makes you wonder at the simple faith and courage of the sons of Allah who build green gardens in the very heart of the sterile desert wastes.

XIII

Ancient People of the Desert World

ONE OF THE PLACES WHERE STONE AGE PEOPLE LIVED WHICH I
remember well is Gara Cheurfa, a flat-topped butte in the Western
Sahara. My companion, Maurice Reygasse, and I first saw it as we
rode into the oasis village of the same name. Our trail passed close
to the base of the table mountain. A narrow, rounded dune of sand
sweeps gracefully from the base to the top of the butte, and that
day a thin haze of sand streamed from the peak like a banner from
a flagstaff.

"The dunes are smoking," said the natives.

The interesting story of Gara Cheurfa, as recorded in the mountain itself, runs through vast geologic ages into the centuries of
man's Stone Age life, then across generations of medieval history
and modern times to the present. A cap of quartzitic sandstone
several feet thick forms the top of this butte, and it is because of
this very hard sandstone that the butte exists, for it has protected
the softer stone beneath against centuries of weathering. Without
that two-acre piece of hard stone, Gara Cheurfa would long since
have been cut away to the level of the plain from which it rises,
just as the rest of the plateau was weathered down in the quaternary
period. The steep-sloping sides of the mountain are covered with
jagged blocks of quartzite broken from the cap-rock by the constant

extreme daily changes of temperature. In winter, the thermometer registers in the lower thirties at five and six o'clock in the morning. By one o'clock in the afternoon it is in the eighties or nineties. The summer sun of centuries has burned the blocks to a warm reddish-brown color, and the desert winds have given them a high polish. On the western end of the Gara the blocks are numerous and very large. Some of them will weigh many thousands of pounds, but they have all been split off from the parent rock by constant contraction in cold nights and expansion in warm days.

The flat, polished, red surfaces of these big rocks served as drawing board and tablet for ancient peoples of the desert. Some of them are covered with inscriptions in Tiffinar characters, the writing of the ancient Libyans and of the modern Tuaregs. Many of these inscriptions have been translated into French, and we know today that they were written by the Tuaregs only a few centuries ago. On the same rocks, mingled with the writings of the early Tuaregs, are carvings of men and camels. These are badly out of proportion and show no sense of perspective. A modern kindergarten child could do as well, but they are the records of the people who have lived in the shadow of the Gara.

When Reygasse and I decided to study the butte, we climbed up among the great blocks of stone near the summit. Reygasse went clear to the top while I was busy getting photographs of the drawings and inscriptions. I heard him shout once or twice but, like many Frenchmen, he was often effervescent, so I kept on at my photography. Finally I scrambled up to join him. He could hardly contain himself, he was so excited—and well he might be. The whole top of the little mountain was covered with small fragments of quartzite, but the western end of the butte had been a quarry for men of the Middle Old Stone Age! There were hundreds of fragments of the red quartzite which clearly showed the "bulb" of percussion. The bulb is a scar produced by a blow, and it is quite in contrast to the angular breaks caused by stresses of expansion and contraction. It was clear that these fragments had been struck from large blocks by the hand of man thousands of years ago, and there was not the least possibility of doubt that we were on the quarry site of a Mousterian type of Old Stone Age culture. The difference between the fragments covering a large part of the mountain and those at the western end was clear cut. Those on the east were angular, uneven pieces produced by the natural processes of weathering, and no two of them were the same shape. On the western end the fragments could all be classified by their shape into discoids, flakes, and blades. We collected hundreds of these pieces, and among them we found a few characteristic Middle Old Stone Age points and scrapers. We also found large fist hatchets, so often associated with such points and scrapers in other parts of the world.

After the collecting was finished I sat on the edge of the butte for a long time, studying the stone tools made by prehistoric people perhaps five hundred centuries ago. A hundred feet below me was the desert plain. Clustering together west of the butte were bunches of mud-walled houses, and off beyond them the long line of plume-topped palm trees, the oasis of the Cheurfa. To the east was the barren gravel plain and in the distance the plateau of Tademait. What was the scene fifty thousand years ago when some Stone Age man sat on this very spot breaking up the quartzite rock with a stone hammer? What did *he* see as he shaped the very tools I was holding in my hand? Was the plain to the east a grassy plain with grazing herds of antelope? Or was it covered with bush and scrub which served as cover for rabbits and coveys of birds? When that Mousterian quarryman looked to the west, did he see a winding river where I saw the line of green palms? Were there trees along that river bank to shelter his primitive home, or did he camp on the open plain, building a large bonfire to keep away the cold and give him courage in the darkness of the night?

The details may be indistinct, but the broad, physical outlines of the desert world have not changed materially in the millenniums during which man has roamed the earth. The mountain boundaries which control the winds and limit the moisture, the internal drainage systems ending in land-locked lakes, the buttes and mesas that dot the landscape today—these are the same geographic features which prehistoric man saw as he looked out from his campsite 30,000 or 100,000 years ago. The buttes and mountains were perhaps a few feet higher. The river banks were much more pronounced. Water flowed more continuously between arroyo banks and stood deep in now-shallow basins. Clumps or bands of trees marked the water courses. Bunch-grass-covered plains, dotted with bushes and scattered trees, extended between the stream beds. Rains came more often in the desert during those wet years of the geologic past when, far to the north, the glaciers were forming and, in temperate climates, flood waters were gouging out broad, deep valleys for the rivers of today.

But the desert world has always been much drier than the surrounding non-desert.

Living crocodiles seen in desert water holes in historic times, the skeleton of a cane rat in the sandstone along a desert trail—these are proof of once-permanent rivers and more abundant river-bottom vegetation, but they do not mean that today's deserts were yesterday's verdant meadows or dank tropical forests.

Archaeologists have found ample evidence that man has lived in the desert world since long before the beginning of historic records, before the age of pottery vessels, and even before he learned to plant seeds and harvest crops. Large *coups de poing* of the earliest paleolithic hunters, weapon points and stone scrapers of the Middle Old Stone Age, and fine and delicately chipped microliths of later paleolithic types are found on desert routes today. Neolithic weapon points, coarse grinding stones for crushing seeds, and weights for digging sticks have been picked up in various parts of the desert world. Even fragments of crude pottery are often found on ancient campsites, although in both the Sahara and the Gobi, modern natives are still using pottery made by the same methods and of the same material as that in use by neolithic peoples. This is why it is not always easy to prove whether the potsherds of a campsite belong to the prehistoric world or are only the leavings of some native camper of yesteryear.

Archaeologists have not done much intensive Stone Age research in desert regions. Tiny flint blades, a half-inch long, a handful of broken arrowheads, or a dozen coarse fist hatchets are not spectacular enough to rate a front-page story in a metropolitan newspaper. Archaeologists need good stories in order to get funds with which to carry on their work, and so the interesting but unspectacular Stone Age story of the desert world has been neglected. But the story is there. The evidence is scattered across the Sahara from the Atlas Mountains to the Niger River. It is on the hilltops and in the sand dunes of the Gobi. You will find evidence that Stone Age Man has lived in all the desert world if you can pick the spots that would have been good campsites in those times.

I have collected the stone tools of prehistoric desert peoples from many of those campsites. At first I believed the popular theories that deserts were once much more fertile than they are now, that they supported many more people in ancient times than they can today. On the basis of these theories I expected to find Stone Age material almost anywhere. Then, when my early efforts failed to find campsites "almost anywhere," I started thinking.

"Supposing the desert was not the fertile paradise the theories claim?" I asked myself. "If the deserts were only relatively more fertile than they are today, where would the Stone Age people have been likely to live?"

When the search was concentrated near today's oases, along the banks of ancient stream beds, on slight elevations overlooking valleys or at the points where two small streams joined, I began to find the ancient campsites. Generally, the evidence left by Stone Age peoples is on the surface of the desert and not buried. This makes it difficult to say that one site is older or younger than another. Desert weathering has been reducing the landscape instead of building it up as has occurred in more temperate regions of archaeological research. Even if one site had been occupied time and time again over hundreds or thousands of years, the evidence of different occupations would all be mingled together instead of separated by layers of sterile dirt deposits. Until the archaeologists find and study truly stratified habitation sites in the desert, we must depend on the study of types of stone tools found to interpret the different ages.

In practice this is not as difficult as it sounds. I have found more than one location on the banks of ancient stream beds where the worked-stone fragments were limited to a distinct area, perhaps fifty yards in diameter, and the artifacts were characteristic of distinct periods like those found in stratified deposits in other parts of the world. On the same stream bank, only a couple of hundred yards away, another site was covered with worked flints of a different type; and beyond that a third. Each campsite was sharply defined on the desert floor and separated from the others by desert plain upon which not one piece of worked stone was found.

Obviously that section of stream bank had been a good campsite some thousands of years ago. Perhaps it was covered with grass when prehistoric man first roamed the region, so that the remains of the first camp were hidden when, years later, the second and third groups came along. Even though all three sites are on the surface so that there is no stratification to prove which campers came first and which last, the difference in the types of tools is so distinct that there is no doubt that each represents a different culture.

On these surface sites only the stone tools are preserved. Many of them, however, are tools for working wood or bone. Some are typical scrapers for cleaning skins, and some are weapon points. These are the durable artifacts of nomad hunters. Some of the flint blades were used to cut and shape bone spear points. Others were inserted in the edge of large animal ribs or other bones to make sharp-edged implements. Some of the sites have yielded true arrowheads, indicating that the people who camped on those sites had acquired the bow and could kill their game from a little greater distance than their ancestors who had only spears and clubs.

Still other Sahara sites have given us stones worn flat and smooth by grinding, so that we know their owners had learned to crush the seeds of plants for making flour. Perhaps they indicate the beginnings of agriculture and the seeds they ground were millet or some other domesticated grain. I have seen Negroes in the Hoggar of the Sahara still using the same sort of stones to grind grain.

Stone Age man has left evidence on campsites along ancient stream banks all across the Sahara from the Niger River to the Atlas Mountains. The type of tools follow the same pattern as those discovered in other parts of the world from earliest Stone Age to Neolithic.

On the other side of the world, in the Gobi of Mongolia, the Central Asiatic Expeditions led by Roy Chapman Andrews discovered sites occupied by prehistoric Dune Dwellers. Three years after that discovery I was with the expedition. In spite of our knowledge of the earlier discoveries the section of the desert we were exploring did not yield much archaeological material at first.

Then, one day about the middle of June, a Mongol hunter rode into camp. His weapon was a flintlock gun, a decrepit, antique affair with a barrel four feet long. The stock was a hardwood board an inch thick. The thing was so clumsy that the hunter had rigged a two-legged standard to support the barrel. To fire the weapon he lay prone on the ground, lowered the two-legged standard, adjusted it with a string, sighted carefully, and pulled the long lever-like trigger. If some ten or twelve other previous operations concerned with charging the weapon had been properly performed, the powder charge exploded and two murderous lead slugs sped toward their mark. To those accustomed to modern, rapid-firing rifles, this relic of a gun looked inefficient, but the Mongol hunter assured us, "One shot, one antelope." We realized then that he spent hours stalking his game before risking a shot, but what is time to a desert hunter?

The gun interested me aside from its efficiency as a hunter's weapon. The vital part of the firing mechanism was not a manufactured gunflint from England or Belgium, but a flintlike scraper characteristic of the Dune Dweller Stone Age culture. I saw it as a new clue in my search for ancient campsites. Where the scraper-gunflint had come from, I believed, there would be quantities of other stone scrapers. By means of signs and a mixture of pidgin English and Chinese, I conveyed the idea to Tsinimbo, one of the expedition Mongols, that we wanted to see the place where the hunter got his gunflint.

Three hours later Tsinimbo came to my tent with the information. The hunter knew of a place "three miles south" which he called "the place of many stones." He would guide us there the next morning at seven o'clock. I had scoured the area of the expedition's camp for a radius of five miles without finding any "place of many stones," but my skepticism did not prevent me from keeping the rendezvous.

The story of that morning's journey to a point "three miles south" is a minor epic, for our hunter-guide led us all over the Gobi. At one time or another our car was headed toward every point on the compass dial except true north, and we crossed all the roughest terrain in the area. Half a dozen times I recognized landmarks which I could have reached by smooth trails but always the hunter turned us away from them. When the speedometer showed thirty-five miles from camp and the hunter gave me a course true west, my patience was exhausted. We had just come to a stall in loose sand with a boiling motor, and I told Tsinimbo that as soon as the motor cooled we would return to camp by trails that I recognized.

"Yes," said Tsinimbo, "Mongol hunter-man bad man no-damn-good but he think this maybe so the place of many stones."

Skeptically I walked over to a wind hollow in the dunes and gazed on its hard bottom. It was literally covered with stone implements!

The Mongol hunter's "three miles south" had proved to be thirty-five miles west by south. But he had led me to the largest and richest Dune Dweller habitation site so far discovered. It, later, took ten men four days to collect all the material from the site which the Mongols had named Baron Shabaka.

The site is a narrow valley which slopes down to an ancient lake basin. The sides and bottom of the valley are covered with solidified sand dunes. Centuries of desert winds have cut mercilessly at these soft stone hills until the large straight-sided hollows have been weathered out all through the valley. On the hard bottoms of these hollows, swept clean of all loose sand by the desert winds, lie the stone tools of prehistoric peoples who lived there when those ancient dunes were live and young. Back and forth across the old camp grounds we walked bent double or crawled on hands and knees to pick up the ancient tools. We kept collecting each day until the long shadows made it difficult to recognize the tiny implements.

We were working on the very spot where Dune Dwellers had camped for hundreds, perhaps thousands, of years. The pieces of hand-worked stone we were collecting had been used and lost by those ancient desert dwellers—lost by them ten or twenty thousand years before.

There were blackened places, where their fires had been, with many fire-cracked stones partially buried in the blackened earth. We found thousands of tiny blades of chalcedony, jasper, chilled lava—all flintlike stones of the Gobi. We found the cores from which these blades were struck. Many of the cores themselves had been made into short, thick, jagged-edged knives after all possible blades had been removed. There were hundreds of tiny disklike scrapers, some of them smaller than the nail of my little finger, some two inches in diameter. There were even a few beautiful arrow points of gemlike chalcedony, and there were coarse spear points of quartzite.

Near the top of the valley slope one of our party found a long rectangular grinding stone; we call it a "metate." The metate was broken, but the two pieces were still in contact. Beside the broken metate was a part of the grinding bar used as the upper stone in grinding seeds or grain. A few feet down the slope was the other piece of the grinding bar. Was this the record of a frustrating day in the life of a Stone Age "housewife"? Had she been putting off too long her need for a new metate and grinding bar until that day when she was late preparing dinner and the worn-out implements both broke? I could well imagine the scene! A Stone Age woman kneeling on the ground, her weight pressed hard against the primitive millstones as she moved the upper one back and forth. Suddenly the hand stone broke and pitched her forward on her face. Angrily she straightened up and hurled the broken piece from her hand. There it lay just down the slope. It fitted perfectly to the broken end of the piece still partly buried beside the metate.

After Baron Shabaka, we found other hollows weathered by the wind in ancient dune lands. On their clean-swept floors we found many other tools. There were stones shaped like the lighter axes once used by the American Indians; we call them "celts." Some have thick, convex edges; others are gouge-like or "hollow-ground." All are slightly curved, so we believe they were once mounted on handles in such a way that they could have been used as adzes, either for digging in the soil or for woodworking.

Ornamentation was already known to these ancient dwellers of the Gobi dunes. We found tiny fragments of ostrich eggshell, yes, and dinosaur eggshell, too, which had been pierced with a small stone drill. Once the shell had been pierced, it was cut and trimmed until it was reduced to a tiny circular bead. Small bivalve shells were also used for beads. We found many which had had the little projecting knob above the hinge ground off until an opening into the shell had been produced. It is an easy and very ingenious way of getting a neat hole in the hard shell.

Fragments of very crude, poorly baked pottery were found among the coarser stone tools, but we did not find any pieces large enough to give us the outlines of the pots of which they once formed a part. The outside of these fragments is marked with lines in such a way that we suspect the maker shaped the vessels with a paddle wrapped with a cord or carved with lines. However, we are certain that the technique of the potter's wheel was not yet known to those ancient peoples.

The type of stone tools found on Dune Dweller sites indicates that only part of the story is left for us. Most of the tools are the sort which would be used for working bone or wood. Similar tools have been found buried in the caves of Europe, where they are associated with a large variety of bone artifacts. It is but simple deduction to say that the principal materials of the complete Dune Dweller culture were bone and wood; but bone and wood are not easily preserved unless they are buried or protected from constantly changing extremes of temperature and humidity. During months of exploration in the Gobi we found no bone tools, no parts of the skeletons of animals eaten by the Dune Dwellers, and no human skeletons.

Near the end of that summer the expedition camped in some dunes just two days' run from Kalgan, China. Here, at the foot of a weathered bank, Bill Thompson, one of the expedition's paleontologists, found some bone fragments. We all joined in the hunt and sifted much of the loose sand. The result was thrilling for the archaeologist. We found one small bone awl, two fine bone needle points, thirty fox teeth which had been drilled near the base, eight shells with the "heel" ground off to make a smooth round hole, and, finally, a small bird bone which had been decorated with a group of parallel lines.

None of the Dune Dweller sites found while I was with the expedition were *in situ* so that they could be dated, but on an earlier campaign buried material was found. The geologists, Dr. Charles P. Berkey and Dr. Frederick Morris, established the fact that the oldest material was probably 20,000 years old.

The largest Dune Dweller habitation sites were all located in the wind hollows of ancient and partially solidified sand dune areas. The belief is that these people lived among the live dunes of their time where most of the desert vegetation existed. There they could snare rabbits and other small game, and they could find some shelter from the wind as well as fuel for their campfires. Perhaps their "homes" were roofless windbreaks with walls of brush or matting near their tiny cooking fires. I have seen such "nests" used by the Negroes living with the Hoggar Tuaregs in the Sahara.

The stone tools of these ancient dwellers in the Gobi were lost or got covered with loose sand. Eventually the dunes became fixed. Rains filtered through the sand dissolving minerals from the upper layers of the dunes to carry them deeper, where they partially cemented the deeper sand and made soft sandstone of the dunes. In the course of time, desert winds have cut away at this soft stone; and implements, long hidden from the surface, have become exposed. As the winds carry away all the loose sand, the clean-swept floors between the dunes are paved with artifacts of ages past.

Dune Dweller artifacts were also found at lookout points on the edges of mesas and on isolated hilltops. However, the evidence of such localities was always scanty. A few flakes and blades, a typical Dune Dweller core of chalcedony or chilled lava made up the usual harvest on such sites. These small workshops were a puzzle for a while. The raw material for stone tools was often fairly common all over the mesa, but the worked pieces were very few and only found at those points which gave a good view of the plain below.

Why did the ancient stoneworker ply his trade on mesa edges

where the view was broad and long? The question really bothered me, until one day I remembered the remark made by the hunter with the cumbersome gun: "One shot, one antelope." Probably the Stone Age hunter had used the same technique and stalked his game before he hurled his spear or drew his bow. If that were true then, of course, he would sit for hours at his lookout point, watching the herds of antelope as they fed on the plain below. Little by little they would work closer to the mesa. Patiently the hunter studied the herd, watched for the straggler and laid his plans for stalking his victim. What better way to pass the idle hours of waiting than to pick up a pretty stone and shape it to his needs? The chips and discarded core were useless, but the finished artifact was carried away with the hunter-arrowmaker when he left the mesa workshop and began to stalk his antelope.

Peoples of the desert world, like desert plants and animals of the arid wastes, have always adjusted to the limitations of the land and climate. The hunters learned to gather roots and seeds. When drought reduced the game or drove it out of easy range, the hunters staved off hunger with more roots and plants while they followed moving herds to new locations. In the Gobi, the hunters and food-gatherers of ancient times are now herdsmen of the plains. They live on milk and cheese and butter; they feast on meat of sheep and goats. They make long journeys on horseback and move their household goods on camel back. A stable food supply, warm clothes, and dwelling places give each man and woman a longer lease on life, make each family group a little larger. Today, many more people roam the Gobi than ever could have lived there when the dune lands sheltered rabbits and the mesa edges were lookout points for the hunter. But the people still must follow the rhythm of the desert climate. If the grasses dry for lack of rain, the herds are moved to mountain valleys. The people follow their herds, just as ancient hunters had to follow game when water holes dried up.

In the Sahara a different pattern developed. As the rivers dried and became intermittent streams, the people planted seeds in river beds when the floods of winter rains subsided. Flocks were pastured on the plains when rains would let the grasses grow. Still, the rivers shriveled even further and went underground. The farmers dug wells and hauled the water back to keep their crop lands fertile. More drying of the river valleys; more people in the desert, with hunters ranging far on horse or camel back; more flocks of sheep, goats, and camels browsing on the arid plains—all have served to concentrate all life near the water holes and stream beds. These became oases, expanding with the population as the labor of the people deepened old wells and dug new ones to bring more water to the surface.

We often think of oasis dwellers as desert people, although nothing could be farther from the truth. Most of them are prisoners of the desert. They dare not leave the green border of their gardens which are cut from the desert on the line of irrigation water.

There are many large oases in the Sahara where the people are numbered in the thousands and date palm trees in the tens of thousands, but many of these people have never traveled out of sight of their own oasis. There they were born; there they live; there they age and die—always inside the sharp green line that marks the boundary of the oasis and the desert.

In contrast to oasis dwellers are the nomads, who live in desert pastures with their flocks or carry desert commerce across the barren plains between oases and between more fertile lands and desert gardens. These peoples, such as the Tuaregs of Sahara and the Bedouins of Arabia, are the true desert people. Their lives are attuned to waterless stretches; their customs adjusted to trading the sheep, the goats, and the camels raised on scanty, arid pasture for the dates and sacks of grain grown in the oases. If we would truly understand the desert world, we must know something of these people who have learned to live with burning heat and freezing cold on waterless stretches, as well as of those who stay within their oasis prisons and hold the desert back with irrigation.

XIV

· ·

· ·

· · · · · · · · · · · · · · · · · · ·

· · · · · · · · · · · · ·

· · · · ·

Veiled Men of the Sahara

IN RECENT YEARS ABOUT THE ONLY QUALIFICATION NECESSARY FOR an author to write about the Tuaregs of Sahara is a bus ticket to Tamanrassett and return. One look at the stately warriors, clothed from head to toe in blue-black robes with their faces hidden by the *teguelmoust,* veil and turban, is enough to start the flow of romantic words. Their hidden faces, their dignified walk, their graceful, flowing garments, everything about them is so strangely different from the world we know that when I first met the Tuaregs my imagination began to clothe them with the attributes of supermen. A little mental effort restored a more scientific point of view, and a few days living in their camp dispelled some of the mystery. Gift exchanges, two or three tea parties with their pretty girls, and a friendly wrestling match with a veiled warrior proved that they were strong but human, and subject to much the same desires and emotions as the rest of us.

Northeast of the Hoggar region is the Tuareg confederation of the Tassili n Ajjer, and in the southwest are the Adrar n Ifoghas; but the group in the Hoggar (Ahaggar) Mountains probably has been the least influenced by foreigners, even though the most often visited by modern writers. Like the other confederations, the Hoggar Tuaregs include three social classes: nobles, vassals and slaves. Legend has it that the nobles are descended from Tin Hinane (the legendary mother of all the Tuaregs), the vassals from her lady-in-waiting, and the black-skinned servants from her slaves. In support of the legend, the Tuaregs point to a huge, ruined stone structure at Abelessa in the Hoggar Mountains. It is twenty hours by camel-back from Tamanrassett.

The trail crosses ridges and slopes of black, barren rock which is more like the slag from a blast furnace than any nature-made stone. There is no bit of vegetation for miles. Nothing grows on the burned black slopes of the Hoggar Mountains—no grass, no bush, not even thorn or cactus. Then the trail leads down off the slopes into a river bed thick with vegetation. Cattle with odd humps on their shoulders graze on coarse, wirelike grass. This part of the Hoggar looks more like a summer-dried Wisconsin marsh than the desert.

While on the Franco-American Sahara Expedition, Hal Denny of the *New York Times* and I followed our guide along a path there through the mass of vegetation. We moved past a few grass huts; then pushed our camels out onto a rocky plain. Ahead of us was a large hill, and from its top a thin cloud of dust was rising.

Denny and I shouted as loud as we could. We saw a pick flash in the bright sunlight, and we shouted again. A man climbed up against the skyline and waved his arms. We waved back and urged our camels forward at the trot. The man came leaping down the hill toward us.

"We've found it," he shouted. "We've opened the tomb of Tin Hinane, Mother of all the Tuaregs." The man was one of our party who had gone by motorcar to Abelessa while Denny and I stayed at Tamanrassett to finish our notes about the Tuaregs. The advance party, with the help of Negro laborers, had cleared the tumbled rock from one room of the huge structure and had just lifted a slab from the floor disclosing a skeleton in the tomb below. We *barraked* our camels in the dry river bed near some tamarisk trees and climbed the hill to see the discovery.

A steep slope extends away from the bank of the *oued* (a dry river bed) for perhaps an eighth of a mile to the steeper slope of a knoll. The top of the knoll is crowned with a huge pole of cut stone, which, although fallen into disorder, still indicates the form of a building. There is a narrow terrace about a third of the way down from the top, and on this, spaced like guards on a castle wall, are fifteen or sixteen small circular tombs built like well-curbs of cut stone.

When we climbed onto the pile of dislodged rocks at the top of the hill, we saw that the workmen had exposed large sections of wall. Some of the undisturbed sections are seven or eight feet high, and the stones, although trimmed to flat surfaces, are of varying shapes and sizes. They were laid into the walls without the use of any mortar or cement. Perhaps their preservation is due largely to the fact that the upper parts of the structure have fallen down and covered the lower sections, for they are held in place and protected by the debris from above. The workmen had exposed enough to indicate that the hilltop had been surrounded by a wall which made a five-sided building with rounded corners. Inside the outer wall is a narrow passage, then another wall. Within this second wall are the seven or eight rooms of the building.

One of the rooms had been cleared when Denny and I arrived. It had been selected only because there was less debris at that point. Nothing was found in that room, but near the center of the floor were four large slabs of stone and one smaller one. Two of these were lifted and the excavations continued below the floor. Fine dry dust, packed hard, was encountered below the stones, and as the dust was removed, bits of badly decomposed wood came to light. It was sufficiently intact to indicate that some sort of ornamental frame had been placed there centuries before. Just as Denny and I arrived they had come upon the skull of a human skeleton.

I got down into the tomb with the guide. With small hooks and trowels we exposed the complete skeleton. On the arms were fifteen heavy bracelets of a metal which resembled untarnished silver. In the dust above the chest of the skeleton were scores of small beads. Most of them were carnelian, but we were as thrilled as if they had been rubies! While the guide and I dug, others sifted the dust we passed out of the darkness to them. They found more beads, a tiny gold ornament, and an earring.

With the burial we also found a shallow glass bowl decorated with silver, a deep glass cup, and a shallow wooden saucer. There was no way of telling what they had once contained, but we also found quantities of date stones and seeds which looked like those from grapes. Bits of leather may have been parts of skins used to wrap the body, or they may have been pieces of clothing. In any event, they were too fragmentary for us to reconstruct.

Fragments of wood which we first found were duplicated at the other end of the tomb and seemed to be parts of the head and foot of an elaborate bed. Even bits of matting which had formed the bed were distinguishable in the darkness of the tomb. All were too badly decomposed to be lifted from the dust, and there was nothing in the desert with which they could be preserved.

The most curious piece which came out of that desert tomb is a grotesque statuette of soft, white stone. It is the figure of a woman with exaggeratedly large hips and crudely carved, pendant breasts. A round knob with a button-like projection is the head but no face is detailed. A hole drilled from both sides pierces the head. The drill was coarse and the driller not skilled, for the two holes are not directly opposite. This little statue was probably a fertility amulet.

The skeleton may or may not be that of the legendary Tin Hinane, but one thing is certain: the fertility amulet was not effective. This individual could not have been the physical mother of the Tuaregs or of any other human beings. Even those who insist that the skeleton is that of a woman "with very fine bones" admit that she could not have borne children.

According to the legend, Tin Hinane and her retinue came from the north. Recent studies by Dr. L. Cabot Briggs indicate that the materials found in the tomb have "a distinctly eastern Roman flavor and may date from as early as the 4th or as late as the 6th century A.D." Neither the legend nor history gives us any other information about the origin of the Tuaregs, but the physical anthropologists agree that they belong to the great Berber family of Northwest Africa, in which their membership has also been established on the basis of language and blood type. Whatever their origin, the Tuaregs of the Hoggar developed an economy and a social organization suited to the severe climate and austere landscape of the most rugged part of the Sahara. Both worked well for these freedom-loving nomads until European control of the desert disturbed the balance.

The Tuareg way of life centered about the camel. Even today camels are their most important livestock, but they also have herds of goats, flocks of sheep, a good many donkeys, and a few humped cattle, as we saw at Abelessa. Except in a few river beds, like that below the tomb of Tin Hinane, permanent pasture with enough grass and a water supply for cattle is lacking in the Hoggar.

A good camel pasture is an ancient lake bottom or dry river bed, where bunches of coarse grass and a few woody shrubs or thorny bushes are scattered about so that the camel can have a leisurely walk between the bites of his dinner. Such a pasture may cover many square miles. It is permanent in the sense that the vegetation is perennial, but it can be quickly overgrazed. Each season's growth is dependent on that season's rainfall. If there is no rain, there is no forage for the flocks and herds. In some areas, where the seeds of the "quickies" have lain dormant for years, a heavy rain will carpet the desert floor with lush vegetation, but such abundant pastures do not flourish every year in any one region. It is sometimes five or ten years between growing seasons for these beds of annuals.

In the Hoggar a pasture may be so small that it will support the flocks and herds of only one family for a few days. It may be rich and large enough for the stock of several families to graze for a few weeks. If there is no well or surface water near, a pasture can be used only in winter or for a few days in hot weather regardless of how abundant the vegetation.

Such pastures have no fences. The flocks and herds must be watched to keep them from becoming too scattered. Someone must hunt the stray animals that wander off by themselves, and it may take hours or even days to find them and bring them back. In the old days guards were also needed to protect the animals from capture by unfriendly tribes. It is still necessary for someone to scout the desert for new pasture before the old is exhausted.

Flocks and herds never did supply all the needs of these pastoral nomads. Millet, wheat and dates are produced in small quantities in some oases of the Hoggar but large quantities have always been imported from the northern Sahara. Blankets, too, are imported from the north in exchange for camels. Trade routes lead into Central Africa where northern products are traded for cotton cloth and leather goods. Some of this trade is still carried by the Tuaregs, but in the old days they carried the commerce of the desert or furnished guides and armed guards for the large merchant caravans. Caravans which were not protected by Tuareg escort or by percentage payments to them were likely to be raided before they reached their destination. Raiding and trading, protection, and share-cropping, all supplemented the pastoral economy of the desert and further diversified the labor of the Tuaregs. Such diversified activities, to be successful, had to be coordinated by recognized authority; and Tuareg society, divided into the three classes, nobles, vassals, and slaves, provided that authority, leadership, and division of labor.

The nobles were the warriors and leaders who scouted the desert for new pasture lands, protected caravans, guarded the pastures and garden plots, raided enemy herds, and captured slaves to be sold in the oases of the northern desert. The vassals were more sedentary. They looked after the herds and flocks and supervised the oases. Some of their men also accompanied the nobles in scouting for suitable pasture. When necessary they helped the aristocrats in battle, but their chief function in the economy was to look after production. The physical labor of making gardens, caring for the crops, doing the daily chores about camp, and getting the meals were all done by the slaves.

Early Europeans who met the Tuaregs assumed that because there were *ihaggaren* (nobles), *imr'ad* (vassals), and slaves, the society was a feudal system like that which had existed in Europe during the Middle Ages. Except for the names of the classes, however, there is not much similarity. The system in Medieval Europe was based on the authority of an autocratic monarch. In Tuareg society authority rests with the people. The *amenokal*, or leader, is elected from members of the noble clan and generally from a particular family in that clan, but the *imr'ad* have veto power over the choice and can refuse to accept an undesirable leader.

The *imr'ad* are tribute-paying allies of the *ihaggaren,* who expect and receive protection in return for that tribute. They fight side by side with nobles when necessary, and they use the same weapons as the nobles. In theory, at least, they can change their allegiance; and, in practice, when the requests for tribute become too burdensome, they simply move far enough away that their patron nobles cannot reach them too easily. In historic times one tribe of nobles was reduced to a vassal tribe after a serious defeat in battle.

However the whole Tuareg system is breaking down now that Europeans police the desert. Raiding, as a means of increasing the flocks and herds, is non-existent. Caravan guards are no longer needed, and tribute for protection is not paid. Although most observers believe that the Negro servants in the Hoggar are practically slaves, they are at least technically free. Their numbers are not increased by new raids, nor is there a ready market for them. Even the big opportunities for profit in trading have been reduced for the Tuaregs, because traders now move their merchandise by motor truck. The loss of raiding, trading, and protection profits have reduced the nobles to near poverty. They still raise their camels and make caravan trips, but even the market for camels is fast disappearing as motor transport increases.

A way of life for which the Tuaregs were well adapted, the freedom of great open spaces which they love, the excitement and thrill of hard journeys and dangerous raids, no longer exist even in the mountain fastnesses of the deep Sahara. Perhaps the young men of today will adjust to becoming truck drivers rather than camel drivers, and young herdsmen will become oil-field workers, and both will willingly exchange the hard and exciting outdoor life for the more prosaic pleasures of steady wages, an eight-hour day, and a television set. I am glad, though, that I knew the desert nomads when automobiles were such a novelty that we could give the girls a thrill by packing them in the car three deep. Gasoline was too precious down there a thousand miles from a filling station for us to take individual joy rides, but it was fun to hear that carload of Tuareg girls squeal with delight as we raced across the desert.

At Tamanrassett we met a large group of Tuaregs. They had come on a formal visit from their pasture and camp some five miles away. There were twenty-five or thirty men in the party, all dressed in their newest and shiniest blue-black robes and with turban veils neatly wrapped. Only their piercing eyes could be seen between the folds of the veils. They made an impressive sight as they sat high on their best riding-camels. The average Tuareg measures only five feet eight inches from the sole of his sandals to the crown of his shaved head, but the lines of his flowing robes and his turban make him look seven feet tall and as husky as a heavyweight fighter. Sitting high on the humps of those slender-legged camels, the men really looked like a company of giants.

They dismounted a little distance from us and stood around like an embarrassed bunch of freshmen stags at a college mixer. It was evident that these desert nobles did not know just how to greet a group of scientists who had come across the Sahara by automobile to study their customs. We were somewhat at loss, too, because a few of us were still under the spell of the legends we had heard in the north about Tuareg treachery, their mysterious abilities, and superman strength. Their appearance in full-dress costume made even the legends seem probable.

After a moment's hesitation, our party walked toward the visitors. Their timidity lessened at once and they came forward to shake hands. Instead of the firm grip and shake that Americans use, the Tuaregs extended the right hand and brushed our palms with a gentle touch, then raised the back of their hand to their own lips. We, likewise, raised our hands to our lips. Everyone of us brushed palms with everyone of the Tuareg party. After these formal greetings we all retired to the shade of the veranda around the fort, where we sat on the floor, tailor-fashion, like desert people in many parts of the world.

The leaders of our party presented each of the Tuaregs with

some present from the lands of standardized production. There were watches, knives, and many other trinkets from the sporting-goods stores and variety shops in Algiers. The most spectacular gift was a small spyglass which was given to Akamouk, the *amenokal,* or elected chief of the nobles. He seemed to be really pleased with the present because "It brings far things close," he said.

While I was photographing the group, two of the nobles came over and asked if I would take their pictures. I posed them on the adobe railing of the porch and got a good close-up of the men in full costume. Their bare feet were on flat, cowhide sandals. Their ankle-length white pantaloons showed a foot below the *gondoura.* The latter is a loose, flowing robe with very wide sleeves which blend with the loose folds of the robe itself. These are tossed back when the man wants to use his hands. A large open "V" allows the wearer to put on the *gondoura* by slipping it over his head, and this "V" is often elaborately embroidered. The needlework, however, is done with thread the same color as the garment, and it can only be appreciated at close view. A large square of cloth sewed inside the robe and below the "V" gives the man a big pocket.

The veil-turban, or *teguelmoust,* is a single long, wide strip of material composed of many narrow strips of cotton cloth woven separately and then tightly sewed together. In fact, all of the blue-black garments were made of these narrow strips woven in the Sudan. The white pantaloons and white *gondouras* worn under the dark garments were made of European-manufactured cotton sheet-ing. The pantaloons are held up by a drawstring, but otherwise all the garments are loose and voluminous. They permit air to circulate next to the skin and give maximum insulation as well as full effi-ciency from evaporating perspiration.

Both men and women carry, or "wear," leather pocketbooks hung from a cord around the neck. Each has several compartments covered by a long flap, over which an outer envelope slides down the cord to cover the several pockets and prevent the contents from falling out. Each man also carries a sharp knife or dagger in a leather sheath attached to a leather bracelet on the arm.

One of the nobles I photographed was named Siderli. After the picture was taken he took a jackknife from his *gondoura* pocket and tried to tell me something about it. I recognized it as the one I had given him earlier that day, but I did not understand what he was trying to tell me. However, he seemed pleased, so I thought no more about it. A few days later at the Tuareg camp, I tried to buy or trade for a blue-black robe. At that time I did not realize that each of those narrow strips was hand-woven and then tightly stitched together by hand, and every Tuareg I approached asked a price which I considered out of all reason. Finally I located Siderli and through the interpreter asked if he would sell me a black *gondoura*.

"Certainly you shall have a robe of mine," he said. I had been bargaining with the Tuaregs for many days and I knew them for astute traders, so I immediately asked the price he wanted.

"Whatever you want to pay," said Siderli. I named a figure about a fourth of what the others had asked me for a similar garment. To my surprise Siderli nodded indifferently.

"Is that price all right?" I asked. Rather patiently Siderli explained.

"You shall have a black robe of mine if you want it," he said. "If you want to pay me five hundred francs ($50.00 at that time), if you want to pay me ten francs, if you do not want to pay anything—it is all the same to me." Such hospitable generosity was new to me. There was no reason why Siderli should give me a robe at my own price. I asked for an explanation.

"You are my friend," said Siderli. "If you want what I have, it is yours. Don't you remember, on the day we first met you gave me a good knife? I told you when you took our picture that I thanked you for the knife and that you were my friend. All my life I have wanted a knife that closed up like that one with many blades. You have given me such a knife. If you want a *gondoura*, it shall be yours. If you pay for it, that is your affair. If you do not pay for it, that is all right, too."

Here was a facet of Tuareg character which I have not seen recorded by either early explorers or modern authors. As I began to know the Tuaregs, I found them less mysterious than other Europeans had found them, and much more interesting and far more human than some of those who have written their history.

There was no pasture for camels or flocks at Tamanrassett so the *amenokal* invited us to come out to his camp in the *oued* Agnar. When we arrived, we found that his people had erected several skin tents for us to use. They were grouped close together but located two or three hundred yards from the nearest tent of the Tuaregs. In this camp the family tents were widely scattered. As one of our party said, "They are close enough to be neighbors but far enough apart to give family privacy."

Each tent is a huge leather blanket made from the skins of goats or, less often, those of sheep. The skins are tanned so that they are as soft as buckskin, then dyed brick-red and sewed together. Thirty or forty skins are necessary for an average tent, but there may be as many as a hundred and fifty skins in a big shelter. The leather blanket rests on one or two center poles, each capped by a wooden "shoe," and these poles are only four or four and a half feet high. Even the shortest of us could not stand erect in a tent, and a Tuareg must bend double to get into one or move about inside without poking his head through the top. At the back and at each end, the leather roof is supported by stakes shorter than the center poles. Sometimes these shorter stakes hold a small ridge pole. Ropes tied to edges of the skins are stretched out to stakes.

The leather shelters are really only roofs. However, in late afternoon, when the desert begins to cool off, large bundles of reed matting are unrolled inside the tent. These long mats, about thirty-two inches wide, when stood on edge around the tent form a wind-tight wall. Some of the mats are bound with leather on the upper edge and decorated with tufts or leather fringe. In the desert this type of tent has one great advantage. During the midday heat the matting is easily rolled away from the sides allowing a breeze to circulate under the low roof. Even if there is no breeze on the open plain, air circulation is created by the black shade of the leather blanket.

Rich or poor, the Tuaregs all live under these leather roofs. The only exceptions I saw were among the Negro servants. One of these families had erected the leather blanket so that the sides hung down to the ground like a true wall tent. Another Negro family had no leather-blanket roof at all. Their home was a sort of nest with a matting windbreak.

Even the "palace" of the *amenokal* was a leather tent. It was much larger than any of the others and had more leather-trimmed matting out in front. This made a private courtyard and gave the king greater seclusion than his subjects.

The Tuaregs sleep on the ground like other natives of North Africa and roll themselves up in woolen blankets. The blankets are colorful, hand-woven products of oases in the northern Sahara, but the Tuareg women also make quilts from cast-off bits of cloth and wool. These patchwork quilts are not the works of art our great-grandmothers made, but they are practical if not beautiful.

Nomad people must carry all their possessions with them when they move from camp to camp. Accordingly, the tent furnishings are seldom numerous or bulky. There is always the saddle and bridle for the owner's riding camel and one or two huge, leather bags elaborately decorated with carved-leather overlay. These are used to store extra clothing. Often there is a small painted or brass-decorated chest which is also used for clothing and other possessions. The giraffe-hide shield and the long spear which used to adorn every tent are hard to find now, but a gun of some sort has replaced the more picturesque weapons. A few wooden bowls and basketwork trays for food, some goatskin water bags and milk containers complete the tent furniture.

In the tent of the *amenokal* is the *tobol,* a large drum, shaped much like a kettledrum. It is the symbol of the chief's authority and is played whenever he wants to call a meeting to discuss tribal business. Even though we were honored guests, the chief did not sound the drum for our pleasure. This was no occasion for an official meeting; therefore there was no reason for its symbolic notes to roll across the desert.

Akamouk was the *amenokal* of the Hoggar federation at the time of our visit. He was a big man, tall and heavy. He must have been at least six feet in height and have weighed 250 pounds, but our interpreter had known him when both he and his wife were very thin. That was before Akamouk was made chief. In those days he spent more time in strenuous exercise and ate no better than the average noble. After his elevation to authority, he had become more sedentary and consumed more food. He was still agile, however. One day as we were sitting cross-legged on the ground in the courtyard with him, he volunteered to prove his suppleness. Casually he slipped off his sandal and, without any effort, raised his right foot above his neck to scratch his ear with his big toe. None of us younger men could duplicate this feat.

After the formal meetings we found the *amenokal* a most friendly and interesting host. He answered our numerous questions promptly and frankly, and he showed keen interest and curiosity about everything we had. This was one thing we liked about all the Tuaregs. None of them was afraid to ask us questions about anything they did not understand concerning our clothes or equipment. The oases dwellers in the northern part of the desert never showed such active interest in anything. The Tuaregs were also much gayer than other desert peoples and readily laughed with us or joined in the songs we sang. If they didn't get all the words, they tried to repeat as many as they could pronounce.

One day when we had been asking questions for an hour or more, Akamouk interrupted me.

"Labisba," he said, "why do you ask so many questions?"

"Because I'm an anthropologist," I said. "I like to learn about people who live far from my country, so that I can go back home and tell our young folks about other people's customs."

"Hmmmmm," said Akamouk. "That's a good idea. I guess I'll be an anthropologist. I'll start on you. Why do you have zippers on your boots?" He reached over and unzipped my high-tops as he had seen me do for some of the less aristocratic members of his tribe. It was then that I asked why Tuareg men wear the *teguelmoust*.

"Because Noah, the hero of the flood, wore a veil," he said. Later I asked other Tuaregs the same question.

One said, "Because Mohammed wore a veil."

No one has ever been able to get any more satisfactory answer to the question from the Tuaregs or from written history. Tuareg men wear the veil because they do. Boys cover their faces with the *teguelmoust* when they are twelve or thirteen years old; and from that time on they never show the lower part of their faces even in all-men or strictly family gatherings. We did get Akamouk to expose his nose and forehead for a photograph, but we had to make certain that no other Tuaregs were anywhere near the secluded corner of the camp at that moment. The veil is not even removed when the men eat. They very carefully lift it away from the face with one hand, so that with the other they can bring the food under the cloth to the mouth.

Tuareg women do not wear the *teguelmoust* and do not hide their faces from the public like other Moslem women. Their outer garments are similar to the *gondouras* of the men, but those that I saw had more voluminous sleeves and the whole garment seemed to drape the body more gracefully. Some of the women wear white pantaloons similar to those worn by the men but shorter. The legs do not show below the robe. Others wear a short skirt as an under-garment. A simple shawl made from many narrow strips of the blue-black cotton cloth, without any fringe or decoration, is worn over the head and hangs almost to the ground. When the girls are exposed to wind and dust, they hold a corner of the shawl across the face, and they may also do this when they are a bit embarrassed or to show respect in the presence of important personages. On formal occasions and for warmth, the women wear wool blankets draped like the shawl over the head.

The blue-black garments worn by both men and women give off crock easily and stain their skins. Those *ihaggaren* and *imr'ad* whose skin color I took under the left arm—the part of the body least exposed to weather—were about the same shade of white as southern Italians. However, they like the blue-black stain and con-sider it beautiful. They also claim that it protects the skin and makes them more healthy. Healthful or not, it seldom gets washed off because there are few opportunities for an all-over bath in the

Sahara. This does not mean that the Tuaregs are dirty, by any means. Desert air is dry and healthful; there are few bacteria; and visible sweat is rare so that body odors do not develop, especially when people wear clothing so well ventilated as Tuareg costumes. Whatever the cause, the Tuareg girls have soft, smooth skin. I found it "the skin you love to touch" as our beauty ads used to say.

The first Europeans who met the Tuaregs got the impression that the women ruled the roost, but modern observers find this an exaggeration. The women do have about equal rights with the men when it comes to property ownership and marital status, but the real rulers are the men. An individual traces his descent through his male ancestors, but he inherits rank and privilege through his mother. The inheritance of material wealth follows Moslem law so that the male heirs receive twice as much as the female heirs. On our visit to the Hoggar only the men made the official welcoming visit at Tamanrassett, and when we arrived at the Tuareg camp on the Agnar the men gave us a welcoming tea party. It was perhaps an hour and a half before the women came to our part of the camp. They stood around in a body a little distance from our largest tent until the men took the hint and broke up the party. Then the women came in and we had a second tea party. The day we gave the girls an automobile ride, they insisted that we let them out of the car in a secluded spot where the *amenokal* would not see them. The interpreter explained that the girls did not think it would show sufficient respect to display such a gay party in the king's presence.

Men and women wear finger rings of silver. They also wear strings of leather-covered amulets suspended from the neck. These are verses from the Koran written on paper and sewed into leather cases. The amulets, and, in fact, most of the items worn or used by the Tuaregs, are also found among other people of the Sahara.

After a few days at the Tuareg camp, my tent was piled high with the things the Tuaregs used. We had wooden spoons and blacksmith's bellows, camel saddles, giraffe-hide shields, manicure sets, and simple spindles for spinning goat hair. As I reviewed the collection I tried to think what there was in the Tuareg culture

which I had not seen in the camps of other desert peoples. Finally
I remembered the ivory plaques worn as the centerpiece of necklaces by many of the noble women. I called Belaid, our interpreter.

"I must have one of those necklaces with the ivory centerpiece,"
I told him.

For a moment Belaid was silent. Then he slowly shook his head,
and in a low, almost awed voice, he answered, "Ah! Now you ask
the most difficult thing of all. I doubt if even you, Labisba, can
get such a prize from a Tuareg. Have you noticed, it is the one
thing they have not offered you for sale? They have sold you many
cherished possessions, but no one has offered you a necklace with
an ivory plaque. This bit of ivory is difficult to get—even for a
Tuareg. They, themselves, pay at least the price of a good camel
for that little piece of elephant tusk. Why, Labisba, even if you
should marry the beautiful Chelifa you couldn't come into posses-
sion of her necklace."

"Thanks for the suggestion, Belaid," I said. "I had not thought
of marrying Chelifa even to get her necklace, but let's have a try
at it through the regular methods of trade."

That afternoon Belaid arranged a tea party at Chelifa's tent.
We provided about a pound of tea and five pounds of sugar. Tea
is an expensive beverage in the deep Sahara, a luxury for which
Tuareg men and women have great fondness. Someone once said
that a Tuareg would kill his grandmother for a handful of tea. This
is malicious exaggeration, of course, but the tea was the bribe I
offered to induce a few of the veiled men to unveil in my thick-
walled American tent while I took scientific measurements of their
faces.

In addition to the tea and sugar, we carried bottles of perfume,
earrings, and bracelets from the Rue de Rivoli in Paris and dozens
of strings of brightly colored beads. Our supplies would have delighted any American young woman addicted to the craze for
costume jewelry.

Chelifa's tent was well filled when Hal Denny, Belaid, and I
arrived. There were ten or fifteen young ladies and a couple of

young noblemen already seated. The girls were busy sewing on white *gondouras*. Three or four of them worked on the same garment at once. They used modern steel needles, but the thread was a raveling from the edge of the cloth they were sewing. One of the girls was strumming softly on the *imzad*, that curious one-stringed and almost monotonal violin. When she saw Denny and me she stopped to join in the shout of her companions.

"Oh, Babahalida, Labisba, sing, sing!" Then laughingly they all chanted, "Eee aye, eee aye oh."

Babahalida and Labisba were the names the chief had given Denny and me several days before, and "eee aye, eee aye oh" were the only syllables the girls could pronounce of the song "Old Mac-Donald had a Farm." Denny and I obliged with a dozen stanzas. Then we gave them about fifteen stanzas of our French translation for "How do you do, Miss Chelifa," substituting the name of another girl in each stanza. By the time we had honored each one of the guests, Denny and I were out of breath, and we thought it was time for the girls to do some of the entertaining. It took a bit of urging but finally the interpreter got Chedma to take up the *imzad*. She played while we listened politely. The music didn't have the boisterous rhythm of "Old MacDonald" but it kept going just as long.

"What is the name of the piece she is playing?" Denny asked Belaid.

"It's one of their favorite tunes," the interpreter answered. "It's called 'The Running Antelope.'"

"Gosh," said Denny. "Doesn't the little fellow ever get tired? That poor little antelope has already done a marathon."

Apparently the girls also preferred our singing, for it required constant urging on our part to keep them at the *imzad*. Occasionally the instrument was passed to another musician, who dropped her sewing. This would be picked up by another girl who seemed to start her seam just anywhere without regard to past, present, or future workers. I have often heard that too many cooks spoil the broth but the number of workers seems to have no effect on the quality of a *gondoura*.

When we began to weary of the entertainment furnished by the *imzad*, a Negro boy, who had been tending a tiny campfire just outside the tent, came in to say that water for the tea was boiling. Chelifa called an old Negro who brought several glass tumblers and two doll-sized teapots. He immediately began the elaborate ceremony of preparing the social drink of desert people. When we had each emptied our third glass in the traditional manner and placed the empties on the sand in front of us, Belaid nodded to me, indicating that this was the time to bring out the presents of jewelry. We had a gift for each of the girls—a necklace, a bottle of perfume, a bracelet, or a pair of earrings. How thrilled they were! How their eyes shown as they put on their gifts and said, "Merci," the French word for "thank you" which they had just learned from Belaid. There was no doubt that our Paris jewels were appreciated by the girls of the Sahara.

"Now," whispered Belaid, "now is the time to try for the necklace with the ivory plaque."

I drew from my pocket a string of glittering red beads and held them up in the sunlight. They sparkled with red fires. The girls gasped. I dropped them in Chelifa's lap. I then brought out a necklace of green and held these beads in the shade so they seemed soft and cool like an oasis. The girls were speechless. I tossed these, too, into Chelifa's lap, and before she could say a word, I added bracelets of purple rhinestones, earrings of topaz and beads of amethyst as fast as I could take them from my pockets. A score of them I poured into her lap before the astonished eyes of all her guests. Then I opened my wallet and showed her a large roll of five franc notes.

"For me?" asked Chelifa, "All for me?"

"Yes, for you, Chelifa," said Belaid as he threw his arms around her neck and tried to unclasp the ivory plaque necklace.

A hush fell on the little gathering. Chelifa's slender hands closed over her necklace. She pushed Belaid away. The other girls covered their ivory plaques with firm fingers.

"Silly one," said Belaid. "Don't you know that Labisba has given you jewels worth the price of a *mehari* (a fast riding camel)?

Didn't you see the roll of money he will also give you? All for one little necklace with an ivory plaque which isn't worth half what he has offered! Silly one, give us the ivory plaque!"

For a full minute no one spoke. Then Chelifa pushed the jewelry from her lap and turned to me.

"You want my necklace to take back to your America. You have offered me more pretty jewels than I have ever seen before. You will pay me more money than my necklace cost when it was new, so that I could buy another like it. But I cannot sell it to you, even for all the pretty jewels you may have in your motorcars. You wonder why I will not sell it to you? Let me tell you.

"I am the sixth of my family who has worn this ivory plaque. Five of my mothers have worn it before me. For more than 150 years it has been in my family.

"The first who wore it was named Chelifa, as I am called. It was given to her by her husband soon after they were married. He brought it from the south when he came back with a caravan of black slaves. It came from very far away, for her husband bought it from a caravan at Timbuktu which had come up from the Land of Great Beasts.

"When Chelifa's daughter was married, this little piece of ivory was her wedding present. A quarter of a century later she gave it to her eldest daughter, and so it has come to me through five generations of my mothers.

"It is not worth as much money as you have offered me. It is not worth the price of the jewels you have laid in my lap. But I cannot part with this ivory plaque. I am a Tuareg noblewoman. It is an heirloom of my family. If I have a daughter I shall give it to her, the seventh Chelifa."

About seven o'clock one November evening we had finished supper and Denny and I were debating whether to go to bed at once or to take a walk in the desert night, when Belaid appeared. He was dressed in full Tuareg costume even to the *teguelmoust*. His little private masquerade aroused our interest.

"Why the fancy dress?" we asked.

"I'm going to the *Ahal*," he said. "Want to come along? See for yourself what one of these famous Tuareg gatherings is like."

Denny and I got up from the ground and followed our interpreter. Years before Belaid had married a Tuareg *im'rad* and lived with the tribe while he was an official interpreter for the French army. When he retired, his wife did not want to follow him north. There was no place for Belaid in the Tuareg economy, so he divorced his wife and took their daughter back to his native Kabylie where she could get a modern education. Each time Belaid was hired by an expedition to the Hoggar, he sent word ahead, and the Tuaregs always managed to have his former wife brought to the meeting place. At the time of our visit she was at the Tuareg camp on Oued Agnar but so badly crippled with rheumatism that she could hardly stand. That is why Belaid was going to the *Ahal* without her.

As we walked away from the three black shadows made by our goatskin tents we felt the chill of the desert night, and were glad we had warm sweaters. Above us the sky was velvet black, pierced with myriads of tiny light points, stars which flickered and dimmed like distant fireflies. In the west was a great lantern, which seemed to be so close that one could reach up and pull it down as easily as one hauls down the masthead light of a schooner. That was Venus; and as we stopped a moment to accustom ourselves to the silence of the Sahara night, it made all the desert romance seem quite real.

All about us were great black rocks. Off across the desert a dozen scattered campfires marked the Tuareg tents. There were no street lights, no brightly lighted windows to show us details of the landscape. The night was so black and the stars so tiny that even the huge black rocks and leather tents could be seen for only a short distance.

"It is this way," said Belaid. We followed him off into the darkness.

Once we came close to a little fire and saw a Negro woman puttering about her master's supper. We called a greeting in

Tuareg. A little later we passed the tent of Akamouk, the *amenokal* of the Hoggar Tuaregs, but we did not stop. Finally, the last fire was left behind, and we began to hear the faint strum, strum, strum of the *imzad*. Then the blackness of the desert became a little blacker and we recognized a dark huddle on top of a large flat rock.

"Here we are," said Belaid. "This is the *Ahal*, rendezvous of lovers. Or, if you prefer a French translation, *la soirée musicale.*"

Our two friends, Chedma and Chelifa, were seated close together on the rock with other Tuareg girls. All were wrapped up in their long, blue-black shawls; but somehow, in spite of the dark night and the uniformity of their dress, we could recognize our favorites. Strangers often say that all Tuaregs look alike but really each is so definitely an individualist that with a little experience one soon recognizes the different personalities.

We had arrived early at the *Ahal* rock. Only a few of the men had come and were seated with their favorite girls. As we climbed up into the gathering, each of us murmured *"Matulas, matulas,"* which is the Tuareg equivalent for "Good evening, good evening." Denny and I sat down back of the circle of girls. Belaid moved more intimately into the circle, but remained close enough to give us quiet translations when we needed them.

Chelifa was just across the circle from me and held the *imzad* in her lap. Now and then she drew the bow across the single string a few times to give a little background music to the low murmur of conversation. It reminded me of a dreamy night at another rendezvous on a college campus in Wisconsin. That night the soft strains of the background music were from a ukelele instead of the *imzad*. Out there in the Sahara there were different costumes, a different language, different music, even a different landscape; but there was no difference in the mood, no difference in the star-dusted blanket overhead.

Soon another dark shadow moved up over the edge of the gathering. I recognized Bayi, a tall young noble, who, experience had taught me, was strong and lithe as a steel spring. Silently he glanced around the group until he saw Chelifa. Then, with a quiet *"Matulas,"* he seated himself beside her. For a moment the *imzad* was stilled, but Chelifa gave no special sign of welcome to the newcomer.

"Where is Hatita, tonight?" I heard Princess Fati ask.

"Oh, he left this morning for Tamanrassett," Bayi answered. "He may not be back until tomorrow. By the way, did you know that Akamouk told him he would have to start for the Sudan with a caravan of fifty camels in a week or ten days? What will you do during the next three months with your sweetheart gone?"

"A lot I care whether he goes or stays," scoffed Fati.

Chedma came to the rescue of her friend by asking why Fatimata had not come to the *Ahal.*

"Not feeling well this evening, I guess," answered one of the girls. "She caught a bit of a cold last night. You know, she and Hadizata stayed out here until three o'clock."

During that bit of gossip, Siderli appeared on the rock. There were several girls without escorts, and Bayi was obviously still devoting his full attention to Chelifa. Nevertheless, Siderli ignored the unescorted girls and calmly sat down on the other side of Chelifa. Gently she drew her bow across the string of her *imzad* and leaned forward ever so slightly away from Bayi.

Softly Siderli began to sing. The song seemed to repeat endlessly like all the other Tuareg songs we had heard, but the man's voice was mellow. It was easy to recognize that he was singing a love song, even without knowing the exact meaning of the words. Belaid later translated them for us.

"I have heard," sang Siderli, "that the beautiful Chelifa will move her camp tomorrow. She will go, so they tell me, to the pastures of the Agnar. There may the Good God provide fine grazing. May she draw much milk from her camels and have plenty to drink."

Before he had finished the song I saw him slip his arm around the shoulders of the pretty Chelifa—and she did not object.

I wondered why young Bayi calmly accepted the arrival of

Siderli, who was obviously stealing his girl. Then I remembered that other explorers have insisted that jealousy is not tolerated among the Tuaregs, and supposedly any show of that emotion would have made Bayi the butt of much ridicule. I am not sure how far this lack of jealousy goes, however. Some accounts indicate that Tuareg husbands are just as jealous as Arab or American husbands, and that wife-stealing reaps the same reward in the Hoggar as elsewhere. Personally, I do not think I would like to take the risk of making a Tuareg man jealous. He seems to have all the other normal human characteristics; why not that of jealousy?

About nine o'clock the night we were at the *Ahal*, the gathering broke up, and the men and girls went back to their tents. Belaid told us that the camels had been returned from pasture and everyone left to do the milking and eat supper. Later many of them met again on the rock to talk, talk, and talk. The *Ahal* rock may not be as comfortable as an automobile parked in lovers' lane, but the conversation is much the same.

When there is a large camp close to good pasture, the young Tuaregs gather for an *Ahal* several evenings a week. Sometimes games are played. One Tuareg game is similar to forfeits once played by American young folks. The girls select a queen and the men choose a king. This couple names the forfeits and fixes punishments. Intimate and potentially embarrassing questions are asked, such as, "Who do you like best, Chedma or Chelifa?" If the young man answers, "I like Chedma," he becomes the butt of much joshing and must pay a forfeit. He should have answered more diplomatically and said, "I like them both."

Another favorite question is, "What would you do if you found yourself confronted with an arguing woman, a stampeded flock of sheep, a donkey which had broken its hobbles, and an overturned kettle?" Most men will answer, "Always first things first. In such a situation I would get the sheep together as quickly as possible. Then I would tie the donkey and put the kettle back on the fire. Finally, when all other problems were solved, I would turn my attention to the woman." This answer will bring the same shouts of protest from the girls as it would if the audience were French, or American, or English. Like the girls of Western nations, the Tuareg women have considerable pride about their importance in the scheme of things.

Some Tuareg women have had great reputations for their ability to play the *imzad* and for their poetic compositions, and men have ridden over a hundred kilometers, we were told, to attend an *Ahal* at which some famous beauty or poetess presided. One of these was Dacine whom we met. Many of her poems were once collected, translated into French, and published. She was no longer young when I saw her, but it was easy to guess from her well-formed features that once her beauty attracted the young Tuaregs quite as much as her poetry.

The young Tuareg has no formal school, but the *Ahal* serves to some extent as a place of instruction. There he learns the proverbs of his people and acquires the ability to speak his thoughts. It is also the place where men and women learn to write. They write each other's names on the rock using a stone for a stilo. Then other words are added. Sometimes these are words of devotion, sometimes complete poems. When a couple decides to become engaged, each draws the outline of his or her sandal on the rock, then ties them together with a single line. On our journey south through the Sahara, we found a large, flat rock surface in the shelter of a steep cliff. On the rock there were hundreds of Tuareg inscriptions. Generations of these desert nomads have used the shelter of the cliff as a meeting place for lovers. Countless *Ahals* had been held there, so we called it Love Mountain.

The *Ahal*, of course, enables young folks to decide about a marriage partner. When a young man has made up his mind about the girl of his choice, he asks a marabout (religious man among Moslem peoples) to tell her parents of his intentions and ask their consent to the marriage. If no marabout is available, which often happens among the Tuaregs because they are not as religious as many other Moslem groups, then he asks an official or important person in the tribe to act as his messenger. Every one of the girl's relatives must be notified of the wedding, even if they live far away. The parents, however, cannot arrange a marriage for the daughter without her consent as they can among most Moslem people.

On the day of the wedding, friends and relatives of both the bride and groom are assembled. The groom names a representative, and the girl's parents select someone to represent them. The girl may make the selection for her family, especially if she has been married before. These chosen representatives decide on the price the groom will pay for his bride. In the case of members of the noble tribe, the price was generally six or seven camels but when hard times reached the deep Sahara the price was reduced. Part of the agreed price is paid at once. It may perhaps be one or two camels, depending on how many people must be fed; and these camels are slaughtered and barbecued for the wedding banquet. In addition to the banquet, which is enjoyed by all the relatives of both bride and groom, there is a fixed ceremony which the couple follow. Banquet and ceremony solemnize the marriage and legitimize the children which may be born to the couple.

Those camels which were not slaughtered for the feast are legally due the bride, not her parents. They may be paid at any time and added to the young wife's herd, for she has her own property which is separate from that of her husband. When the young folks make a successful marriage, full payment of camels may not be made for years, but if the man wants a divorce the balance due on the agreed bride price must be paid at once. If the full payment was made at the time of the wedding or later, then no further payment is demanded when a divorce is asked. One might say that among the Tuaregs the amount of alimony is agreed upon at the time of the wedding ceremony. It saves court costs and prevents the ex-husband from getting behind on his payments.

Before we visited the Tuaregs we heard many stories and legends which painted them as treacherous, vicious, sly, hostile, and dangerous nomads. These legends were so generally accepted that we carried a machine gun on one of our cars, as well as rifles and revolvers. At Ouargla, in the northern Sahara, we asked the French commandant what he thought of the machine gun.

"It is excellent," he said, "for shooting gazelles. But if you want to shoot Tuaregs, extra film for your camera will be more practical."

We left the cumbersome weapon at his *poste* and found the Tuaregs hospitable, dignified, friendly and courteous—just as the commandant had predicted.

The Tuaregs are desert nomads. Like other natives of the desert world, they are conservative and reluctant to accept changes in a way of life which, for centuries, has been well adjusted to their needs. In general they have come to terms with nature's elements. They have learned to endure extreme heat in summer and cold in winter. They expect long periods of dryness, and know how to conserve water. They get along with little food, but know how to enjoy a banquet on occasion. They know the limits of the land which can be grazed or used by their family and their tribe. They know who are their friends and who are their enemies. They understand what to expect from both and how to act toward each of them. They know the rules. They believe in these rules and they act in accordance with that belief.

When Europeans, armed with modern weapons, their camels loaded with abundant supplies, invaded their land the normal adjustment was thrown out of balance. Some of the Europeans claimed peaceful intent but displayed their superior arms. Others claimed innocent "search for knowledge" but trespassed on the nomads' territory without so much as by-your-leave. Individual Tuaregs or small groups acted in accordance with their rules to restore the normal balance and repulse the trespassers. The legends grew accordingly in the minds of the "peaceful" and self-righteous Europeans.

Desert nomads are believers, and their lives are less complicated than the lives of people in more advanced civilizations. The desert makes them that way because it imposes harsh conditions of dis-

tinct values. The line between life and death is sharp, and there are
no gradations. The same is true of the nomad's thinking. He believes that right is right and wrong is wrong and his duty to God
and himself requires that he maintain this distinction. The only
difference between him and a normal European or American is
that he is closer to the realities.

"The members of a normal family," said Sir Arthur Keith,
speaking of human beings in general, "are prejudiced in favor of
one another. Their attitude towards their own family is different
from that which they hold to other families. They resent the in-
trusion of strangers to a place in the family circle. . . .

"The same mental bonds which hold a family together give rise
to those which unite members of a social group or tribe. . . . That
group spirit implies a discrimination between groups. A tribesman's
sympathies lie within the compass of his own tribe; beyond his
tribe, begin his antipathies; he discriminates in favor of his own
tribe against all others.

". . . If a group no longer considered its own things more
precious than those of other groups, in no need of defense, then
patriotism would be superfluous. . . . But this would be against
all human nature. The group spirit at whatever level, 'family pride'
or 'team spirit,' 'community spirit,' 'nationalism,' 'patriotism,' or
'religious unity,'—call it what you will according to the breadth of
its embrace—is a defense mechanism that is shared with man by
many kinds of social animals including the great apes. . . ."

As Mr. Justice Holmes said in 1881, ". . . But it seems to me
clear that the last resort, not only of kings but of private persons,
is force, and that at the bottom of all private relations, however
tempered by sympathy and all social feelings, is a justifiable self-
preference. If a man is on a plank in the deep sea which will float
only one, and a stranger lays hold of it, he will thrust him off if
he can. When the state finds itself in a similar position it does the
same thing."

The desert nomads are no different than Americans or Europeans
except that they still see the issue in its simple terms and act

accordingly. The Tuaregs and other natives of the desert world did try to defend their way of life, their "plank in the deep sea"; but their weapons and their numbers were no match for the power of civilization, and they now try to make the best of their adversity while clinging to as much as possible of the way of life they value.

XV

. . . .

. . . .

. . . .

. . . .

. . . . .

People of the Gobi

A GROUP OF MONGOLS RODE INTO THE GOBI CAMP OF THE CEN-
tral Asiatic Expedition one day, dismounted, and hobbled their
horses. I had never seen such sleek, well-groomed animals before.
Their manes were clipped short but their tails were beautifully full
and thick. These were no bangtails, the long hair actually dragged
on the ground. The saddles and bridles, however, were rather plain
compared to the colorful trappings I have seen on horses in the
Sahara and Arabian deserts. Only one of the horses carried a nicely
tooled leather saddle and a silver-mounted bridle. Apparently the
Mongols consider a well-groomed horse sufficiently beautiful in
itself without elaborate ornamentation. The hobbles tied both front
feet together, but there was also a rope which tied one hind leg
to the front feet. The animals had little chance to move about the
camp or travel far to look for food while the riders were visiting.

I got my camera and began taking pictures of those horses, and
in a few minutes I noticed that Tsinimbo, the nineteen-year-old
Mongol who had been with our motor caravan all summer, was
also admiring them, just as an American boy looks over a new
model automobile.

"How about it, Tsinimbo?" I asked. "Can you ride a horse?"

The lad looked at me in amazement. When he saw that I was

· 230 ·

asking a serious question, he turned away and nodded an affirmative. He evidently did not trust his voice to answer, but the look he gave me was charged with meaning.

"Of all the stupid questions!" his eyes exclaimed. "That takes the prize. Ride! Of course, I can ride! You might as well ask an eagle if it can fly, a fish if it can swim, or a wolf if it likes meat!"

That look left no doubt in my mind that Mongols consider themselves horsemen above all else. They are desert nomads, and horses are by far the dominant element in their culture. A Mongol, boy or girl, is tied onto a horse almost as soon as the child can walk and is made to race with other babies. A horse is always tied or hobbled in front of every camp, and an adult will mount a horse to go fifty yards rather than walk. Some observers have said that all Mongols are bowlegged because they ride so much. Many *are* bowlegged, but, like our Western cowboys, their bent legs are actually caused by an unbalanced diet in their youth, not from bending their legs around a horse's barrel.

During the twelfth century, and later, a horse thief in the Gobi, if caught, had to return nine horses for one stolen. If he could not meet this payment, he had to give his children as compensation; and unless he made restitution with either horses or children, the horse thief was slaughtered like a sheep. Horses meant much more to the Mongols than just transportation. They were food, shelter, friend, and measure of prestige. In the shamanistic period a horse skull was even an object of worship. Every Mongol had a horse and everyone could remember any horse he had ever seen.

A traveler could go the length and breadth of Mongolia by lasso relay. This was an interesting system which emphasizes the Mongol love of freedom in great open spaces and his respect for horses. A rider leaving home on his own horse galloped on course until his horse was tired. At the next herd he lassoed a remount and turned loose his own animal. On the return journey the rider picked up the same horses he had ridden out and returned them to their own herds. If he came back by way of another route it made no difference. Individual horses were so easily recognized that someone else would return each to its rightful owner. Horses really had great prestige. While they could carry riders, no one would dare degrade the animals by using them as pack horses.

Mare's milk was and still is a common drink among the Mongols. It is used either fresh, slightly fermented as *kumiss,* or distilled into *arrak,* a very intoxicating liquor. In making *kumiss* the fresh milk is placed in a rawhide bag, hung in the sun for a few days, and stirred two or three times each day. *Arrak* is distilled from the *kumiss.*

On long marches, the Mongol soldiers of the Middle Ages sometimes opened veins in their horses and drank the blood. They did not take enough to kill, or even weaken the animal, but enough to give the soldier nourishment and keep him fit until more conventional food was available.

In the twelfth and thirteenth centuries complete unity between horse and rider gave the Mongol a mobility which enabled him to sweep down on his enemies with the suddenness of a man dropping from empty space. These hardy men under Genghis Khan conquered most of Asia and even part of Europe—apparently just for the pure joy of conquest. Their love of freedom was so great that free migration and conquest was the only glorious career considered suitable for a Mongol noble. When the fun of conquering wore off, they just quit the subjugated lands and came back home.

Many Western observers have said that the Mongols have degenerated and are no longer the men they were in the days of Genghis Khan. It is true that in recent centuries they have been dominated as a group by their neighbors, but their ancient capacity for hard riding and vicious, brutal attack still exists. In 1921 a band of 300 Mongol cavalry annihilated 4,000 Chinese near Tuerin, a lamasery between Udde (or Wuteh) and Ulan Bator. In 1939 Outer Mongolian cavalry clashed with the Japanese a few times on the borders of Manchukuo in a "rehearsal for war," as one reporter said, but both sides decided that no easy victory was possible. In 1942 there were 18,000 hard-riding Mongol cavalrymen in Meng Chiang, the puppet state of Inner Mongolia set up by Japan as a buffer between China and Russian-controlled Outer

Mongolia. However, when the Japanese poisoned their general in hopes of getting a more dependable puppet, the whole army went over to the Chinese.

The desert nomads really haven't changed a great deal over the centuries. They can still be led by a strong leader, but they cannot be pushed around too much, as both China and Japan have found out. Russia has been more successful in getting their cooperation, but the Russians have operated with thorough and systematic planning, based on a complete understanding of these nomad peoples.

North of the desert, the Russians have succeeded in collectivizing and industrializing the Mongols around the city of Ulan Bator (Urga); but out in the desert the nomads are still freedom-loving herdsmen who resist organization into collectives. They like the open spaces and a wild ride across uncultivated plains. The Mongol believes his way of life is gay and free. He has only contempt for the city dweller or the earth-bound peasant who prefers a tame donkey to a fresh-caught horse. Of course, his Chinese neighbors hold him in equal contempt as a barbarian who is too stupid to rise above the discomforts of a rough outdoor life and too ignorant to appreciate the artificial beauties of civilization.

Americans, as a rule, find it easy to get on friendly terms with the Mongols—perhaps because we are not too far removed ourselves from the freedoms of the pioneer life. Their sense of humor is not much different from our own, and they dearly love a practical joke. Some who have lived with the desert people find that they enjoy natural beauty, that they have a most dignified etiquette, and that they possess a real appreciation for aesthetic and ethical values. They understand these values and recognize their intrinsic worth, to the extent that they have long resisted the less soul-satisfying elements of civilizations, whether Chinese or Western. For instance, it was long considered unethical to sell milk. Yaks, sheep, cattle, and camels are all milked, and their milk is relished in that order of preference; but it was not for sale. Mare's milk is preferably drunk as *kumiss*. Milk was given away without hesitation to anyone who needed or wanted it, but only recently have the Russians succeeded in establishing dairies and commercializing the distribution of fluid milk. The breakdown of the ethics about selling milk is an indication of the ruthless pressure neighboring civilizations are exerting against the Mongol's way of life.

Mongol etiquette is well established, and it seemed to me to be based on the supposition that individuals are free and dignified personalities. Their forms of greeting a stranger are quite different from our own. Once when I was photographing a group, one or two of the men stuck out their tongues. I supposed they were being childishly unfriendly, or at least smart-alecky like some young folks in almost any American group. Later we learned that sticking out the tongue is one form of a friendly "Hello." Another casual greeting is to extend a closed fist with thumb up. Nearly all Mongols carry snuff bottles, and on meeting strangers each presents his snuff bottle to the other. None of us on the Central Asiatic Expedition carried snuff, nor did we care to use it, so we made a gesture of acceptance but did not actually sample the contents before returning the bottle.

The most formal greeting among the Gobi peoples is the presentation of a *hata*. This is a light blue silk scarf about a foot or so wide and from one to two feet long. It is held on both hands, palms up, and extended with a gracious bow toward the one to be greeted. The receiver also bows and accepts the *hata* on his extended palms. The courteous response to the bearer of a *hata* is some gift—a trinket, a useful article, or money. One may also return the *hata* if no other gift is available or if, as sometimes happened with us, visitors became so numerous that it is suspected that the *hata* presentation is becoming a racket. The return, however, must be done most graciously and on extended palms. The *hata* is sent to announce an important visit and is given before making a request. It is also used as an expression of high esteem, as when acknowledging an important favor. In that case the recipient keeps the *hata*. Old friends shake hands when they meet, and if they are exceptionally glad to see each other they use both hands.

The courtesies and etiquette of the *ger* (a yurt, or felt-covered, portable house) and the tent are so formalized that some of them have the force of law. The yurt generally faces the south on account of desert winds, and a visitor is expected to approach from the east, like the sun. If one comes toward a camp from any other direction, he is expected to circle the yurt at a decent distance so that he comes within hailing distance from the correct direction. Only clandestine or enemy approaches are made toward the back of the dwelling.

It is neither necessary nor expected that a stranger will call out or knock before entering a dwelling. Mongol visitors often came to our camp and entered one tent after another. Once I was taking an all-over sponge bath when my tent flap was unexpectedly opened. A Mongol woman stepped inside, casually walked over to the cot on the left side of my "bedroom," and sat down. I will admit I was nonplused for a moment. However, the woman was so far from the pristine beauty of her youth that I quickly lost my embarrassment and continued with my bath.

You may enter the dwelling without knocking, but you must do it correctly. The door is opened with the left hand and you enter on the left side. This is so a visitor will not step into the wife's side of the yurt. Also one must step over, not onto, the doorsill, and leave his whip or club outside above the door of the yurt. The wife's place is to the right of the entrance, and her claim to that part of the dwelling is a legal right. She is even allowed to beat anyone with a stick or piece of furniture who tries to take her place in the yurt.

The yurt and the Mongol tent are both excellently adapted to the Gobi climate, but although both are portable, the tent is more easily moved. On the Expedition we used Mongol tents which are made of lightweight cotton cloth, blue outside and white inside. These are the triangle or "A" type like the old army pup tents. They also slope from pole to ground at front and back. In other words, there are no straight sides and the tent presents very little resistance to the wind from any direction. During very hot days we could prop up the tent walls from the bottom to let air circulate, but such days were few. Once we were wakened in the middle of the night by a terrific wind and had to put extra ropes over those tents which withstood the first onslaught of the sudden gale. Ordinarily the tents met the desert conditions very well.

Unlike the tent, the yurt consists of a circular wall perpendicular to the ground, which is topped with a conical roof. It is built as a lattice-work frame of bamboo or other lightweight wood, and covered with a thick sheet of felt lashed to the frame with goat-hair rope. The top of the cone-shaped roof is open like the smoke-hole of an American Indian tepee. Again like the tepee, there is an extra flap which can be placed over the smoke-hole if necessary. The felt covering of the yurt is excellent insulation, and the structure is warm in winter and cool in summer. The circular shape presents the minimum resistance to Gobi winds at all seasons.

Inside the yurt, the hearth is near the center with a large iron kettle of Mongol tea always bubbling. At the back, opposite the door, is the *Burkan*, or altar, with a picture of Buddha. This part of the dwelling is also the place of honor for visitors. Chests of drawers and the household equipment are kept on the wife's side of the yurt. There may be a low bed platform, or the family may sleep on felt pads laid on the ground. Young lambs or other baby animals may be kept on the woman's side of the yurt if they need special attention, but dogs are never allowed inside the dwelling. They are the guardians of camp and flocks and belong outdoors at all times. Yurt etiquette requires respect to both the altar and the hearth. Whether sleeping or sitting up in the dwelling, one never points his feet in those directions.

Mongol yurts are erected almost anywhere on the open plain but generally not very far from a well and within only a few miles of suitable pasture for the flocks and herds. There may be only one or two yurts and there may be as many as eight, but there will not be seven, for the number seven is considered as unlucky among the Mongols as thirteen is among Americans. The number of families camping together depends on the amount of pasture. If there is forage sufficient for large numbers of animals, then the ideal group is four or five tents together. They can group their flocks into bands of a thousand, and so make the most economical use of their man power. As the pasture dries up, the Mongols load their yurts onto camels and move to greener fields. Those who live near the mountains may go to higher altitudes as the summer advances, but by November each family will be back at its winter camp.

Summer camps are located chiefly in regards to water and pasture, but the winter camp is in a sheltered valley or in the lee of a hill. A large supply of fuel is always stored at the winter camp and this is considered personal property. Even so, the Mongol pastoral nomad abhors private ownership of land as much as he looks down on agriculture as a means of livelihood.

Almost every individual is a Jack-of-all-trades as far as personal equipment is concerned, but division of labor is practiced between the sexes. Women are skillful at needlework, and make clothes, do fancy embroidery and trim felt. It is their job to milk all animals and make the milk products, butter, cheese, and *kumiss*. They also wash and dress the meat and guts from slaughtered animals. None of these jobs would be done by a man except, perhaps, on a caravan journey where no woman could be found to do them for him.

Man's work includes the more strenuous jobs and those which require strength. They are concerned with all the caravan work of loading and unloading camels, with herding camels and horses, catching and breaking horses, slaughtering, gelding, and with leatherwork and woodworking. None of these tasks would be done by a woman.

Gathering dung for fuel, herding sheep and cattle, and making rope are generally considered women's work, but a man can do those jobs without loss of dignity. He may even help his wife with such jobs or do them for her if she is sick.

At most wells I saw men or teen-age boys hauling water for the flocks. The man stands on the edge of the well and drops a leather bag attached to the end of a four-foot pole down to the reservoir.

The pole is tied to his wrist by ten or twelve feet of rope, and with this rope he pulls up the stick and bag. The stick acts like the handle of a dipper and enables him to empty the bag of water into a trough where the animals drink. At the camp of the Mongol hunter who guided me to the prehistoric Dune Dweller site (see Chapter XIII), it was apparently the wife's job to water the sheep in the morning. I recall that the hunter was most annoyed because, on the morning I have described, his wife decided to get sick. He had to water a big flock of sheep before he could join us for that wild automobile ride across the desert. He also had to carry two large casks of water up to the yurt. These were slung on either side of a small camel. They were unloaded at the well and filled, but I decided to speed up our departure and hauled them back to the yurt half a mile away in the car rather than wait another fifteen minutes for the camel to make the journey.

Each tribe has limits prescribed to its wanderings, but within the tribal territory families move pretty much on a "first come, first served" basis. There is, however, so much exchange of news and plans between groups that actually cooperation exists in determining who goes where.

Throughout the Gobi the dung of sheep, camels, and cattle is the only fuel either for cooking or for heating the yurt. As I have said, a collected pile of such fuel is considered private property; but if a family announces that they do not intend to return to a winter camp where they have stored such a fuel supply, then any other family may camp there and use the dung. The droppings of sheep, camels, and cattle around such a campsite are pressed by hand into a wooden mold to make bricks. These are then dried in the sun and used to build the winter corral for the sheep. In summer the animals are bedded down in the open near the yurts, but in winter they are shut up inside the wind-tight dung walls. If the animals become restless during the night, it is the duty of the oldest daughter to leave the yurt and quiet them. If the sheep have been made restless by the girl's lover, it may take her an hour or two to quiet them.

Horses are pastured at greater distances from the camp than sheep and are watched day and night by the herdsmen. These men are mounted on horseback and carry an eighteen-foot pole with a rope noose at the end. When they want to catch a horse they gallop alongside and slip the noose over the horse's head. It looks like an easier type of lasso to handle than that used by American cowboys, and it is very effective.

The Mongols are also good camel men. They raise the Bactrian, or two-humped, species, which is much shorter legged and stockier than the one-humped dromedary of Arabia and Africa. The Asiatic camel is the chief means of freight transport between China and the cities of Central Asia; and desert mystery and the romance of far places are in the sound of such city names as Kalgan, Kobdo, Uliassiutai, Urumchi, Turfan, and Samarkand, all of which, for centuries, have been ports for these Asiatic ships of the desert. For thousands of years the Mongols have furnished both the camels and the caravan men to lead them over the thousand-mile trails through the most rugged and arid deserts of Asia. They have always been content with the freedom of the desert, the joy of months spent in the open air pitting themselves against burning heat and freezing cold, and they leave the financing and trade to the Chinese merchants who risk fortunes in hope of good profits.

The contrast was made vivid for us one night out in the western Gobi. Soon after we had set up our camp near a bit of open water we heard the creak and groan of camel boxes and looked up to see a large merchant caravan approaching. The caravan stopped near us. Two well-dressed Chinese merchants dismounted from their riding camels and, with their backs to the gorgeous sunset, sat upon a couple of camel boxes. Arms folded, staring straight ahead like wooden statues, they sat there while the caravan men made camp. As soon as their tent was erected they disappeared from sight. The caravan men went about their work with laughter and gaiety, and when their work was done they sat around their campfire laughing and talking like American campers on a holiday. Perhaps the Chinese merchants had a fortune in their money chests, but the

Mongol caravan men had companionship by a tiny campfire beneath the stars of a desert night.

The Mongols prefer to keep their camels in pasture all summer and work them during the fall or in late winter and spring. Even though the camel can go many days without food and water, it must be in good physical condition at the start of its privation and it must be allowed to recuperate after the ordeal. Where good pasture is available along a route there may be several hundred camels in a single caravan, but if pasture is scanty or water points are of small capacity the numbers are reduced drastically. Their owners may even be obliged to carry supplies of dried beans bought from Chinese farmers who live on the edge of the arid wastes.

Camels shed their wool in July and August and caravan men pick it up as it falls. They also pull off the loose wool in large mats, but they never clip the camels the way they do sheep. Some men card the wool in camp and spin it into yarn the next day as they walk along with their charges. Both the spun yarn and the raw camel's wool are sold to Chinese merchants.

The nomad peoples of the Gobi, like those in other parts of the desert world, depend on their neighbors for part of their material needs. They exchange wool, hides, and surplus animals, including horses, for non-animal products such as tea, sugar, flour, matches, cloth, and shoes. Before the Communists dominated Asia, the Mongol trade was with Chinese merchants who wandered over the desert with ox-carts loaded with the products of civilization. Now that Russia has industrialized the area around Ulan Bator, though, the Chinese merchants may have been replaced in the desert by Russian traders. The nomads may pay outrageous prices for the products that they want from civilization, but they accept only the styles which conform to their traditions.

Individual Mongols vary a great deal in appearance, especially where there has been racial mixing with their neighbors. Generally they are of medium height, and the body is thickset and sturdy with a small waist and small feet. A typical Mongol does not have the slanting eyes of his Chinese neighbors, because he lacks the Mongoloid fold, and his skin color is more like copper than the yellow of the Chinese. His face is broad with prominent cheekbones; his hair is black and straight and, until a few years ago, it was worn in a braided pigtail. His eyes are dark brown. In fact, he could easily be mistaken for an American Indian if dressed in buckskin and feathers instead of a caftan and a straw hat.

The Mongol caftan is a long coat with sleeves that hang way below the hands. It is a double-breasted garment which fastens to the right of the neck, or even out on the right shoulder, and down the right side below the arm. Other designs include sleeveless coats, short jackets, and waistcoats. Trousers, worn by both men and women, may be similar to our Western chaps, that is, a pair of leggings sewn together or joined to a band at the waist. They may also be true trousers with a central section inserted between the legs. Petticoats for men and women are two separate panels of cloth on a belt which can be worn as a split skirt. Another type is made up of five panels which form a wrap-around skirt, and this may be worn under or over the waistcoat. A sash is worn around the middle of the caftan by men and unmarried women, but married women let the caftan hang free. Winter clothing includes trousers lined with wool or sheepskin and coats made of fur or sheepskin with the wool on.

In general there is so little difference between the costume of the men and women in Mongolia that I once gave a young man a package of needles because I thought he was a woman. He was quite puzzled by the gift, and I could not understand why until some of my colleagues pointed out that his head was shaved and that he did not have the two braids and the silver ornaments a woman would have.

Garments worn by the lamas, the priests of Tibetan Buddhism, are red or yellow and they do not wear other colors. The lay population avoid red or yellow but wear any other color which strikes their fancy.

Men and women wear any of three types of boot. They are the same for the right and left foot. One type has a flat horizontal sole onto which a moccasin-like foot covering and calf-length upper is attached. These are made of leather, cotton, velvet, or satin, and sometimes they are elaborately decorated. A second type has the sole pointed and turned up like the front of a ski. It is almost always made of leather and may be decorated with colored leather strips. The third type is usually made of pliable skin and resembles a moccasin shoe pack. Some of these have a top facing of velvet embroidered in chain stitch. Cotton stockings are sometimes worn inside the boots. These are tailored to the shape of the boot and the back seam is left open except over the heel.

In winter the men wear fur caps with ear flaps. During the summer they sometimes go bareheaded, or they may wear a cone-shaped straw hat with a tassel on the point. The lamas and the women wear a hat that looks rather like a cone placed in a soup bowl.

When we stopped at the camp where Tsinimbo and the other Mongols of our caravan lived, we were impressed by the elaborate headdresses worn by their wives. The ladies had supplemented their own hair with huge, detachable crowns of hair as black as their own. Over these were open networks of silver chains, coral, and semiprecious stones. Large chain and colored-stone ornaments hung from either side of the headdresses almost to the women's shoulders. They made me think of very fancy earrings but were part of the headdress. Regular earrings also dangled from the pierced ear lobes.

Tsinimbo said that each married woman receives her headdress as a dowry, but he did not explain who pays for it. Each Mongol tribe has its own style of headdress. In Outer Mongolia it takes the form of artificial hair "horns" rather than a mere crown. These horns are set with silver or gold and precious-stone ornaments. Among some other groups no extra hair is used, but a sort of cap made of gold or silver chains and silver fringe studded with coral or precious stones is worn.

Mongol men carry a long knife and a pair of chopsticks in a sheath which is stuck into the sash. They also carry a flint purse on a chain and a snuff bottle. The flint is for striking fire. Both men and women carry their own food bowls tucked into their caftans.

There are three principal dialects of the Mongol language which are sufficiently different to cause difficulties of understanding, but enough alike for speakers to get the general meaning of each. In Mongolia five other languages—Chinese, Manchu, Russian, Tibetan, and (by the lamas) Sanskrit—are also spoken; and many a Mongol speaks at least one other language besides his own Mongol dialect. Under Chinese rule the free schools which were operated in Mongolia taught in Chinese, but in Russian-controlled territory the teaching is in Mongol. Mongols attached to American scientific expeditions were quick to pick up enough English words to get along quite nicely.

Once when Dr. L. Erskine Spock, a geologist, and I were out by ourselves we located a formation which Spock wished to have placed on the official map when the topographers reached the locality. We located it in relation to a native well which we could see near-by, but we needed the native designation of the point.

"What name, that well?" We asked Tsinimbo. The boy immediately started off on a dead run.

"Hey! Come back here," we called. Tsinimbo returned.

"You understand?" asked Dr. Spock. "We want the name of that well. What are you running away for?"

"Me understand," said Tsinimbo. Then he pointed to our motor car. "English name, *motacah*. Mongol name, *chug-chug*." Then, pointing to the well, he continued. "English name, well. Mongol name, me go find out." This time we did not stop him as he raced away to talk with the herdsmen who were watering a flock of sheep.

Mongols are also quick to understand and communicate in sign language. Once a missionary asked the expedition's surgeon to visit a Mongol who had been kicked by a horse. The man's son had ridden to the mission for help and was to guide us back to the family yurt. Doc asked me to be his chauffeur. There was no particular problem going out, for the boy sat in the back seat and tapped me on the shoulder when he wanted my attention, then pointed in the direction he wanted me to turn. He was the best back-seat driver I have ever ridden with. Part of the time we were bouncing cross-country, but most of the time we followed trails. The family yurt was located in a valley up in the hills some twenty miles from our camp, and as soon as the boy had jumped out of the car and driven away the dogs, we entered the dwelling.

The injured man lay on the dirt floor to the left of the door in front of the hearth. His face was covered with a dirty rag which Doc lifted. The poor fellow's face was turned wrong side out. Doc looked around the yurt, but there was not much to aid him there— No table on which the physician could place the man so he could work on him comfortably, no sterile cloths, no pans adequate for heating quantities of water.

"If I could only get him back to the mission," said Doc, "it would be easy. But what would these people think if we tried to kidnap the poor fellow?"

The man's wife was fluttering about the place like any distracted spouse in more civilized parts of the world. Apparently she was worried because she had not extended us a hospitable welcome, for she finally found a piece of stone-hard cheese which she gave to me. Food is the standard indication of hospitality in all parts of the world, and I accepted the gift with the same elaborate bow I would have used if she had presented a *hata*.

While I had her attention I pointed to the man on the floor. Then I made a cradle of my arms and turned toward the door as I said "Chug-chug. Hatt In Sumu." Those were the words for automobile and the name of the missionary's home.

The woman nodded her assent and went out of the yurt.

"I guess it's all right, Doc," I said.

Until then I had not noticed an old man sitting at the back of the yurt smoking a little pipe. He coughed to attract my attention, then beckoned me toward him. Without a single word he pointed to the injured man and held up his fist with the thumb up, then turned the fist thumb down.

"How about it, Doc? The old man wants to know whether your patient will die or get well?" I said.

"He'll live, all right," Doc replied. So I turned to the old man and showed my fist with thumb up. We both smiled, and he nodded his head several times as much as to say, "That's good. That's good."

"There's two things I'd like to ask the old boy," said Doc. "I'd like to know how long ago this accident happened. It looks like a couple of days have elapsed. I'd also like to know how a horse could kick a man in such a way as to tear his face down from the nose the way this is."

I turned to the old man and again pointed to the patient. Then I laid my head on my arm and closed my eyes and held up one finger, then two fingers, then three fingers. The old man shook his head at the three fingers but held up two.

"It is two nights since the accident," I said.

Next I got down on all fours near the old fellow and kicked out with one hind foot. The man laughed out loud but shook his head. When he had stopped laughing at me, he made a pawing motion with his hand. I understood then. As the patient had stooped to hobble his horse, the animal had raised his front foot and caught the man's face just above the nose. The blow literally tore off his face.

About the time we had completed this sign-language conversation, the boy and the woman came back to the yurt. The boy was carrying a lunch, so we knew that he was expecting to go with us. We loaded the injured man into the car and made him as comfortable as possible, and that afternoon Doc and the nurses at the mission worked on the patient for several hours. When we left the mission a few days later the patient thanked Doc by showing his fist with the thumb up, the "all's well" sign language in many corners of the world.

This incident high-lighted a Mongol custom concerning the disposal of the dead. They do not like to have a person die in the yurt, and if possible they move a dying person outside before the end. When we got the doctor's patient back to the mission, the interpreters confirmed our sign-language conversations, but they also learned that the man had been so certain he would not get well that he had asked his relatives to carry him out of the yurt and leave him. Some Mongols bury their dead; some cremate the body; but in many parts of the Gobi the body is exposed to the elements, the beasts of the plains and fowls of the air. According to the religious beliefs of the Mongols, this is "so the body may fulfill its last earthly function by entering into and supporting life in some living creature." In other words, if a Mongol has led a good life, then dogs, wolves, and scavenger birds will quickly dispose of his flesh.

Lamaism, a modified form of Buddhism, is the religion which has dominated the Mongols for several hundred years. It is also the religion of Tibet. As practiced in Mongolia the original teachings of Buddhism were changed by the addition of nature worship and magic. Lamaism also adopted many of the shamanistic practices in which the Mongols believed before they came into contact with the Tibetan form of Buddhism.

Collections of buildings which form the lamaseries were the only permanent structures in the Gobi when we were there. Glaring white walls bordered with bands of red and trimmed with gold made a spectacular splotch on the desert landscape. Flocks and herds of the lamaseries were the largest in Mongolia, and huge stacks of *argol*, the dung of sheep, camels, and cattle, piled near the buildings, guaranteed ample fuel to warm the buildings in winter. Much of the fuel was gifts from passing caravans.

The eldest son of every family was claimed for the priesthood by Lamaism. If the family could afford to spare other sons, then they, too, were claimed by the religion; and this resulted in about a half or more of the male population taking the vows of celibacy. The fact that these vows were not always honored has been blamed for the wide spread of syphilis in Mongolia.

Lamas are called upon to select auspicious days for every under-taking. They are necessary for performing ceremonies and prayers for the sick and the dead, and at marriages or births. Lamas are needed to drive out evil spirits to cure sick animals, and to purify a house which has been defiled by the presence of a corpse. All these services require payments of clothing, food, or animals.

As I have mentioned, each dwelling contains an altar opposite the door, and offerings to the spirits are placed there near the picture of Buddha. Every day the head woman of the family offers milk to the gods. With a dipper she throws milk to the east, the north, the west and, finally, to the south, for spirits are thought to inhabit these various points as well as other places in nature.

A most prominent feature of the Mongol landscape is the *obo* or large monument of stone. *Obos* mark territorial boundaries and serve as "lighthouses" or trail markers for caravans; but they also have religious significance and are the abode of spirits, so they are the sites of religious festivals and celebrations. On such occasions the lamas decorate the structures with *hatas* and leave food for the spirits. The *hata* becomes a prayer flag and, constantly whipping in the wind, it wafts aloft the lamas' petitions to the spirits.

When one sees the great collections of substantial buildings in the desert where the lay population lives in portable homes, when one realizes the man power consumed in collecting the fantastic stacks of *argol* to heat the buildings, and when one watches the crowds of lamas who swarm out when visitors approach—it is easy to believe that the religion of the Gobi has placed a terrific drain on the economy of the Mongol people.

In the north where Russia dominates the country, they claim that the oldest son can no longer become a lama and that this edict has reduced the number of lamas from nearly 60 per cent of the male population to only 3 per cent. If these figures are correct, there must be large quantities of good timber to be salvaged from abandoned lamaseries in the Gobi.

Originally the Mongol tribe was the *aimak,* which actually consisted of the personal followers of a ruling prince or leader and his related princes. On the death of a leader, the *aimak* might break up and become several smaller, independent groups. A strong leader, however, might unite several such groups, and even so greatly extend his authority that his *aimak* was enlarged to the size of a nation. This happened under Genghis Khan.

When the Manchus conquered China they had the help of Mongol princes. Each prince and his tribal following was given a territory with specific boundaries so that several petty states or Mongol principalities were established in the lands along the border of North China. The princes ruled the Mongols, but the Manchus kept the princes in line through subsidies, honors, and obligatory attendance at governing centers. They were never given enough freedom to develop strong leaders or coalitions large enough to threaten China. The princes found it more advantageous to maintain the *status quo* of established principalities and protect their personal wealth than to risk their wealth in tribal wars which might have united the tribes and built up a strong Mongol nation. Lamaism, with its heavy drain on man power and huge accumulations of wealth, was another important factor in keeping the lands along the border safe for China.

Mongol families are patrilocal, that is, the wife goes to live at her husband's camp unless he is an orphan, or her family has no son and needs another man to help with the herds. When a son reaches maturity he is no longer under his father's authority. If he wishes, he may take part of his father's herd and become a direct subject in his own right rather than in that of his family.

Mongol nobles trace their descent through the male line back to Genghis Khan, and the man whose descent is most direct from the Great Khan has the highest rank. Commoners or Arrat families among the Khalka Mongols were sometimes attached to noble families as *hamjaanai ail,* or supporting families. The relationship involved reciprocal rights and obligations. The commoner helped the noble meet his debts and rendered certain services, and in turn the noble paid for the commoner's funeral and was responsible for misdemeanors on the commoner's part. This relationship was hereditary and followed from father to son, but it was not a kinship relationship. That is, the two families were never related by blood or marriage. Nobles, lamas, and commoners mingled socially in a democratic manner, although the nobles were addressed by titles of honor. Sometimes the commoner was wealthier than the noble and would hire the latter to work for him.

Marriages are more in the nature of a civil contract than a religious rite, but a first marriage is celebrated at an elaborate feasting ceremony attended by relatives of both the bride and groom. Formal law states that the man may divorce his wife if she disobeys him, if she is barren, or if she has syphilis. A woman may divorce her husband if he is impotent or has syphilis. Recent observers say that divorce is now by mutual consent. If the children are very young, they belong to the father; but if they are old enough they may make their own decision as to which parent they will live with.

There is no stigma attached to a divorced man or woman, and both are free to remarry. If there is a second marriage, there may be a banquet served to close relatives of the contracting parties, but this is not necessary. Although legally a wife is expected to obey her husband, there seems to be practical equality between the sexes in most respects.

A good wife always has "tea" bubbling on the hearth in a Mongol yurt. This is different from any other standard diet I know of. Basically it is black, brick tea boiled in milk—and it is strong! Added to the tea and milk are butter, salt, and often flour or grain. We might call the drink soup or gruel, but the official name is *manja,* tea. The Mongol diet also includes fresh milk, cheese, and sour milk. The hard, dry cheese is stored for winter use and eaten melted in hot tea. Like the cheese in other parts of the world it is very nourishing.

The Mongols also eat meat, mostly mutton. If a group is large enough to use up a whole sheep in a day or so, some meat is eaten in summer; but much more is eaten in winter. The winter supply is butchered in December and quick-frozen. Where cattle are available, beef is also butchered. Like mutton it is quick-frozen for winter use, but it is also dried for year-round use.

There is a certain ritual in killing both sheep and cattle which is performed by individuals appointed by the lamasery of an area.

This butchering ceremony is considered so important that Mongols will wait, even when quite hungry, until an authorized butcher is available. Some wild game—especially antelope, which are sometimes found in great herds—is hunted and eaten by the Mongols. During our stay in the Gobi we almost always had antelope meat twice a day. If the Mongols who accompanied us expected to share the meat which our hunters had shot, they would rush out and perform the ritual killing before the antelope breathed its last.

As civilization encroaches on the life of the Gobi nomads, other foods are added to their diet. In addition to tea, traders supply noodles, millet, wheat, flour, sugar, wine, dried fruits, and cakes. Tobacco for their tiny pipes and snuff are also obtained through trade.

In summer the Mongol diet is supplemented by wild onions, either the hot, strong, little ones like scallions or the large highland onions which are eaten raw as we eat apples. The little ones are also eaten by the sheep, so summer mutton often has a strong onion flavor, as does the milk. There are also two kinds of rhubarb, or pieplant, which can be eaten; and in some sections of the Gobi dune plums can be gathered in edible quantities.

The winter diet is often so lacking in necessary vitamins that the nomads develop scurvy. The Mongols say that plenty of fresh milk will prevent or cure the disease. It can also be cured by any green plants, including grasses.

The Russians believe that all civilized people must eat bread. They have, accordingly, made a serious effort to force the Mongols to become bread eaters. Bakeries have been established north of the Gobi, but how widely the bread-eating habit has been spread is not known. Probably it has not spread far beyond the city of Ulan Bator.

Undoubtedly the central Gobi of Mongolia will continue to be a back pasture of the desert world for many generations. It will be a land of the partially free, where young swains can gallop past their sweethearts' families, showing off their horsemanship on the way to special ceremonies or demonstrating their stamina in ten-mile races across the open plain. In years of plentiful rainfall, Chinese farmers on the south and Russianized Mongols on the north will plant seeds and harvest crops in fertile grasslands closer and closer to the true desert. But these farmers will retreat in arid years, and the nomads will continue to pasture their flocks and herds wherever desert grasses can take root.

XVI

. . . .

. . . .

. . . .

. . . .

. . . . .

Desert Arabs—A People in Transition

ARABIA IS A LAND SURROUNDED BY THE CRADLES OF ANCIENT civilization, Phoenician, Assyrian, Egyptian. It is the birthplace of three great world religions, the Jewish, Christian, and Moslem. In this part of the world parts of Greco-Roman culture were preserved while Europe struggled through the Dark Ages and slowly made ready to build once more on Greek and Roman foundations.

In spite of its nearness to past splendors, a million or more Bedouins still live in this rugged desert kingdom as they did in the time of Abraham, 4,000 years ago. Here vast numbers of people who reckon time by days or seasons mingle with time-conscious Americans who keep appointments on the minute and synchronize their watches with radio time-signals.

Arabia is a land where transportation and communication have jumped a 5,000 year gap—from camel courier to diesel trains and radio—almost overnight! Donkey freight runs feeder lines to air freight; and a single family may go from the light of campfires to neon tubes, from illiteracy to a college degree, in less than a generation. Within a few years their barter economy has been replaced by a sound and stable currency; and a chaotic tribal rule of raid and plunder has been replaced by stable government and security for travelers in less than half a century. A local less-than-self-sufficient economy is rapidly giving way to world-wide commerce and major importance as a world supplier. Homewoven tents and "camper's plumbing" are being replaced by central air-conditioned efficiency apartments and modern sewage disposal.

We Americans pride ourselves on our "adaptability" when we go from a centrally heated apartment in Washington to a centrally air-conditioned house in Arabia, but the Arabian is trying to adapt from walking transportation and ignorance of the laws of speed and momentum to an age of heavy trucks hurtling across the desert landscape at a mile a minute. Hundreds of new experiences and new situations confront the Saudi Arabian every day and each forces him to make some new mental adaptation.

The Saudi government and the Americans in Arabia both realize the shock these constant new adaptations naturally cause the individual. This is why Arabians are clinging to as many of the old ways as they can, and why whenever possible new ways are introduced gradually to give the people time to adjust.

Americans with intelligent understanding are welcome in Arabia. They are the ones who have patience, more patience, and still more patience with a people who are trying to span 5,000 years of world progress in a couple of decades.

"Do-it-yourself" has been the principal "industry" in Saudi Arabia for centuries. Lack of raw materials, absence of water power, and scanty agriculture have forced the people to rely on themselves to produce their own basic necessities.

Camels, sheep, and goats supply the dairy products and a little meat for food, as well as wool and hides for clothing and tents. Each family weaves its own clothing, tent cloth, rugs, blankets, and saddle bags from the wool or camel's hair of its own herds. Before oil was discovered, camels were exported to Egypt for food and horses exported to Arabia's other neighbors for military and transportation needs. Some hides were also exported.

In the oases, date palms supply the basic food for both the oasis dwellers and desert nomads, or Bedouins, but nearly half the dates consumed in Arabia are imported from Iraq. The Bedouins trade sheep's wool in the oases for dates. The date palm also supplies leaves and fiber for the local weaving of mats, and wood for framing adobe houses and for burning. In addition, the oases produce rice, millet, vegetables, and fruits. The Bedouins raise some wheat in desert hollows where water accumulates after a rain.

Irrigating water formerly was hoisted in a handmade leather bucket on a handmade rope pulled over a squeaking, handmade wooden pulley by a donkey or a camel. Since the discovery of oil and the increase of government-financed water wells, the donkey and camel are being replaced by power pumps. Every animal replaced by a power pump releases garden space for plants for human food, space which was formerly needed for alfalfa.

A considerable tourist industry centers around the annual pilgrimage of Moslems from all over the world to the holy city of Mecca; and this brings in a considerable amount of foreign exchange. This tourist industry has rapidly improved since the King established definite law-and-order security, and pilgrims to Mecca are able to travel safely in the kingdom.

Since the development of oil, some 800 to 900 types of services and industries have been introduced into the country. Arab-owned industries are increasing daily, and these range from electric generating plants to filling stations and automobile agencies, ice plants, and dry cleaning and laundry establishments. Dry ice plants, which also produce oxygen, carbon dioxide, and acetylene; soft drink bottling works; bakeries; cement block and brick plants; and machine shops—all are owned and operated by Arabs. Arab contractors, who build roads, houses, hospitals, schools, office buildings, and stores, regularly meet their own payrolls for scores and even hundreds of men. Each year they take on more complex jobs.

Still, there are large numbers of the Bedouins who prize their freedom above the economic security of a clock-controlled existence. Between freedom and comfort, they choose freedom and continue to live in a "do-it-yourself" economy. There is little protection against summer heat or winter chill for these nomads. During the dry seasons when their animals give little or no milk they often endure near-starvation. In case of long droughts when their animals die, they turn to the King for help. This help is never refused whenever it is justified.

But the new era is affecting these roamers of the desert waste. Water wells drilled for the government make it possible for the nomads to shorten their annual journeys to greener pasture. Many no longer go hundreds of miles to the north in summer, as they were forced to do in the days before oil.

Since the King has enforced internal security, raiding has stopped. Mechanized transportation for civilians and the military throughout the Middle East has almost wiped out the market for horses and camels. Power pumps have reduced the demand for donkeys. All these marks of progress have reduced Bedouin man-power needs. It takes fewer men to guard the herds from wolves than it did to protect them from intertribal raids and to go on reciprocal raids. Much of the surplus man power is being absorbed by the industrialization and oil development on the eastern, or Persian Gulf, side of Arabia.

Thousands of Bedouins have been settled on newly irrigated acreage; and the King has established experimental and demonstration farms for the improvement of oasis agriculture and food animals.

All these radical changes, which have taken place in a single generation, naturally produce social tensions as well as economic strains. For example, one oasis produces a special kind of date which can be made into a delicious confection and sold at a much higher profit than unprocessed dates. This was an ideal situation as long as only the surplus of the crop was processed, but with prosperity in the east and expanding export markets, more and more dates were processed for export. Eventually the export of luxury dates reduced the supply of staple food dates in that oasis and food cost was raised. This high price, in turn, attracted food dates from other oases until their export business used up all that locality's surplus and cut into *their* home consumption needs. The price of food dates skyrocketed so that oasis dwellers could not buy their basic food. When gardeners' wages would no longer suffice to buy their food, wages were raised. This caused a wage spiral among oasis gardeners, and along with it the same grumbling about higher prices common in other parts of the world. Eventually the King stepped in. He put a quota on confection date processing in the oasis where the trouble had started. This brought food date prices more into line.

Now this is only one example of the way that "progress" can disrupt a way of life which has run along in a contented manner for centuries. There are thousands of others. It is difficult for us Westerners to understand the vastness of this sudden social and economic upheaval.

Two things are important in understanding the explosive changes taking place in Arabian industry. First, while it is possible to take a young camel driver away from a caravan and make him an efficient truck driver in six weeks, it takes a long time for him to make the countless other adjustments that go with his new job. He has to learn how to spend his ready cash and provide for his family under a new way of life. He has to learn to read and write, and to wear different clothes. A family man at heart, in a land of strict customs regarding man-woman relationships, he has to learn to live for long periods as a bachelor. It is a most difficult adjustment to make. The new wage and money economy which has replaced his do-it-yourself and barter economy raises all kinds of family problems when his wife and children no longer have flocks to watch, and wool to card, spin, and weave into family clothes and shelter. These are some of the more obvious adjustments being made or attempted.

Second, the numerous public works being constructed in Saudi Arabia are not paid for by public taxation the way they would be in the United States. New water wells, hospitals, clinics, schools, railroads, agricultural and animal-improvement experimental farms, and roads—all are government-financed from oil royalties. In America such royalties are spent by private landowners entirely for their personal accounts; but in Arabia the Bedouins have never believed in individual or private ownership of the land over which they pastured their flocks. This is the tribal or government land—

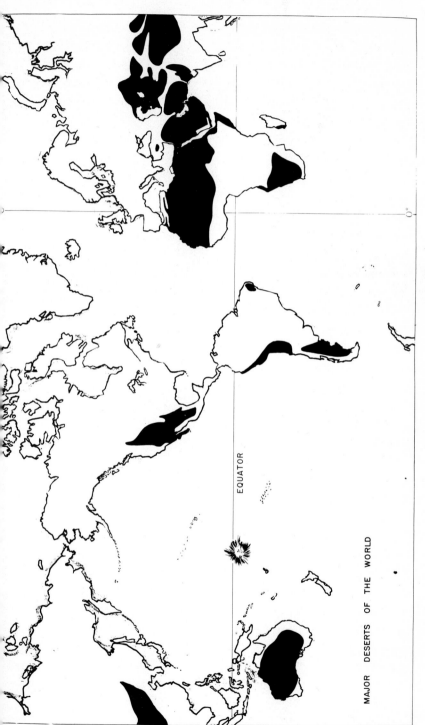

MAJOR DESERTS OF THE WORLD

EQUATOR

Major deserts of the world.

A typical desert canyon south of In Salah on the way to the Hoggar. Far more of the Sahara is barren rock than sand.

The northern edge of the Sahara—not sand but rock which is slowly being broken by daily extremes of heat and cold.

Great rock cliffs in the Sahara.

A vivid pattern of erosion gullies in the southwestern Sahara appears in this aerial photograph, showing how rare torrential rains cut into the desert floor.

Tamanrasset, the capital of the Hoggar in the Sahara. This village was completely wiped out by a three-day rainstorm in 1910.

The dunes of the Sahara.

The sand dunes of Tit, west of In Salah in the Sahara. The crests of these dunes are "planted" with palm leaves to prevent the dunes from encroaching on the oasis.

The "Forest of Tidekelt" in the Sahara. The roots of these wind-tormented trees have held the clay together for centuries while desert weathering has cut away the plain for eight or ten feet.

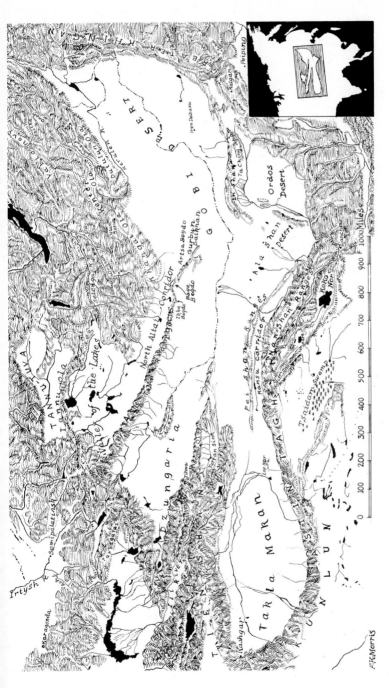

The Gobi Basins.

Cairns marking the old boundary between Inner and Outer Mongolia.

Trees are a rare sight in the Gobi.

Great desert rivers like the Colorado in the western United States are
carried through the desert by the volume of their waters.

The "goosenecks" of the San Juan River near Goodrich, Utah.

Desert scenery in America: Looking south at the free abutment of Rainbow Bridge.

The fantastic desert scenery of Monument Valley.

The deserts of the southwestern United States have more vegetation than those of other parts of the world.

Sheep and goats in pasture in the western Sahara in February. A heavy
rain produced this great field of flowers.

The poisonous melon of the African desert, *Citrullus colocynthis*.

A thorny, desert-blown tree at Oued Talha in the Sahara.

The author on Ole, a "swift" riding camel of the Sahara.

Camels at a watering trough in Saudi Arabia.

A small caravan crossing the Western Dunes of the Algerian Sahara.

Primitive plank-wheeled oxcarts are used to haul traders' freight across the Gobi.

hence the royalties belong to the King. The Saudi does pay some taxes, to be sure, but most of the government income is from oil.

The best way to understand the people of Saudi Arabia is first to consider features of our own American culture which most Americans never think about at all, but which are the real reasons we act and think like Americans. These characteristics make up our starting point, and they are so different from the starting point of the Saudi Arabians that Americans have great difficulty in understanding the Arabs and the Arabs find us incomprehensible. If we will recognize these American fundamentals, we can see why the Arab point of view is different. Once we understand the differences between *our* fundamental ideas and *his* fundamental ideas, his way looks just as logical and makes just as good sense as our own.

Americans believe in *progress!* They started "taming the wilderness" more than 300 years ago, and they have been making *progress* ever since. To do that job our forefathers abandoned family tradition, country, everything their ancestors had held sacred and had depended upon—except their faith in God and their confidence in themselves as individuals. The millions who followed the earliest settlers made similar breaks with their past; and this break with the past is fundamental in the background of Americans. It is a basic difference between us and the people of Saudi Arabia, who have lived by traditions for 4,000 years. They know the old ways and those ways have proved right for them for centuries. Why change an established way for a new idea that has not had time to prove itself? Until we recognize this basic difference, we will never understand or get along with the Saudi. When we do recognize it, we find that we have a lot in common.

Another basic difference is the American desire to be comfortable. For a hundred years we have been making life more comfortable with more things by using power tools, swift transportation, and mechanical gadgets. We pride ourselves on our "adaptability" because we have learned to run the new machines as fast as they come on the market. Saudi Arabs are now receiving all at once the whole batch of products it has taken us a hundred years to accept and understand. Not only are they getting all of our gadgets and ma-

chines at once, but they are getting them on top of a way of life
which has ignored comfort, speed, and even time, for at least forty
centuries!

Arabians conquered their wilderness, the Arabian Desert, not
just three centuries ago but forty centuries ago. The country has
always been a rugged wilderness with a minimum of resources to
be exploited. The Arabs conquered it without machines or gadgets,
but by adapting themselves to one of the severest and most rigorous
climatic areas in the world. They learned to ignore physical comfort and to live without "things" as a matter of course. Their history
makes our ideas of comfort and health "necessities" seem like nonsense to them until they learn to accept these new ideas, just as we
ourselves had to learn to appreciate their importance. Burning sun,
barren soil, and scanty water make life difficult—hard indeed to
get the barest necessities of food, clothing, and shelter. Only those
strong enough to ignore hardship and disdain physical comfort
could survive, and even they were forced to depend absolutely on
the cooperation of the family and tribe in meeting the daily problems of living.

Saudi Arabians *believe* in that cooperation with family and tribe
because the facts of life, as they know them, emphasize its importance. Members of an Arab's family have first claim on his loyalty.
Every Arab can trace his ancestors back for ten or fifteen generations, and he is proud of his background. His family has always
stood by its individuals, even unto the third and fourth generations,
against all enemies. It is only just that when he has the opportunity
to favor his relatives they get preferential treatment.

"The Westerner," Ibn Saud once said, "should know and understand our Arab psychology. If possible he should be conversant with
our manners and customs. Above all he should be acquainted with
our Arab pride and our hopes. He should read something of God's
Holy Word in the Koran. . . .

"Because of the Arab's nature an act of kindness will buy him
body and soul but those who treat him harshly or deal unjustly with
him will discover that he has made an implacable enemy for all
time.

"We Arabs believe implicitly in God's revealed Word and we know that God is faithful. We care for nothing else in this world but our belief in the One God, His Prophet and our honor. Everything else matters nothing at all, not even death. We are not afraid of hardship, or hunger or lack of this world's goods. We are quite content to eat camel meat or dates to the end of our days provided we hold to those three things, our honor, the Prophet and one God."

In Saudi Arabia customs and traditions are so closely tied to religion that they are generally inseparable from it in the mind of the average Saudi. A good example of this is our use of the camera. There is nothing in the Moslem religion which forbids pictures of people or buildings. The King of Saudi Arabia is often photographed, and so are the most sacred religious buildings in the kingdom, even in Mecca itself. Nevertheless, many Moslems object to having their pictures taken. Some orthodox religious opinion takes the view that to create images of living things is to give human beings the prerogative of God. This objection may be a part of their belief in the evil eye, which they rationalize by claiming that the Koran forbids pictures. Regardless of whether this belief is right or wrong, it will do us no good to try to convince a Moslem that the Koran does not prohibit pictures. Most of the Arabs will co-operate on photos, but when one objects you simply "fold up your camera and silently steal away," or smile and wait for a more cooperative subject.

Not only customs and traditions are tied to religion; even the laws of the land come from the Koran. Religion and law therefore are from the same source. They are the same thing. The laws of God and the laws of man are not administered separately, and the judges of the courts are first religious leaders. Their function is to hear disputes relative to personal rights and liberties and to try persons charged with an offense against the laws of Islam.

When the King wanted to establish radio communication in Arabia there was considerable opposition from the religious leaders. Recognizing this opposition, the King arranged a meeting of influential religious men for the first broadcast. The message which came from the loudspeaker was a reading from the Koran, and the devout

Moslems were no longer able to oppose the use of the new device, for anything which spreads the words of the Holy Book cannot be bad.

The Moslem's belief in the will of God is so complete that it is almost impossible to surprise him with the products of civilization. Airplanes fly—but so do birds! Flight is not surprising, therefore; it is simply the will of God.

The Moslem religion has about 322,000,000 believers. This is a great many more than the Hindu, Confucian, Buddhist or Jewish faiths can claim, and it is second only to the number of Christians in the world. The main features of the Moslem religion are a necessary background for understanding Saudi customs and traditions.

Mohammed was the founder of the Arab's religion, but he is not worshipped. It is, therefore, not really correct to call his followers Mohammedans. They are and prefer to be called Moslems, "Believers." Their faith is Islam, meaning "surrender" (to the will of God). The Koran is the religious book revealed to Mohammed, and a great deal of it is similar to the Laws revealed to Moses and to the teachings of Christ.

The Koran gives the Moslem detailed and explicit instructions for everything he does. The food he eats, the work he does, his conduct toward his wife, family, landlord, or tenant are all covered by the Koran. It is his civil code of laws governing marriage, divorce, in · heritance, and contracts, as well as the criminal code covering theft, murder, rape, and everything else. Islam is a positive religion which gives the Believer direct instructions for his conduct from dawn to dusk and from dusk to dawn, as well as from birth to death, including the depth and orientation of his grave.

The five pillars of Islam are Faith, Prayer, Alms, Fasting, and Pilgrimage. Each day a Moslem proclaims his faith: "God is Great, God is all powerful, there is no God but God and Mohammed was His messenger."

The Arab's prayers are not petitions and requests; they are adoration. He says them five times daily: before dawn, about noon, in mid-afternoon when a shadow is as long as the object by which it is cast, after sunset, and after dark. Any suggestion of sun worship you see is avoided. Each prayer has two, three, or four sections and an epilogue. These are passages from the Koran and they are accompanied by "setting up exercises" while the worshipper faces Mecca. He must be ritually clean at the time of prayer. Some pollutions necessitate a complete bath, but generally face, nostrils, hands, and feet are washed. If water is not available, sand or dust may be used. A good Moslem stops whatever he is doing when prayer time comes and goes through the ritual wherever he is. I have seen him praying in the desert or in the lobby of an office building; and wherever he may be, he performs the rite with simple dignity and without self-consciousness, utterly secure in his belief that before God he is the equal of every other Believer, be it king or lowly shepherd.

He needs no intermediary whether priest or saint to plead his cause in heaven, and this certainty enables the penniless Moslem to sit at ease in council with silk- and satin-robed peers. Accordingly, he cannot feel inferior to any foreigner. In fact, he is more likely to have an inner sense of superiority because he is a Believer while the foreigner is not.

Islam also teaches that man's original nature is essentially good. This is contrary to the Christian idea that we are all born sinful and must be baptised to wash away that sin. According to the Koran, God says: "Verily we create man in a perfect state—a state of purity that may be destroyed only by subsequent wrong behavior."

Almsgiving is prescribed in specific detail by the Koran, but the Moslem realizes that his need for the reward of giving is greater than the poor man's need of the gifts.

Fasting takes place during the ninth month, named Ramadan, of the Moslem year. Arabs follow the lunar calendar, so Ramadan begins eleven days earlier each year. During this month the Moslem does not eat, drink, smoke, or have carnal intercourse between dawn and dusk. He can and does enjoy his food and drink (non-alcoholic) during the darkness. When Ramadan comes in summer, it works a real hardship on the desert people, who cannot even drink water during the daylight hours of fasting. Winter or summer, employers make unlimited allowances for their workmen during that month. It is a time when religious fervor runs high and the devout are least tolerant of the backsliders. "During Ramadan the gates of paradise are open and the gates of hell are shut and the devil is in chains," is an Arab saying. Another is "He who fasts has two delights, breaking his fast and meeting his Lord."

Pilgrimage to Mecca is the duty of every Moslem if he be of age, of sound mind, and can afford the expense. On the pilgrimage he wears pilgrim dress—a single, unsewn cloth, draped like a toga, leaving the arms and one shoulder bare. Many Moslems all over the world consider the pilgrimage to Mecca a goal for which they will make the greatest sacrifice. Industrialists throughout the Middle East say that the pilgrimage is the principal cause of labor turnover. Men will work hard to save enough for the pilgrimage, just as in America housewives will work in a canning factory or a laundry for a short while to earn money for a glossy white refrigerator, a new davenport, or a TV set. Some return to their jobs after the pilgrimage with increased social standing in the community.

In addition to the five pillars, there are six points to the Moslem code of honor. These apply perhaps more commonly to the Bedouin than to Arabs in transition to modern industrialization, but they are deep-seated in all Arabs. The Arab will do a great many things for money, but money will not tempt him to sacrifice his honor. He sticks rigidly to his code. This he believes:

1. A man's first duty is to God.
2. He must protect his tent neighbor.
3. The laws of hospitality are sacred.
4. He must protect a traveler under his "safe conduct."
5. He must give attention to the laws of personal protec-
   tection and sanctuary.
6. He owes a duty to himself; to raid when he can and to
   keep what he has captured.

The late King Ibn Saud eradicated the point about raids. He also removed the socio-economic justification for raiding by drilling water wells at government expense, settling nomads in enlarged oases, improving agricultural production, and subsidizing the tribes when rains fail or famine threatens.

Every sheik must obey these rules of conduct and loyalty if he expects to remain in power. The late Ibn Saud was recognized by his people as the exemplification of these desert virtues. It was not often that he failed to abide by the rules; and his strict adherence to the laws of hospitality, his generous treatment of the sheiks he conquered, and his assumption of responsibility for the families of those leaders slain by his men kept his prestige high throughout Arabia. His adherence to the virtues of the desert, as well as his complete understanding of the desert and its austere way of life, made it possible for him to attract and hold the most individualistic warriors on earth, and to weld them into a nation able to move toward modern industrialization.

Raiding has been honorable for generations, not only among the Bedouins of Arabia but among nomads in other parts of the desert world. The difference between honorable raiding and dishonorable theft may be a pretty fine line of distinction, especially for a nomad who encounters a foreigner. However, Ibn Saud realized that one of the basic requirements for modern civilization is the prospect of retainable rewards for effort. This, of course, means stable government in which foreigner and native are protected against "honorable raiding" as well as against theft. To encourage foreigners for the pilgrimage traffic, the Saudi government promised swift, sure punishment for theft or molestation of caravans. Amputation of the hand for theft is still the legal punishment.

Today Saudi Arabia is one of the safest places in the world to travel. The certainty of severe punishment is a great deterrent to lawbreakers, and in Arabia laws are intended to stop the practice for which they are made. American magazines have sometimes complained that Saudi traffic fines are too high. The well-posted and enforced speed limit in the city of Dhahran is twenty kilometers per hour, on heavily traveled highways forty kilometers per hour. The purpose of the fines is to protect the people who live in a walking culture. Fines are not intended as a sort of nuisance license fee for those who can afford repeated payments to continue to endanger the lives of people who must walk. The difference between our attitude toward laws and that of the Arabs is perhaps one reason that life and property are safer in Saudi Arabia than in certain large American cities. The Arab sense of justice is strong, well-developed, and clear-cut. It is not weakened by maudlin pity or pleas of extenuating circumstances for violations against the laws of God.

Duty to himself may be the last of the six points in the Arab's code of honor, but it is as well developed in most individuals as the other five. An austere land like Arabia forces a man to recognize his duty to himself. Countless generations aware of this fact have developed an acute practical instinct for survival in the average man. One manifestation is that business is done on a cash basis or with what the English call "irrevocable letters of credit." The practice is understood by the Arabs and accepted. In dealings with these people one should not be offended if asked to pay cash, and they will not be annoyed when you expect the same treatment.

This brings up the custom of bargaining. Where Western merchandise is sold, fixed prices are fast becoming the rule in Arabia as elsewhere. When one goes out into the desert away from the modern oil cities, or when buying native crafts, the old customs are still in effect.

Americans seldom understand all that is involved when dealing with native merchants. In the first place, these merchants are somewhat like our collectors. They really enjoy handling and looking at their merchandise. Secondly, they like people. They like to talk and visit, especially with people who appreciate the kind of merchandise they handle. To these old-time merchants a sale is as much a social transaction as it is a business deal. You might say that part of their pay for an article is the fun they get in bargaining over it. When we pay a dealer's first asking price, we cheat him of his fun. We display our ignorance of the article's value, or show that we are no match for the dealer's skill in conversation and have no respect for the value of money. Lacking so much which the dealer respects and appreciates, we are worthy only of his contempt. You can gain his utmost respect and even come close to friendship with a dealer if you display real skill in bargaining. To do this you will have to know the true value of the article and be able to recognize its good points. Expensive things may take several visits before the transaction is completed, but you will get a lot of fun in the meantime matching wits and visiting.

The important thing is that one cannot back out of a verbal agreement to buy. If I say, "I'll give you 100 riyals for that rug," and the dealer agrees, I have bought the rug even though I have paid nothing down, see the same rug elsewhere for less money, or just change my mind about it. Saudi law recognizes the verbal agreement, and I cannot get out of it legally.

The older Saudi Arabs cannot understand our American custom of getting signatures and witnesses' signatures on contracts. They believe that among men of good will a man's word is a guarantee of the fulfillment of the agreement. One must be careful when one gives his word to an Arab. Never give it lightly because he expects that it will be kept.

Under the code, protection of a tent neighbor, protection of a traveler under "safe conduct," and laws of sanctuary emphasize a point of view which greatly differs from ours. We think in terms of the individual: "It's my life," we say. The Arab thinks in terms of the family and tribe. If he is injured or insulted, his whole family is damaged, because every member is needed as provider and protector in their rugged way of life. They are entitled to compensation or revenge for any loss. If an Arab is crippled or killed by an auto accident, the driver of the car may be held responsible for the support of *all* the injured man's family for the rest of their lives. This extends to all who have just claim as family, not only to his wife and children. Likewise, if an individual gets into trouble, his whole family is responsible and must placate or recompense the injured family. Under such a system, insults or physical injury to an individual are much more serious than in our American society. It is truly against the law in Arabia to strike a person by hand or by tongue or to treat him with scorn or contempt.

The Arab is proud of his family. His whole society is much more concerned with personal ties and responsibilities to family, tent neighbors, or others claiming his protection than is American society; and the value he places on these personal ties is what makes the shift to modern industrialization such a difficult adjustment. A new job means cutting personal and traditional ties with his idea of home, family, clan, and community. It means a new house, instead of the traditional tent or ancestral home. It means departure from the lifetime association with village elders or group leaders, intimate friends, and religious leaders—in fact all those people whose ways and customs are known, understood, and trusted. These long-established relationships in the community of one's birth give the Arab his main source of psychological security and balance, and the new order upsets this balance and forces tremendous adjustments. The presence of foreigners in his land is just one more element to which adjustment must be made.

Hospitality is an Arab custom of the utmost importance. A man's character, his reputation, his standing in the community, even his own self-respect depend on his adherence to the laws of hospitality. Prince and tribesman alike consider hospitality so important that either will starve himself rather than be inhospitable. Manners are so closely associated with hospitality that I shall consider them together in this chapter.

The seriousness of violating hospitality was emphasized by a European who knew the Arabs of the mandated countries. "Their complexes are mainly social," he said, "and our Western snobbery has made more enemies than our policy." Then he explained that being turned out of a club, insulted by a foreign soldier, or snubbed by a supercilious mandate official are violations of hospitality which cannot be forgiven.

Arab standards of hospitality have been set by long custom and one could not be treated with more courtesy or graciousness in Buckingham Palace than in the home of an Arab, rich or poor, or in the tent of a Bedouin. Even an enemy may count on safety and courtesy while he enjoys the status of a guest.

In the desert, a traveler is certain to receive food and shelter in a Bedouin camp. A Bedouin whose food is low may camp away from traveled routes to avoid company, but he will not refuse food and water to visitors who approach his camp.

Serving coffee—nowadays in cities this is often replaced by a popular soft drink—is the first and most common gesture of hospitality among all Arabs. Coffee is the social drink in the town house or desert tent. Even as a total stranger stopping on the street to ask a question and tarrying for a few minutes chat with an Arab, I have been offered coffee. The cups are small, without handles, and they are only about one-fourth filled. There is no hard and fast rule about how many cups you must accept. Some claim that good manners require one to accept one cup or three cups but never two or more than three. In any case, shaking the cup when the server comes around is the sign that you have had enough.

American etiquette about noisily sipping a drink differs from good form in Arabia. There you sip loudly to indicate enjoyment of the drink.

Guests at an Arabian dinner party will arrive at the host's house after evening prayers. Formal greetings are exchanged and each asks after the health of the other and his male relatives, even to that of his fourth or fifth cousins. One does not mention the wife or other female relatives. Hot, spiced, black coffee is served and drunk noisily.

When dinner is announced, the guests go into the dining room where a clean white tablecloth is spread on the floor. A whole sheep, boiled or roasted, and resting on a tray, is the central dish of the spread. Distributed in great profusion over the white cloth are small dishes of chicken, vegetables, salads, condiments, pastries, and sweets. The sheep is generally stuffed with rice and surrounded with steaming buttered rice.

Guests are seated on cushions, rugs, or mats around the cloth. Knives, forks, or spoons are not generally used, but if Westerners are guests they will be supplied. Guests may tear off chunks of the meat, then dip them into the rice or other dishes. Only the right hand is used in eating. If you are a southpaw, then learn to eat with your right hand before visiting the desert world. Arabs have their rules of sanitation even if they are called manners, and the left hand is reserved for bodily functions not connected with eating. Since one is eating from a common dish he does not lick his fingers. If a spoon is used, one must be careful to operate in his own little excavation in the common dish.

Sometimes the host will not eat with his guests but will make certain that each is well served. Before starting to eat, each diner will say "Bishmillah," which is comparable to our saying grace, except that each individual says it for himself. When a guest has satisfied his appetite, he leans back or arises with a word of thanks to Allah. Audible belching is an indication that the diner has eaten abundantly of delicious food, although among sophisticated Arabs who have had extensive Western contacts this custom is somewhat modified. The Arab's natural good manners and innate courtesy enable him to make some allowances at first for a foreigner's ignorance of his customs.

As each guest finishes eating, he leaves the dining room and goes into the courtyard. A servant brings warm water, soap, and towels for the guests to wash their hands. Guests then go into the living room where coffee is served, then tea, and then coffee again. Following the last cup of coffee, a servant brings perfume for the guests' hands and a brazier over which the hands are waved. Then each guest spreads his head cloth as he leans over the brazier and traps the fragrant smoke. This is the end of the dinner party. They do not sit around and visit for hours as we so often do at home.

A guest asks permission to leave and etiquette demands that the host must smile and protest at first; but eventually he rises, accompanies his guest to the courtyard gate, and bids him "Go in God's company."

There are no chairs or benches on which to sit in a conventional Arab home, but there are plenty of thick rugs and cushions. This necessitates sitting cross-legged or tailor fashion. One must never stretch out his legs so that the soles of his feet are exposed. This is considered extremely bad manners and it is just not done. To do so is a breach which will cause a shadow of annoyance to darken the face of even the most perfect Arab host.

Ordinary social blunders, caused by ignorance of his customs, do not arouse resentment on the part of an Arab. They are naturally good humored, kind, informal, and courteous. Accordingly, outright discourtesy, ridicule of their customs or religion, and comment which implies inferiority labels the speaker as undesirable.

The Arabs have a number of simple salutations and replies which are standard for each time of day and for the region of the person being greeted. There are local variations in customary greetings, too, so those common at Dhahran, say, are not as common in some other community.

Good-humored small talk and the exchange of health inquiries are usually longer extended than in America, but even business conversations are preceded by such pleasantries. It is not good manners to "go straight to the point" or "get down to business" too quickly. Social exchange in Arabia is just as important as commercial exchange and should not be neglected.

"Speed comes from the devil," say the Arabs, and impatience, haste, or preoccupation with other affairs are all evidence of a lack of self-confidence or of just plain bad manners. A host must never terminate a conversation with his guest. Even the King does not signal the end of an audience. It is up to the guest to make the first move toward departure.

In conversations, family affairs, except the health and well-being of male members, are private and not suitable subjects, at least until long, long friendships have been established. Religion and politics will be accepted in conversation long before family. The family women are never mentioned with casual acquaintances.

Some questions which we consider impertinent, such as asking you what you have paid for your clothes, your watch, or other personal effects, the Arab asks as a form of compliment to your taste and financial standing. Also one must be cautious in his admiration of a host's possessions when visiting in his home, for he may offer the admired object on the spot as a present. This is a common custom in Arabia, and it can be embarrassing to us Americans.

Arabs do not drink alcohol; exceptions are few, and it is bad form to offer them an alcoholic drink. It is even worse form to offer them ham, pork, bacon, or any food containing pig meat. Pork and beans, sausage, or even food cooked with lard is ritually unclean to a Moslem. During Ramadan, when the Arabs do not eat in the daytime, a courteous foreigner will neither eat, drink, nor smoke in the presence of one who is fasting. Respect is also shown when a Moslem is praying. No one will stare at him, nor will they walk across his prayer rug or mat.

Arabs shake hands somewhat as we do but never with a vigorous grip. Among themselves men often embrace close friends and relatives, but this type of greeting does not extend to foreigners. It is also not uncommon to see young men strolling hand in hand—a gesture of sincere friendship with no other implications. The boisterous backslapping sometimes indulged in by Americans is considered bad manners and unduly familiar. Playful wrestling is likewise avoided. One does not ask an Arab to take off his headdress, for this is worn indoors or out, and to have it knocked off even by accident is not funny to an Arab. It is much more embarrassing than for us to lose our hat in a high wind.

Customs concerning women in Arabia are deep-rooted and firmly respected by both Arab men and Arab women. Violations of the code are very, very few. One reason is that the penalties are sure, swift, and severe. City women are veiled when they are about twelve years old, and from that time on their faces are not seen by men outside their own families. They have separate quarters in the house and in the tent, but in the desert they go about with face exposed. There are no mixed social gatherings, and it is considered vulgar and disrespectful to even mention the women. They prepare the meals and can hear the conversation of the diners through the tent walls, but they do not eat until the guests have had their fill. All the food is put before the guests. Women and children eat at "second table" from the same dishes. Servants and hangers-on follow them. The great heaps of food left by the guests are never wasted.

Marriage is governed by Shariah (religious) Law, its details laid down by the Koran. Polygamy is permitted with a legal maximum of four wives at one time. Most of the population cannot afford the luxury of plural wives, for there are far more responsibilities connected with polygamy in Arabia than newspaper columnists and travel writers realize. Each wife must be treated in a manner equal to the others. This can mean maintaining separate apartments, and supplying equal jewelry and clothes. It also means that each wife has her claim on an equal share of the husband's evenings. Theoretically, divorce is easy—three times renouncing the wife before witnesses constitutes the ceremony for separation—but there are still responsibilities and the lady has recourse to the courts to force the man to show just cause. In actual practice, divorce in Arabia is no more common than it is in America. No statistics, of course, are available, but those who know the Arabs well believe divorce is probably easier and more frequent among certain American groups than it is in Arabia.

The strict code for man-woman relationships makes infidelity and prostitution extremely rare. The punishment is so severe that the rewards are not worth the risk. Writers who have lived among the Arabs for a generation generally collect one or two stories, but often even those are rare examples of "what happens if . . ." and are gleaned from an earlier time.

In general, Arab customs are more leisurely and social, less time-conscious, and more closely tied to religion than American customs. There is more emphasis on courtesy, kindliness, and good humor, even in casual contacts, than in America, and also more sensitivity to discourtesy, brusqueness, and impatience.

XVII

. . . .

. . . .

. . . .

. . . .

. . . . .

Starvelings of the Desert World

IT SEEMS LIKE A PARADOX THAT CIVILIZATIONS BASED ON THE cultivation of plants have prospered in the deserts of Africa, Asia, and America—and yet there are only a few corners of the desert world where man can survive on wild foods alone. Irrigation, of course, can guarantee the water for agriculture, but wild plants are dependent on the vagaries of weather. Most people who inhabit the arid waste lands would die of starvation in the season of "abundance" if compelled to live on native plants and animals alone, and they would perish from thirst in times of drought. Nevertheless, in each desert there are a few families—and in some areas, like the Kalahari and the Australian Deserts, even whole tribes—who keep alive with little more than the natural resources of the desert landscape.

Desert people generally depend on their flocks and herds, but occasionally they vary their diet with wild foods, such as onions and dune plums in the Gobi, or mushrooms in some parts of Arabia. Such foods are usually important only as vitamin supplements or variety.

In Arabia members of the Sulaba tribe depend a great deal on wild food and utilize every edible morsel they can find. Apparently they have no food prejudices and can, accordingly, exist where camel breeders and sheep herders would starve. As they are so dependent on natural resources, their knowledge of the desert is very extensive, and they are often hired by the wealthier tribes as hunters or guides. However, they are considered inferior to all the other nomads. They cannot marry into the wealthier tribes, and they do not accompany them on raids. Neither do they take part in defending the camp of those for whom they may be working. On the other hand, they are protected from plunder in raids and any of their possessions which are misappropriated in the excitement of battle will be returned.

The Sulaba are the blacksmiths and coppersmiths of Arabia. They keep the Arab horses shod and maintain the metal equipment of their superiors. They are also breeders of donkeys.

Even though they know how to find the few edible plants of the Arabian wastelands and are expert at tracking a gazelle or finding lizards and grubs to satisfy their hunger, they depend primarily on food from domestic sources. Such food, and any manufactured products such as clothing and pots or pieces of metal which they need, are obtained in exchange for their services or in trade for their surplus donkeys.

Like other nomads they depend on wells for their water supply, but their intimate knowledge of desert geography makes them better than average at locating natural water holes and drainage cisterns hidden in rocky desert areas. Such water supplies exist only for a limited time after rains, but the Sulaba are good weathermen, too, and keep close track of rains or signs of rain which guide them to the favored spots.

On the fringes of the Hoggar in the Sahara and in outliers of the Tibesti Mountains in the Libyan Desert, explorers have occasionally met small wandering groups who were long distances from their fellow men. Apparently, these are examples of marginal families who, for reasons unknown to the explorers, have wandered far from their usual tribal routes. For a few days or weeks they haunt the desert near natural cisterns, but they return to their less venturesome tribesmen when their secret water holes are exhausted.

In the deserts of Australia, native peoples absolutely dependent on wild foods are still able to survive. Lizards, grubs, and wild roots make up a large part of their diet. They are excellent trackers and skillful spear-throwers, so they feast on larger game whenever they can catch up with it. These are the desert people who made life miserable for the telegraph linemen when the wires were first strung across Australia. They climbed the poles to get the glass insulators, and consequently broke the line almost as fast as the repair men could put in new insulators. In the days before the telegraph, the Australians made their spear points of stone, but the glass is a much better material. It can be worked by the same techniques as the stone they had used, and it works more easily. Telegraph-line insulators became standard raw material for Australian spear points, until in desperation the white man replaced them with porcelain.

The Australian natives' knowledge of natural water points, however, lets them survive where others would die in a few days. Some of the water holes are hidden under acacia trees and covered with sand when not in use. To the average desert traveler, one acacia looks very much like any other and not many of them hide water. Perhaps the good sites have characteristics recognizable by the Australian native, but more likely those which mark the water are known by all the tribesmen and this knowledge is passed on by word of mouth. There are also springs trickling from rock crevasses, and soaks where a man can scrape away the sand and in a little while find water in the cavity. White men can, of course, memorize the locations once they have learned them from the desert people, but not many have the patience to observe the minute details which the natives recognize as characteristic of a specific rock, tree, or hollow in the desert plain.

In the Kalahari, the Bushmen are also almost wholly dependent on the natural resources of the desert. These hunter-gatherer tribes have been pushed into the desert regions from other parts of Africa where game and wild foods are more plentiful. They survive, but one can hardly say they prosper in the desert, for it takes most of the day to gather enough food for that day's needs.

Each family group has a fixed territory with definite boundaries which limit its wanderings, although naturally it takes a very large area to supply enough wild food for a group during the nine months of the dry season. In the wet months, game is plentiful and surface water can be found in every depression on the plains. Sometimes, however, rain showers follow a fixed path and clouds drop their moisture on the same pans or flat areas day after day, while missing others altogether. This phenomenon doesn't last for all of the rainy season, but it has been observed for periods of several days.

Camping groups are not large because they are dependent on the wild food which can be gathered daily. They also must move frequently. The usual group consists of the parents, their children, and the husbands of the married daughters. Visiting relatives may join them for a few weeks and some members of the family may go visiting. The size of the group is constantly changing, but it is always dependent on the amount of food and water available in the area. There are no recognized chiefs, but each group has its natural leaders in whom the others have confidence. Usually everyone in a group is related to all the others either by blood or marriage. Everyone else is considered a stranger even if he speaks the same dialect and occupies contingent territory. If a hunter follows wounded game into another's territory, or if he needs and takes food or water belonging to another group, he makes a serious attempt to find the owner and tell him about it. These desert dwellers make every effort to avoid any source of conflict, either among themselves or with their neighbors.

The Bushmen move often and have no other transportation than their own two legs, so they have few possessions. The men wear a loincloth, which is drawn between the legs, and carry a skin which can be used as a cape. Women wear a leather apron and the whole skin of an animal, which is tied at the waist and on the shoulder to make a burden carrier. Ostrich egg-shell beads are worn as ornaments. These beads, animal skins, and some wild honey are the few articles Bushmen have to trade with neighboring tribes.

Every woman has her digging stick which may be weighted with a stone "doughnut." Fragments of such digging weights are common on the prehistoric campsites along the ancient river beds in the Sahara and in many other parts of the world. The men carry bows and arrows. The latter are pointed either with bone or with pieces of metal. Their effectiveness depends more on the nerve poison with which the point is covered than on the seriousness of the wound the arrow can inflict. Men and women both need a knife to keep the digging stick sharpened and to shape the bone arrowheads.

Bushmen hunters, like all their counterparts in the desert world, are excellent trackers. Once they have hit an antelope with an arrow, they will follow it all day until the poison takes effect and brings down the animal. If the quarry is too big to carry, the hunter protects it from vultures and other scavengers, and then goes back to camp and brings the family to the feast. There will be no "leftovers." The bones are cracked for the marrow, and even the gristle inside the ears is eaten.

The women search the desert plains for roots and tubers. Some of these are swollen with moisture during the dormant season, but with the first hint of spring, new shoots start up and the root begins to shrivel and lose its moisture. Even that moisture which is left in the root becomes bitter, so the labor of digging it is wasted.

Not all tubers of the Kalahari are fit to eat even when they are firm and filled with moisture. Back in 1885 an American named Farini crossed the Kalahari and for some reason became separated from his party. During that time he ate a poisonous tuber which paralyzed him totally except for his hearing. His companions finally found him and began discussing whether or not the man was dead. He could hear the conversation but was powerless to respond in any way. Fortunately, he recovered in time!

The baobab tree is a feature of the Kalahari landscape which has considerable value to the Bushmen. The tree towers from sixty to two hundred feet in height and may be as much as thirty feet in diameter. From roots to topmost branch the tree furnishes shelter for snakes and animals, birds and insects—all of which the desert people can eat. The great trunk is so big that it can be climbed only by driving pegs into the smooth pink bark to make ladder-like paths up into the branches. Bees nest in the hollow branches high above the rocky ground, and in their efforts to steal the honey some of the Bushmen fall to their deaths; but the food wealth of the baobab lures others to the golden sweet. Hollow trunks of old trees serve as rain reservoirs, from which thirsty Bushmen can get drinking water in the dry season. When the long, sausage-like fruit ripens just before the drought begins, its pulp makes a cool and appetizing drink. Even the seeds, alum-like, powdery stones are eaten.

More important to the Bushmen in the Kalahari are the melon and cucumber plant families. The melons range from tiny ones no bigger than a walnut to round ones the size of a honeydew. Some of these have furry skins and others are covered with prickles, but the Bushmen know the edible ones and pass by those which are poison. The large melons are called *tsamma,* and sometimes they grow in great numbers—so thick, in fact, that one cannot walk through a patch without stepping on them. Both men and animals eat them, and in the dry season they are often the only source of water for many square miles. They taste like our vegetable marrows and give some nourishment, but their chief value is their moisture. When the *tsamma* is mature, it has a hard rind which protects it from losing moisture during the drought, even though it is exposed to the direct heat of desert sun. The tough rind can also serve the desert wanderer as a container or dish. The brown seeds of the melon are eaten by some groups, and sometimes they are ground into flour.

The Bushmen say that there are two kinds of *tsamma* but that they cannot be distinguished except by tasting. In fact, they claim that if the melon grows in ground fertilized by the dung of one animal it will be edible, while a melon growing in the dung of a different species will be bitter. Be that as it may, the photographs I have seen of the edible Kalahari melons look very much like the poisonous ones from the Sahara, so possibly the kind of soil *does* determine the edibility of the fruit.

Another moisture-bearing fruit of the Kalahari is a cucumber-like plant. This fruit has a bumpy exterior like our cucumbers and it tastes much like them, but the desert species is shorter.

The Bushmen surpass all other desert peoples in the world in their water conservation and in their ability to extract that life-giver from the arid lands. They not only know where to find the roots and tubers filled with moisture and how to recognize fruits with potable moisture, but they bottle water in the rainy periods and store it against the drought. Their storage bottles are blown ostrich eggs. Instead of just breaking the eggs to make an omelette as we do, they make a single hole in the shell and extract the contents. The shell then makes an excellent water bottle. It may be filled and carried in a net bag made of fiber string on their long marches into dry country; or, after the egg is filled, the single hole can be plugged and the water buried a foot or more below the desert surface. There may be many water-filled eggs in such a buried nest, so that the Bushmen will be assured of water when they travel in that section of their territory long after the rains have ceased.

Even more ingenious are their "sucking-wells" first reported by Dr. Livingston. Nowadays these are called "sip-wells" and we have described them in Chapter XI.

According to Elizabeth Marshall Thomas, the Kalahari Bushmen also practice an unusually efficient desert survival technique. They go about the daily gathering of food in the cool of early morning and early evening but rest during the intense heat of the desert midday. This practice is followed by all desert dwellers, but Mrs. Thomas says the Bushmen go further than this in conserving body moisture.

One of their choicest foods in the dry season is *bi,* a root rich in moisture. The *bi* is scraped, the scrapings squeezed dry, and the juice is drunk. When daytime temperatures climb up around 120°F., the Bushmen dig shallow trenches in the shade. They urinate on the dry scrapings of *bi* and line the hollow with the wet pulp. This is their bed during the daytime heat. Here they lie quietly, conserving their sweat by complete inactivity, and letting evaporating urine keep their temperature near normal.

Modern physiologists have recommended that desert survivors in emergencies conserve their sweat by soaking their clothing in urine and letting its evaporation cool the body; but, so far as I know, Mrs. Thomas is the only observer who has reported this intelligent use of urine among native desert dwellers.

Bushmen are living proof that man can adapt himself to the

desert world if he will live the way the desert dictates. They take advantage of each favorable hour in the desert day, and they retreat in those moments when the desert demands more than frail men can give. Perhaps the Bushmen would continue to wander in their corner of the desert world for many centuries if food and water were their only worries. But unfortunately they have Bantu neighbors who need herdsmen for their cattle. White ranchers, too, push closer to the arid wastes. The Bushmen prefer to run and hide rather than meet the stronger strangers. They know no way to resist the pressures along the desert edges and can only retreat further and further into the arid wastes. Each year some of them are tempted away to the outside world, and those who cling to the freedom of the open spaces in spite of its physical hardships become fewer and fewer. But who knows? Perhaps their ability to run and hide and their extensive knowledge of their rugged world will always keep a few of them free from encroaching civilization.

XVIII

. . . .

. . . .

. . . .

. . . .

. . . . .

Desert People of America

THE DESERTS OF THE NEW WORLD ARE AS DRY AND HOT AS ANY of the arid corners in Asia, Africa, or Australia. There are sections in Death Valley and the Sonora Desert as bare of vegetation as the Rub' al Khali in Arabia or the Tanezrouft of Sahara; but the most arid American deserts, like their Old World counterparts, are not inhabited and rarely, if ever, visited by native peoples. There are, of course, springs of potable water on the edges of Death Valley, and there are natural tanks in rocky canyons of the Sonora which sometimes fill with rain water. These water holes enabled the more venturesome Indian hunters to make excursions far beyond their usual range and even occasionally to cross the sterile lands; but, on the whole, native Americans avoided these badlands as well as some of the less arid regions and confined their habitats to areas with more vegetation.

Although the American southwest is a region of scanty rainfall, there are numerous canyons where water seeps from rocky walls, and where plants and animals find sustenance, even though the surrounding mesas support only sparse, non-edible, desert plants. In these canyons American Indians find food and a way of life less rugged than that of food-gatherers in some other corners of the desert world. They can also range from the low, hot desert to cooler, higher altitudes, where they find a wider choice of food plants and animals than are available to Old World desert peoples. Furthermore, there are permanent streams—the Colorado, the Rio Grande, the San Juan—and their tributaries which traverse the American arid zones and make drinking water available at all times. Desert vegetation is also more varied in the American desert than in Asia or Africa. One botanist states that there are several score more species of plants on a few acres of an American desert canyon than he found in hundreds of acres in a section of Sahara with comparable rainfall.

Until the coming of the white man, population pressure on the edges of American deserts was probably far less intense than, for instance, it has long been around the Kalahari. Even the poorest Indian food-gatherers were not forced as far from rivers or permanent water holes as the Bushmen were. Neither were they pushed into regions of such scanty food supply. In fact, by the time white men reached our desert regions, agriculture was well advanced and food-gatherers had begun to do some planting and harvesting themselves, or at least had access to the products of agriculture through trade with their neighbors. The desert world in America has apparently always offered greater natural resources, a more abundant life, to nomad peoples than the Old World deserts ever did.

In desert country large game is always scarce; but within the range of nomadic food-gatherers small game was often abundant enough for organized drives. Several families—perhaps as many as fifty men, women, and children—might participate in one drive for rabbits. Long nets, woven from fiber string, were stretched along the sides and across the end of a valley, or in a semicircle in more open areas. Armed with sticks and clubs, the crowd of beaters spread out beyond the nets and advanced noisily toward the trap. The frightened rabbits scurried from their hiding places and raced away from the shouting crowd toward the nets. As the crowd closed in on them, the frantic rabbits became entangled in the nets where they could be shot with arrows or easily beaten to death with clubs. Such a hunt not only served to collect large quantities of food and furnished pelts for warm rabbit-skin blankets, but it also offered the people a social gathering with plenty of fun and activity.

In some areas ground squirrels were fairly numerous, and the women had a clever way of catching them. Using the digging stick, they scratched little channels to direct tiny streams of water from a near-by creek to the ground squirrel burrows. The little animals were quickly flooded out so that the women could strike and kill them with their sticks. Sometimes one woman would divide a stream to flood two holes at once, but even this mass-production method never quite exterminated the supply of ground squirrels.

Other small animals were trapped with little deadfalls. A frame of sticks was weighted with a heavy rock and either baited or just placed in a runway. When a desert rat sprang the trap, the weighted frame dropped and killed the animal or held it until the hunter could collect his prey.

Grasshoppers were often abundant in American deserts, as they are in other sections of the desert world. Wherever they are found, they have been prized as food. Whole families would participate in harvesting these insects. In the southwest a favorite site was a hill-side, because the grasshoppers prefer to hop downhill when disturbed. To catch them, the Indians dug trenches a foot or so deep on the hillside at right angles to the slope, with "wings," or branch trenches, sloping uphill so that the grasshoppers could not get around the ends of the trap. The trenches were covered loosely with grass, and one would think that the insects could have crawled over the trenches on the grass bridge, but they didn't.

When the trenches were ready, the family, armed with bunches of grass, formed a line uphill from the grass-covered traps and slowly walked down, beating the ground with their grass flails as they came. They were careful not to travel too fast but give the insects time to jump ahead of them. Soon the hillside was a seething mass, flowing toward the grass-covered ditches. When the grasshoppers reached the traps, they did not crawl across the grass cover but crawled down through it into the trench. Then, because of the grass cover, they were not able to jump or crawl out. When the beaters reached the end of their drive, they set fire to the grass over the trenches. The heat killed the insects, burned off their wings, and partially cooked them. It was not uncommon for the trenches to be half-full of dead grasshoppers when the fire was out, for hardly any of the insects had escaped. The Indians scooped them up by hand and packed them into their burden baskets for transportation back to camp. Grasshoppers can be eaten either raw or cooked. After a big harvest they were pounded into paste and stored. When needed, they were mixed with flour of ground seeds and made into bread.

Apparently, civilized man has not been able to invent any better way of catching these little insects. Once, in North Africa, I saw shiny metal troughs on the slopes of a hillside. Like the primitive food-gatherers' grass-covered trenches, these metal troughs were intended to catch locusts on the hillside. However, instead of killing them by firing a grass cover, the Locust Control sprayed oil and set them afire.

In the higher altitudes of the desert regions, deer and other large game were hunted both by individual hunters and by small groups. Men sometimes organized to drive the game toward hunters in ambush, but large game has always been less abundant in the desert lands than in more temperate regions.

All grass seeds are edible and they are relatively easy to collect. The southwestern Indians bent the ripe heads over a container and beat the seeds into it with a stick, much as the Wisconsin Indians still do in gathering wild rice. Desert Indians, like the Bushmen and natives of Australia, also collected a variety of roots and tubers. They used a digging stick to get them out of the ground just as other food-gatherers still do. In the Great Basin area, the Piute collected quantities of tiger lily and spike rush bulbs.

Close to true desert country, the fruit of all kinds of cacti is eaten, as well as the stems and the fruit of yucca plants and the pods of mesquite. Cactus fruit can be pressed into large balls which keep indefinitely. The black seeds, especially those of the giant cacti, were separated by soaking in water, then dried and ground into flour. Variety in foods is much more characteristic of the American desert than it is of other parts of the desert world, and when there was a poor crop of one species the American Indians could turn their attention to another.

Another excellent desert food plant is the agave or century plant. When this plant is about seven years old and signs of the flower stalk appear, the whole plant is cut near the base and trimmed of its leaves. These stumps are placed in a heated pit, covered with earth, and a fire is built over the top and kept going for a day or so. The cooked agave is then sun-dried and pressed into bales to be eaten as needed.

In times of excessive drought, the desert Indians suffered less from starvation than those Indians who lived in more temperate climates and who depended almost entirely on only one or two species for their food supply. Even the great herds of buffalo sometimes migrated suddenly and left the plains Indians short of food, but in the desert there would always be cactus fruit because these plants can store water and will produce some fruit even in years of meager moisture.

American desert dwellers had still another advantage over Old World food-gatherers, for the abundance of some wild foods at harvest time enabled them to store large quantities for use in the dormant season and even for years of less abundant wild crops. They were also able to rob seeds from the hidden food stores of desert rodents.

The most important wild food for storage by desert dwellers was, and still is, the piñon nut. There are several species of low-growing pines which produce these edible nuts. Although they grow at higher altitudes than the cactus plants, they are nevertheless within travel distance of the desert food-gatherers. When the pine cones are ripe, men bend down the branches or break them off with long poles hooked at the end. The women then collect the cones, which are covered with pitch, into large piles, cover them with brush, and burn them until the pitch is removed. Then each cone is squeezed by the ends so that the seeds, or nuts, drop onto a blanket. The piñon nuts have a hard shell, so they keep well and may be stored for many months or even a year or two.

Someone has said that a survivor in the desert would starve to death trying to make a meal of piñon nuts. That is not too great an exaggeration, if one tries to open each cone without burning off the pitch and cracks each nut individually. The desert dwellers, however, developed more efficient methods—one might say assembly-line procedures. Instead of cracking each little nut, they placed a handful or more on a stone *metate* and rubbed them with a hand stone. The edible nuts were then easily separated from the crushed shells and could be eaten a handful at a time. Southwestern trading posts now package piñon nuts in cellophane bags and sell them to tourists like salted peanuts.

In northern sections of the Great Basin desert region, the Piute had learned to increase the harvest of wild foods by irrigation before European explorers reached their land. Apparently they only channeled water from streams out to individual wild plants in the same manner that Indian women channeled it to ground squirrel holes. This system assured each desirable wild plant plenty of water during its growing season without being wholly dependent on the scanty rainfall. Sometimes the Indian even built temporary dams of mud and brush like the beaver, and so made water available for their little channels. The dams were destroyed when the wild plants no longer needed the extra moisture, and this allowed the streams to continue watering the erosion fans at the foot of the hills and so encourage the growth of wild vegetation on the edges of the barren wastes. The Piute did not, however, sow seeds in these flood plains, nor did they transplant the desirable species to concentrate a crop and increase their harvest.

The desert peoples of America were seldom far from sources of drinking water, but occasionally when traveling they were obliged to use emergency supplies. In dune country, one early explorer, Major Howard Egan, has told how his Piute guide found water by scraping away the sand in a dune hollow to a depth of six or eight inches. When he found damp sand, he deepened the hole to a foot and widened it to a foot or more in diameter. This shallow "well" soon filled with water, from which all the party, including the mounts, were able to satisfy their thirst. The guide then filled in the hole, because, "Otherwise there would never be water again at that point," he said.

Major Egan considered this statement a mark of superstition, but whether the Indian realized it or not there was some logic on his side. If the temporary well were left open, water flowing to it would evaporate in the dry air and soon exhaust the dampness of the dunes in that vicinity. Even six or eight inches of loose dry sand above the damp layers of a dune contain enough dead air spaces to insulate the water-saturated layers below.

The big barrel cactus, *Bis naga,* was another source of drinking water when the Indians were caught far from their usual supplies. As we will explain in the chapter on "Desert Survival," one can cut away the top of this big cactus and either get a drink by mashing the pulp of the plant stem or by sucking the moisture from large chunks of the pulp. Apparently the American desert people were seldom forced to such extremes in obtaining drinking water as those which the Bushmen and the Australians knew.

Summer shelters in American deserts were not elaborate affairs. Sometimes they were little more than brush canopies to provide shade, but where winds were chilly, even in summer, brush and dirt or even stone walls were put up as windbreaks. Those parts of American deserts which have been inhabited by the Indians are generally colder in winter than either the Kalahari or the Australian deserts, and accordingly the Indians needed shelters somewhat warmer than those of food-gatherers in other parts of the desert world. Their shelters had a frame of poles. The large gaps were filled with brush, and the whole structure was covered with dirt. Smoke from heating or cooking fires escaped through a door or window between the top of the door and the peak of the house. These earth-covered houses could keep out most rains, but in a long-continued downpour they would sometimes leak. However, they were warm protection against the desert winter.

Clothing among the American desert peoples before the white man dominated the area was sometimes very scanty, but often it was much more elaborate than that of other desert food-gatherers.

Nowadays the Indians have easy access to ready-made cloth garments, but originally they made shirts, leggings, skirts, and moccasins of skins. Some of these garments were semi-tailored and elaborately decorated with fringe. One of the most interesting cold-weather garments worn by desert dwellers who otherwise went almost naked was the rabbit-skin blanket. It is now almost impossible to find one of these outside of a museum, and even there they are rare. This blanket was made from narrow strips of dried rabbit skin, and the animals had been skinned so that the hide was turned wrong side out but kept intact. After a skin was scraped of all flesh, it was cut in a spiral so that a narrow strip eight or ten feet long was produced from a single hide. These strips were tied together and fastened over a frame to make a continuous strand warp for a blanket. The warp strands were not crossed by woof strands, but were knotted together at intervals with sinews or with fiber cords. The resulting blanket was warm and quite waterproof. If rabbit skins were not available, serviceable blankets were made from sage-bark cord. Sometimes, of course, the desert people went naked. At other times groups, such as the Piute women, wove and wore little aprons of milkweed fiber.

An outstanding feature of American desert peoples is the variety of baskets made by them. Large lightweight burden baskets, heavier storage baskets, basket hats, sturdy trays, and even water bottles— all were made of split willow or sumac. Those which were intended to hold water were coated inside with pitch. The gum was softened in hot water and then placed in the basket to give a thin, smooth coating. Once it was well-coated inside, the basket became impermeable and was easily cleaned.

Dyes for decorating the baskets were made from the roots of mountain mahogany, which gave a red, and barberry, which made a yellow stain. Geometric designs—triangles, rectangles, bands, and circles—were used extensively, but they represented natural objects to the Indians. Each design was given a name which indicated that it represented a trail, a house, or some other object.

These baskets are still made in the desert area and they are produced by a coiled process. That is, three or five long rods of split wood are wrapped with thinner fiber and the flexible strip coiled on itself, but each coil is also bound to those on each side of it. The coils continue around and around until the basket is built up to the desired size. This interesting technique is responsible for the most embarrassing moment of my travels in the American desert. At Flagstaff, Arizona, the museum curator showed me around his collections which included a great many coiled baskets.

"It's interesting," I said, "that this technique is found all over the world." The startled look that flashed across the curator's face puzzled me.

"Well, as a matter of fact," he said, "it is extremely rare. This type of basketwork is found only here in the southwest American desert region and somewhere in North Africa."

I had seen so many coiled baskets in Algeria that when I found the same thing in Arizona I had taken it for granted that the technique was universal, instead of limited to two widely separated areas which I happened to know.

In America the baskets were developed by non-agricultural people, but in the Sahara I found them being made by oasis dwellers, all of whom depended on agriculture for their subsistence. So far as I know, there is no evidence that the coiled basket was developed by food-gathering peoples of Africa. Now, at any rate, they are made in the oases from the split stems of date palm leaves and wrapped with strips of leaf blade. Such material was not available to African food-gatherers, although other materials could have been used if they had discovered the process.

Did the American Indians develop baskets, some pieces of tailored clothing, semi-permanent house shelters, and woven rabbit-skin blankets because their food supply was sufficient to give a surplus and hence a little leisure in contrast to the grind of a day-to-day food hunt forced on the Bushmen and the Australians? Or were the Americans just blessed with individual geniuses who invented these things?

Before the Spainards reached our southwestern deserts, the Indians knew nothing about pastoralism or herding. They had domesticated turkeys which furnished a reliable supply of feathers for ceremonies and clothing, but apparently they did not raise them for turkey dinners and turkey-egg omelettes. As pets, the turkeys were properly housed, fed, and cared for, but they were ignored as a source of food.

When the Spaniards brought sheep and horses to the arid regions, some of the nomads, such as the Navajo, recognized their economic value and adapted both animals to their own culture. Sheep became a source of meat and their wool replaced cotton and wild fibers for weaving, but, unlike the desert peoples of Asia and Africa, the Navajo did not use sheep's milk.

The horse quickly became important as an aid in herding sheep, in moving camp, for excursions into distant territory, and for pure sport, but mare's milk was ignored as food and drink. A good herd of horses gave a man economic prestige. He could also be proud of a fast horse and with it gain fame, prestige, and even wealth by winning bets on his races. However, horses among the Navajo never gained a position of such symbolic importance as they held with the Gobi Mongols, nor did they have the luxury status which they hold with the Bedouin of Arabia. No mare became so important among the Navajo that ownership would be shared by half a dozen different men, as it is with the Bedouins—each owner expecting to realize his share by claiming a colt at some future time, perhaps six or even eight years distant.

The Navajo made beautiful saddle blankets for their best riding horses, but their pride centered upon the beauty of the weaving and the skill of the weaver. Among the desert peoples of Arabia and North Africa the elaborate gold-and-silver thread embroidered harnesses were intended to enhance the beauty of the horse rather than to be admired in themselves.

Some of the American desert dwellers engaged in local wars and raids for loot, prestige, and protection of their own territory or possessions. But desert warfare in America never equaled the elaborate techniques developed in Old World deserts. Possibly this is because the American desert had not become as heavily popu-lated as Arabia or the western Sahara. Its borders were not dotted with large cities, and agricultural villages were not always pushing their flocks into the territory of the nomad to reduce his scanty pasture. Neither were there any large commercial caravans to be raided or "protected." Whatever the reasons may be, American desert peoples had a less warlike existence than those of the Sahara or Arabia.

Nevertheless, the desert Indians were not immune to the ravages of war. In the southwest by the time exploring Spaniards reached the desert, large tribes of Indians had advanced beyond a food-gathering and pastoral economy to complete dependence on agriculture. Some of the surplus from their harvests was traded to the nomads for game and wild foods, and later for sheep and wool to add variety to their products of cultivation.

The cultivators were well aware of the risks in desert agriculture, and they stored great quantities of corn, beans, squash, and other products for winter use. They sometimes went much further and often kept a full year's supply of food in their storage bins as insurance against a year of crop failures. Such thrift and industry naturally tempted nomad peoples from beyond the desert, as well as the pastoralists near at hand, in times when their livelihood was threatened by drought.

Instead of attempting to meet the threat of war and plundering by developing a strong warrior class for retaliation, some cultivators located their dwellings on easily defended ledges under overhanging cliffs in almost inaccessible canyons. Others chose promontories reached by steep, tortuous paths. In these protected locations they built extensive "apartment houses" with scores of rooms. These are the famous cliff houses. They were built of timber and stone, with roofs of packed clay. Some were built with walls of adobe. There were rooms for living quarters, others for food storage, and still others were reserved for religious ceremonies. Access to the upper stories was gained by ladders leading from balconies or from the roofs of lower rooms to the roof above, and entrance was down into the rooms through holes in the ceiling.

Sometimes the fields tilled by the people of these well-protected villages were several miles distant. Such fields were often watered by irrigation ditches supplied by low dams in the rivers. Other groups had their fields on the valley floors along the sides of the canyons, where springs and seepages gave enough water to facilitate plant growth. Still others were on the flood plains at the mouth of a gulch or a canyon, and these received periodic soakings after a storm. Dams and irrigation ditches were often used to spread the water beyond the limits of natural flooding, but not always. There is one large irrigation system on the Salt River which in prehistoric times watered about 200,000 acres. In this case the main canal was nine miles long, seven feet deep, and four feet wide at the bottom. The bottom and side walls were of hard-packed, possibly baked clay. This canal carried water from the river to Los Muertos, a city of thirty-six communal dwellings. Side canals carried water off to the fields, and although the system had been abandoned before the arrival of the white man, the posts for the gates were still visible some seventy years ago and some of the canals have been cleaned out and used in modern times.

Both flood-plain agriculture and canal irrigation were practiced in other deserts, but the crops raised in the American desert were different. All had been domesticated from native wild species found elsewhere on this continent; but, although corn was the staple, it was handled quite differently in the desert regions from other parts of America. Instead of planting three or four kernels in a shallow hole, the desert people planted ten or twelve seeds at a depth of ten or twelve inches. They also planted their hills several feet apart. Deep planting gave the roots less chance of drying out in the hot summer, and large clumps of plants offered protection against strong winds. Often those stalks on the outside of the clump were cut away by wind-blasted sand before the summer was over, or at least their leaves were cut to ribbons; but some of the center plants generally survived. Beans, squash, or pumpkins might be planted in the same fields with corn, or they might be planted in different plots. Some of the desert cultivators still protect their low-growing plants against strong winds by building fences of brush. Such fences check the force of the winds and cause them to drop wind-borne sand before it has a chance to cover the low plants or cut them to ribbons.

The desert dwellers adapted their methods of agriculture to the rugged conditions of their environment, but they did not lose sight of their dependence on sun and wind and rain. These, they recognized, were controlled by forces outside themselves, and they believed that these forces could be influenced in their favor by ritual prayers and ceremony. Like the desert dwellers of Arabia, those in America are *believers*. True, they believe in many gods instead of one, but their belief is strong and they keep faith with that belief. Even after more than 400 years of contact with the white man and his religion, the desert peoples of America still believe in their own gods, still practice their native religion, still perform the sacred ceremonies and rituals of their ancestors.

They have separate rooms or special structures in their villages which are reserved for secret rituals and religious ceremonies, and there are specialized costumes and body decorations reserved for specific ceremonies. Religious dances are pageants or dramas in which the priests act out the stories of their myths and legends, and so carry messages to those gods who influence the lives of men.

The conduct of men, women, and children living in the close contact of compact villages is regulated through their religious belief. Religious functions and civil authority are so interwoven in the persons of the religious leaders that it is difficult to separate them. It takes several years for an individual to become "letter perfect" in all the prayers and ritual forms, the dances and the sand paintings which go with the offices of priesthood. Unless each performance is perfect, it cannot produce the desired influence on the gods. When the people are not rewarded in accordance with the plan of any ceremony, then everyone—whether he participated in the ritual or was only an observer—examines every phase of the performance in an effort to discover the flaw. What went wrong? What offended the gods?

Only among people who are guaranteed a surplus of food can such time-consuming ceremonies and the decorative arts which accompany them be developed. In the American desert regions, agriculture made possible this abundant food. It also gave them time to develop artistic expression in pottery-making and blanket-weaving, some of the designs of which carried out their religious motifs. In fact, the desert dwellers in America were able to develop a very complex culture of community dwellings, religion, ceremony, poetry, and art quite different from desert cultures in any other part of the world.

Non-cultivators of the desert who now depend more on herding, like the Navajo, probably got much of their religious form and ceremony from the cultivators, but they, too, are strong "believers." Those Americans who have known the Navajo intimately give us vivid pictures of the importance of religion in their lives and the strength of their belief.

"Whether a thought is spoken or not, it is a real thing," Wolf-killer, the Navajo, told Louisa Wade Wetherill. "It has power. It does good or it does evil. So my grandfather taught me years ago.

"When it is a good thought," continued the old man, "it does good. When someone is ill and the medicine man sings for him, all the people must believe that he is going to get well. If one or two people in the *hogan* (an earth-covered house) do not believe, all the work of chanting and the prayer and the sand painting will be lost. But if they believe, the words of the prayer are true—'All is peace, all is peace.'"

Everyone who has lived close to these desert people and has learned to understand their language has found constant reference in their poetry and in their legends to "the path of light." Those who have departed from the traditional right way of living are urged to return to this path of light. The whole group will participate in a ceremony to wipe out the wrong thinking.

Another thought which repeats throughout the Navajo mind is reference to beauty. They see the beauty in the stars of night, in distant mountains, in the sunrise. Not only do they *see* beauty, they *feel* it deeply. Their craftsmen translate it onto silver bracelets and belt buckles. But a silversmith, they say, cannot copy another man's design unless he, too, can feel its beauty within his heart. The true Navajo believes that a beautiful piece of jewelry is conceived in good thoughts, and that one who has strayed from the path of light is incapable of producing beauty, even if he tries to copy a good design.

When one has been away from the people (as, say, soldiers returning from World War II), or if he has become contaminated in any way such as by helping to dispose of the body of a deceased relative, he must go through a ritual cleansing including a stay in a sweat lodge. This may be a temporary house. In it many hot stones are placed until the little room is heated to a very high temperature. The man enters this "Turkish bath" and stays until he is thoroughly cleansed. Then he rushes out to roll in the snow, if it is winter, or to be rinsed with cold water. Not only is he cleansed physically, but all the time that he is building his sweat lodge and getting his steam bath his thoughts are on the ritual prayers. He returns to the people clean in body and pure in heart.

When evil befalls individuals or the group, it may be due to evil thoughts of one or more persons. At first glance, this seems similar to the white man's early belief in witches; and Mrs. Wetherill tells of curses placed on two individuals by an insane Navajo which did cause their deaths, so strongly did the victims believe in the power of evil thought. There is, however, a distinct difference between the Navajo's belief in the power of evil thought and the New Englander's belief in the power of a witch. The white man believed the evil was in the person of the witch and that the person should be destroyed. The Navajo believes that the evil is in the thought, not the person. Therefore the person who starts an evil thought can remove its power by a good thought.

An evil thought can cause trouble even if the thinker does not intend such harm. An example is a successful raid on the Navajo by a band of Piutes. They carried off four young girls and left behind many dead who had fought valiantly to protect their people. Eventually one of the girls returned after real hardship and suffering. She admitted that some time before the raid she and her friend had commented that a certain young Navajo would soon be ready to select a wife. Both girls had expressed the hope that he would choose them. This in itself was an evil thought because it is not the right of a girl to do the choosing. However, this maiden had gone even farther and in her heart was jealous of her friend. When the raid took place, she was convinced that her evil thinking had brought the harm to her people.

When the old men heard her story on her return from captivity, they recognized that she had suffered and was repentant. They forgave her and instituted a cleansing ceremony, which included the ritual prayers and the sweat bath, after which she was accepted again by the people because her thoughts were now good thoughts.

The desert world is indeed a strange world. Some it terrifies, making them cringe in fear. Some it siezes with its beauty and makes mystics. But those who have learned to meet the rugged, uncompromising conditions of the desert world seem to enjoy a freedom of the spirit not often found elsewhere.

XIX

. . . .

. . . .

. . . .

. . . .

. . . . .

Pablo Valencia and Desert Thirst

THE HISTORY OF THE DESERT WORLD IS REPLETE WITH RECORDS
of thousands who have died of thirst, or rather died of dehydration,
for the sensation of thirst is only a warning and not a killer. In the
latter part of the fourteenth century, Tamerlane (1336?–1405), the
great Mongol leader, subdued the Ottoman army by turning away
the only stream of water to which they could gain access. Five
thousand of the Ottoman soldiers died of "thirst."

During the 1860's more than 400 gold seekers who took the
Devil's Highway in northern Mexico as a short cut to the gold fields
died for lack of water. In 1877 Captain Nolan of the United States
Army lost four of his twenty-six men in three and a half days on
the Staked Plains of West Texas without water. Dr. Sven Hedin
very nearly died of thirst in May 1895 out in the western Gobi.

In World War II an American army detachment of about 800
men on maneuvers in the southwest desert failed to reach their
objective because of lack of water, and I believe that one or two of
the men died from dehydration. Lack of water also stopped a Ger-
man advance against the British in the Sahara of North Africa. The
crew of *Lady Be Good,* a bomber returning from a raid on Italy,
parachuted over the Sahara, leaving their water and coffee in the

plane. They died of thirst in the desert. The discovery of their bodies made headlines in 1960.

The record of death from lack of water, whether you call it dying of thirst or dying of dehydration, is continuous. Every year Arabs in the Arabian Desert and Americans in the Mojave will leave their stranded car or truck and start walking without adequate water. The record of their ordeals by thirst can be brought up to date any summer by reading the newspapers published in desert regions.

Throughout this 600 years of history about desert thirst there is nothing comparable to the story of Pablo Valencia. Pablo should have died. To be specific, he should have died on August 20, 1905, five days after Jesus Rios left him alone near El Camino del Diablo, the Devil's Highway, with only one day's supply of water.

According to his own story, Pablo *did* die two days later, on August 22, for on that day he knew his soul left his body; but, hovering outside its broken husk, it drove the body seven miles across the Yuma Desert to rescue.

The experience of Pablo Valencia in the desert along the U.S.– Mexico border is probably the most remarkable historic case of desert survival ever recorded. Even the absolute silence of the desert played a major role in his final rescue. The facts are well established.

Pablo was a Mexican forty years of age. He was five feet, seven inches in height and weighed 155 pounds on August 14, 1905—a husky, well-built man. Few of his countrymen were as barrel-chested as Pablo. Fewer still had as sturdy legs. He would rather walk than ride a horse, and he even preferred to walk barefooted unless the furnace-hot desert floor forced him to wear sandals. In fact, his quick stride and his springlike step often carried him over the trail as fast as most horses of the region could travel. In younger days Pablo had sailed in Pacific ships. He had been a miner and a prospector for years. During the summer of 1905 he was raising watermelons near Gila City, but Pablo was a desert man and prospector, not a farmer. He liked to drowse in the sun, to eat heartily, sleep heavily, and yet, when occasion demanded, he could be energetic and stubbornly persistent at the job at hand. Pablo Valencia boasted that he could starve longer, thirst longer, and endure more desert hardship than any man in Arizona or Mexico. Physically he was equal to his boasting; a man of action not overly endowed with the finer mental sensibilities, but religious and, regarding alcohol, a teetotaler. The latter fact may have contributed to his rescue.

Deep in the desert there is a "lost mine." Pablo knew about it, and he had even been there months before. It was a rich, gold-bearing ledge. If he could stake a claim and collect the yellow-spotted samples to prove its worth, Pablo could drowse in the sun for the rest of his life. He could eat as much as he pleased and hire others to raise the sweet watermelons which quenched his thirst. Watermelons are ambrosia to desert people. Even better than rain-water, they slake the thirst and restore strength to desert travelers.

But it is not good to travel the *Gran Desierto* alone. Even gold-hungry Pablo knew that, and it was why he hired the old man, Jesus Rios, as guide and companion for his desert journey. Jesus was about sixty-five years old, a typical Mexican *vaquero,* who claimed to know the desert southeast of the Gila Mountains and the Tinajas Altas. Perhaps, long ago, he had known the Devil's Highway and the desert sands beyond, but at sixty-five a man's memory plays him tricks. Roads and trails are not always just where an old man remembers them.

It was Monday, August 14, just about noon when the two Mexicans rode into the meteorological camp of Dr. W. J. McGee near the High Tanks. The Tinajas Atlas, or High Tanks, are pot holes in the rock on a canyon floor. They catch rain water and some seepage from the granite above. In 1702 Padre Kino first placed the tanks on his map, but modern maps apply the name to the whole ridge southeast of the Gila Mountains. At the turn of the last century Tinajas Altas was the only sure water on the Devil's Highway, that terrible short cut between Quitobaquito in Mexico and Yuma, Arizona. No water for eighty miles to the east! Even the Indians shunned the area except when the cactus was in fruit.

Pablo rode Jim Tucker's best horse, a sturdy animal well acclimated to desert work. Jesus rode his own grass-fed animal. They

were well outfitted by Tucker at Yuma, and their supplies of pinole
(parched wheat meal) bread, cheese, sugar, coffee, and tobacco
were ample for a week. They even had enough pressed alfalfa and
rolled barley for the horses. Only their water was inadequate. Two
canteens of two-gallon capacity, two of one-gallon; six gallons of
water was all they could carry for two men and two horses! Even
good horses must water regularly to keep their strength in the desert
heat.

The horses were fed and watered at the camp. Pablo and Jesus
feasted on jerked cimarron (meat of the mountain sheep) from
Dr. McGee's supply, then dozed till late afternoon.

"Moon's about full tonight," said McGee. "Better wait till mid-
night or one o'clock before you start."

The advice was ignored. About five in the afternoon the two men
rode out from camp toward the southeast. But McGee had made his
point. The desert was still hot. It had been comfortable at the camp
with the scientist and his helper, Papago Jose. Anyway, the horses
had not drunk much, thought Pablo, as he rode. Maybe the doctor's
advice about a moonlight start was good.

"We'd better go back and let the horses drink some more," ordered Pablo. By 5:30 P.M. the two were back with McGee and
Papago Jose.

Pablo was a heavy sleeper. Neither he nor his guide, Jesus, was
awake at moonrise. Not until nearly dawn did Papago Jose get the
guide up. Together they pulled the sleeping Pablo from his blankets.
It was daylight, about 3:45 A.M. on August 15 when the guide and
prospector again rode out from camp.

The desert was pleasant that morning. Faint color washed the
eastern sky. McGee's official thermometer would register a cool
77°F. just before the sun sharpened silhouettes of jagged buttes to
break the monotony of the flat desert plain. In the cool, dry air the
horses made good time for about three hours, but as the sun climbed
above the horizon the shaded instruments of the meteorologist at
Tinajas Altas moved up through the high 80's. Twenty miles away
to the southeast there was no ventilated shelter for the riders and

their horses, and by ten o'clock the official thermometers were swinging into the upper 90's. Horses and riders were absorbing direct rays of the sun and catching reflected heat from the desert floor. Sweat from their bodies evaporated too fast to moisten the skin. Relative humidity that day was never more than 25 per cent. The horses slowed their pace, and their heads drooped as their body water was lost to the dry air in order to keep the body temperature normal.

About noon they reached the sand hills thirty-five miles southeast of McGee's camp. No longer could the horses move easily. The men, too, were tired. More than half of their water was gone, but they were far from being refreshed. While they rested and listlessly ate a little bread and cheese, McGee's official thermometer reached just under 100°F. Out in the sand hills Pablo, Jesus, and their horses were enduring heat stress at least 30°F. greater than the official temperature.

"Horses are no good, here," said Pablo. "I walk better in sand than they. You go back to Tinajas Altas and water the horses again. Fill canteens with more water. Meet me tomorrow. Maybe one o'clock like now. Maybe seven o'clock tomorrow night. I'll be other side that sierra on the road you tell me is over there."

Jesus Rios took the empty canteens and turned the tired horses back toward the camp at High Tanks. Pablo kept a two-gallon canteen of water and some pinole. The sun beat down on the sand hills, and shimmering waves of heat reflected skyward and made mirage lakes in the flat places between the dunes. Pablo strode away across the sand toward the distant mountain ridge.

As he walked he remembered how prettily the yellow gold speckled the rocks on the ledge. The mine would be all his. So simple. All he had to do was to stake his claim, as he had done many times before. This time he did not have to share with anyone. His guide, Jesus Rios, had been hired outright. Twice that afternoon Pablo ate a little pinole. Three times before sunset he drank a little from the big canteen. Not much. Not enough to replace the quarts of body water lost in sweat to keep his temperature near the normal 98.6°F. Sometimes he stopped to rest, but before dark he had traveled ten miles through the dunes. Then he stopped for the night, drank once more from the canteen, and slept.

When the morning star showed bright above the horizon on August 16, Pablo was roused from sleep by his parched mouth and throat. Immediately he reached for the canteen. He shook it. Water sloshed about freely. There was less than two quarts in the big canteen. He took a few swallows, little more than enough to wash the dust from his mouth and throat. Then he ate a handful of pinole, rolled up his serape, and walked on across the desert. Even that little water which Pablo had drunk revived his sluggish muscles. Free air temperature was in the 80's and relative humidity was about 40 per cent. This pleasant weather of early morning made walking easier, but the loss of body water left the man vaguely uncomfortable. He was impatient and feverish but still eager to reach his lost mine.

Now he plodded across the desert. His steps had lost their spring; his stride was no longer quick. Pablo had to think about his walking as he moved toward the mountains and the lost mine. Two hours after sunrise the heat began to slow his pace, although official thermometers were registering only in the low 90's. By nine o'clock his mouth and throat were so dry that he had to rinse them from the near-empty canteen, but he used the water so sparingly that it only relieved his mouth's dryness. It gave him no more strength; gave no relief from the fever building in his dehydrated body. It would have taken several quarts of water to restore his body weight and give him back his normal strength.

It was mid-morning when Pablo reached the ledge of his lost mine. The sight of the gold-flecked rock roused his flagging energy. Eagerly he built monuments necessary to stake his claim. He posted legal, mineral-claim notices. The sun climbed higher. The dark rocks of the ledge became oven-warm as Pablo broke off hunks of ore samples. The sun had reached its zenith by the time the job was done. There were no shadows long enough to protect a man's body, no shelter from the desert heat, as official instruments registered 99.5°F. But Pablo had staked his claim. He had proof of his wealth in gold ore samples. Perhaps by nature he was too phlegmatic to want to celebrate. More likely his dehydrated body was burning so with fever that his brain refused to recognize the meaning of his wealth.

He tipped the big canteen to his lips and drank. One swallow, another swallow, and a third. Three swallows of warm water, but how sweet they tasted! How good to feel the dust washed from his throat! Pablo took the canteen from his lips and looked at it. Then he held it near his ear and shook it. The water sloshed loudly. Less than a pint was left. Another swallow would taste good now. But how far must he walk to the rendezvous with Jesus Rios? How far was the road Jesus had told him about? When would he get more water? Pablo corked the canteen and started north. For perhaps a mile he kept his steps directed purposefully to the north, but as the desert heat accumulated his once firm steps began to falter. Hot sand dragged at his feet. He no longer held a true north trail but wandered almost aimlessly. His mouth and throat were constantly dry. Now and then he tipped the canteen to his lips and let a few drops moisten his mouth, but he never tipped the container far enough to swallow the water. At last the canteen was dry. Still he wandered northward. Jesus Rios had said the road was not far. He would be waiting there with filled canteens and the big horse.

The sun moved down toward the western skyline. Low hills threw long, long shadows so that a man could hardly tell their shape. Pebbles on the desert floor were stretched out by their shadows to look like parallel sticks all pointing to the sunset. Had old Rios lied about the road? Did the old man plan to follow Pablo's tracks and steal his claim? The thought drove the prospector's fevered body to new effort. He would yet live to feel his knife in the traitorous heart of old Jesus Rios! A guide who leaves his party to die of thirst deserves to die himself. Again his steps were heading due north toward the non-existent road.

It was past sundown now, still hot but without the direct sunlight beating down on his body, and he had a little more strength to walk. A few minutes after the sun disappeared, Pablo saw the winding course of an arroyo. Would there be water under the black bank of the big bend? He tried to run, and stumbled. For a moment he just lay sprawled on the desert. This was what the guide had planned, thought Pablo. But he would fool the old man. No one cheated Pablo Valencia! He would beat the desert, guide or no guide.

Under the bank on the bend of the arroyo he scraped with his hands. The sand was loose and still warm as he started to dig. Eight inches down it was cool but still dry. Frantically he dug deeper. The sand wasn't even moist. His fingers tore at stones as he tried to dig deeper and deeper, but there was no water. Finally he abandoned the useless hole and struggled farther along the arroyo. Somewhere in that dry stream bed there must be a sheltered pool; at least some wet mud where he could squeeze out a few drops of water to wet his parched lips. But there was none.

As darkness blanketed the desert, Pablo staggered northward along the arroyo. Soon after he left the dry sand hole he had tossed away his heavy load of gold, but his mind clung to the hope of evening the score with old Rios. Once, as he fell, he noticed the bag of pinole he still carried. The thought of food nauseated him and he tossed away the parched grain as he had thrown away his gold. Even his coat became a burden and he abandoned it. Finally he dropped his serape on the desert but still he kept staggering toward the north. As the night air cooled, he used his canteen to catch his scanty urine. At last he realized that he would find no water in the arroyo. He lay down on the sand and dropped into exhausted sleep.

About two o'clock on the morning of August 17, Pablo was awakened by his dry mouth. Soft moonlight bathed the plain. There was no wind, no sound, no movement. The desert was a dead world. Neither the eerie light nor the silence touched his mind. Only the awful dryness of his throat demanded recognition. He uncorked the canteen and filled his mouth with the salty urine. Slowly he sloshed it around his mouth. He tilted his head back; let the liquid reach his throat and gargled. Before his throat could dry again he lay back on the sand and slept.

Just before sunrise the thermometers in their official shelters five feet above the ground at Dr. McGee's camp were showing just under 80°F., but on the unprotected desert floor it was colder. Without his coat or serape Pablo was chilled to wakefulness. Slowly he crawled to his feet. Like a sleepwalker he turned his slow steps northward. A faint shadow of a trail led slightly from his course, but on it his feet stumbled less. Perhaps it would lead him to Tinajas, but the trail, if trail it was, petered out in rocky desert. Again the prospector had to pick each step until he found another elusive trail. Always these pathways, whether real or figments of his fevered brain, led northward. Was it the desert man's deep knowledge that only at High Tanks was water to be found in August? Perhaps this kept him headed northward, but Pablo later thought that the hope of knifing Jesus Rios never wholly left him and drove his limbs from step to step that morning.

Before noon the sun beat down from a cloudless sky, and the temperature climbed fast to the high 90's. Black stones on the desert floor became too hot to handle. Back at the camp that day the relative humidity stayed around 25 per cent. Who knows how dry the air of Pablo's breathing? Bent half over he staggered and stumbled like a drunken man. But always he headed northward.

Near noon he fell over the bank of an arroyo. There on the dry sand were half a dozen *calabasitas,* wild gourds that look like small round watermelons. The thirst-crazed man broke one open and swallowed the juicy pulp, then broke open a second gourd, but the bitter liquid of the first had reached his stomach and he retched. The only moisture in the desert was a violent poison! Pablo lay there inert while those recording instruments being watched by Dr. McGee climbed to 103.4°F. On the ground where Pablo lay it was at least 130°F.

The hot hours passed, and as the sun went down Pablo roused from his stupor. His legs and feet were uncomfortable. He threw away his shoes, then his trousers with money, knife, and tobacco in the pockets were cast aside. Delirious from lack of water, he still could hold direction and moved on northward. Now and then he followed old trails. Some faded out. Some led for a few miles to end in deep sand or impassable rocks; rocks which cut his feet. They slashed his arms and legs when he fell, but Pablo was too numb to feel his cuts and bruises. One trail actually led to a large tank, but there was no water. Dry desert air had evaporated the last rain accumulation, just as it was drying out the stubborn body of the man.

Often during the day he rinsed his mouth and gargled with the urine he had saved at night in the canteen. Even in his delirium, when he had discarded all his clothes, he clung to the canteen. It was now almost impossible for him to swallow. Dehydration had reached more than 10 per cent of his body weight. That the man could still walk is a miracle, a tribute to his determination. Many desert victims of water shortage have not survived under far less stress than Pablo had experienced by the night of August 17.

During that night the temperature dropped and cooled the prospector's fevered body. Humidity rose to 60 per cent which also reduced the stress on the dehydrated man. Pablo slept. Sometimes he roused and used the canteen to catch a trickle of urine.

Soon after dawn on August 18, he was again staggering across the desert, but he traveled only a few miles. The sun on his near-naked body soon forced him to seek the shade of a paloverde tree growing over the bank of an arroyo. The day was partly cloudy at the meteorologist's camp and the high temperature was only 96°F.; but Pablo, weak, almost naked, and without water could not move even in that mild midday heat. All day he huddled on the sand in the scanty shade. When the shadows began to lengthen, he roused and tried to chew the twigs of the paloverde. They were bitter and had no moisture. They only irritated his dry mouth.

The hours of rest had restored a little of his strength. Again he started north. He found some mescal and chewed a few of the stipes. They seemed to have a little moisture, and even a few drops were precious to the water-starved man. He caught some flies and a spider. These he chewed, but they were too dry and he could not swallow them. Always when he could move a step or two, he kept headed north. There was still a chance that he would meet Jesus Rios or find the Old Yuma Trail he remembered from his youth. And so he walked and staggered, stumbled, crawled, and kept on northward. All night he struggled on. Toward morning of August

19 he was convinced that Jesus Rios had abandoned him. Now that his suspicions had changed to a certainty, his desire to avenge the treachery was sharpened. Anger spurred him to greater effort. He walked faster and held a truer course to the north. Only a few times did he stop to relieve his mouth dryness with urine; then he pushed on again—always to the north. How could a man half-dead from dehydration keep going as Pablo did? Dr. McGee believed that Pablo's anger and determination to knife the old guide drove him to that spurt of walking which brought him to the Old Yuma Trail.

It was full light on Saturday morning, August 19, when the prospector recognized the mule-wagon tracks of the Yuma Trail. Still far from rescue, but on a familiar trail, strong hope was added to the spur of revenge.

Pablo pushed along the trail, following the ancient wagon tracks as hundreds of gold seekers had done half a century before him. By mid-morning the heat drove him to the shelter of an arroyo. Overhead he saw vultures circling high on hot air currents. All day he lay under the bank keeping his body in the scant shade. Late that afternoon a large green scorpion crawled close to him. How cool and lush the light-green insect looked! Pablo caught the poisonous creature. He ground off its sting with a stone. He ate it. Throughout the day, whenever his dry throat became intolerable, he rinsed his mouth with urine. Sometimes he swallowed a little, but dehydration had now progressed so far that it was extremely difficult for him to swallow at all.

Toward evening he crawled over the arroyo bank and continued along the Old Yuma Trail. This is hideous desert—a land of black volcanic rock. Jagged mountains rise abruptly from the flat, grassless plain. Rarely a stunted tree, gnarled and grotesque, makes a patch of dull, ashen green on the edge of a waterless stream bed. Thorn- and spine-covered little bushes sometimes speckle a shallow saucer where water from a winter rain has stood a week or so. It is a land so parched in summer that rain from clouds coming up from the Gulf of California evaporates before it reaches the ground. During eight years, some 400 gold-seekers died of thirst along this Devil's Highway. There are sixty-five graves in one stretch of thirty miles. This is the road Pablo Valencia found early on the morning of August 19. He was still fifty miles from McGee's camp and water at High Tanks.

He walked north through the night. Often he stumbled in the old ruts and fell. Sometimes he crawled on hands and knees a few yards before he could get on his feet and stagger again toward the north. Once, when he fell, he caught a glimpse of a coyote in the road behind him. Another time he thought that he found the tracks of Jesus Rios, where he had wandered in search of the impossible rendezvous three days before.

Now that he was on a recognized trail, Pablo had new hope. The old Tule Well was near this route. Perhaps he could reach that thirty-seven-foot pit and lie in cool mud at the bottom. He dreamed of dying there in the damp, cool pit. Even while he dreamed, he recognized the insane hopelessness of the idea. Still, it was a goal, an incentive to his tortured mind and fevered body. He kept to the road. His urine now "mucho malo" was still used as a mouthwash despite its foulness. The road swung west and Pablo rested.

Sunday morning, August 20, he again moved west on the wagon trail. His strength was failing, and often he had to sit down in the trail. The pair of buzzards circling in the hot sky were not such tiny specks as they had been yesterday. When he tried to walk, he fell so frequently that he decided it was easier to crawl. The buzzards circled lower. Pablo knew they watched him as a dying animal. He staggered upright and made better progress on his feet.

The desert was a silent place but Pablo could not even hear the rattle of stones stirred by his stumbling footsteps. His sight, too, was blurred. Mountains in the distance danced and disappeared. Cactus plants and chaparral moved and jumped to strange positions as his eyes refused to stay in focus. Dehydration had now reached nearly 20 per cent of his normal body weight. Why did the man keep on living? All the medical rules, all dehydration statistics, show that Pablo should have died that day, if not the day before. True, the relatively low cloud cover at night and morning which ranged from 10 per cent most of the week to 80 per cent on August 18 and, for the desert, the high relative humidity of 40 to 50 per cent all contributed in his favor. Even so, the man *should* have died, for he abused his body by travel in the heat and by drinking the salt excretion from his kidneys. Certainly his will to live and his desire to knife old Rios were more powerful motives than most men ever have.

Tule Well is north of the rut-marked wagon trail by at least a mile or two. In 1905 a guidepost indicated the turn, but Pablo's eyes were so weak and blurred by dehydration that he staggered past without seeing the post. He kept on westward. It was nearly high noon by the sun when his wracked body stumbled against the second Tule Well guidepost. Those sheltered recording thermometers at Tinajas Altas were showing only 91°F. But out there, unprotected on El Camino del Diablo, Pablo found the sun too strong for his weak body. He knew that he could never work his way back along the northeast spur-trail to the wells he had passed. He saw the buzzards circling lower.

Perhaps missing the first turn to Tule was a good omen, a sign that rescue was near. He hung his hat on the signpost and crawled to some *tinajas* he remembered from his long-ago journey over this cursed road. But the tanks were dry—bone dry. The rocks offered shade, however, and in their less-hot shelter Pablo rested and waited for lengthening shadows. Urine dripped involuntarily now, and he hoarded every drop to moisten his burning mouth.

The thought of the old guide returned with the lengthening shadows. Again he dreamed of sweet revenge; his knife twisting in the body of the traitor. He crawled from the rock shelter and struggled along the trail. All night he moved ahead. Each time he fell it was torture to rise again, but foot by foot he labored westward.

Actually he seldom walked more than two or three steps at a time. Mostly he crawled on his hands and knees among the thorns —but always in the right direction. Few men have had such tenacious trail sense as the phlegmatic Pablo.

At daybreak he recognized an old campsite. His all-night struggle had carried him only three and a half miles from Tule Well. Still nineteen miles from McGee and Tinajas Atlas!

Monday, August 21, was a cool day by official records. It never got above 91°F. in the shade, but, of course, for Pablo there was no shade. The sky was overcast, about 60 per cent cloud cover, and the relative humidity ranged from 40 to 50 per cent. Pablo was stark naked now. He had discarded his underwear when he hung his hat on the Tule Well guidepost.

He made no attempt to travel after sun-up but was so certain of rescue that he lay across the trail so that searchers could not possibly pass him by. All day he slept or dozed. Sometimes he thought he heard wagon wheels and started up. Once he was sure he heard the beat of horses' hoofs. Perhaps it was his imagination; more likely the grunts of buzzards. They came so close, while he lay naked and hardly able to move, that he could almost touch the ugly scavengers waiting for his death.

Sleep and the cool day restored a little of his energy, and at sunset he started west again. His disordered brain told him that he might even find the full canteens Jesus Rios was to bring to the meeting place. Old Rios had indeed left them, but at such impossible places that even a mildly thirsty man could not have found them, much less one as near death as the prospector.

With the hope of rescue driving him along the Devil's Highway, Pablo walked and crawled, staggered and fell for twelve miles that night. Much of the route was downhill and along the arroyo. He crossed the black *malpai's mesite*. Graves of other desert victims are thick there but Pablo believed he was beating the desert. Rocks cut his body when he fell. Thorns made deep gashes in his limbs, but he felt no pain. His thickened blood was too stiff to flow from the slashes in his flesh. His eyes no longer served him. He could no longer even see the mountains which were the landmarks of the trail. Still, he kept to the trail by feeling with his hands every few yards.

Illusions became more and more common. Often he was certain that he saw the High Tanks just ahead. He even thought that he could see the food and water at McGee's camp. Then he would feel some familiar landmark on the trail and know he was still distant from his goal. Still he did not lose hope. Step by step, for twelve long miles, he traveled in the night.

It was early dawn on Tuesday, August 22, when Pablo believed he was really close to Tinajas Altas. As the light brightened, he could dimly see a milepost just ahead. He staggered on until he touched it with his hands. He felt it over top to bottom. But there were no canteens of water hanging there. He identified this post as the six-mile marker. Slowly hope gave way to reality. Without water the prospector knew he could never walk the six or almost seven miles across the sand to Dr. McGee. For days he believed that his urine mouthwash had been a help. Now even urine had ceased to flow. This was the end.

Only six miles away, Dr. McGee was reading his meteorological instruments. Temperature 90°F.; relative humidity 32.5 per cent; sky one fifth cloud-covered. Pablo found a little bush that cast a shadow. Piously he knelt down in the cool shade and prayed the final prayer for the dying. He lay down under the bush, consciously turning his face to the east. He made the sign of the cross, regretting only the absence of holy water for his last rites. Quietly he made his peace—and "died."

This, Pablo said later, was the clearest and most real experience of his ordeal. His body lay lifeless as the sun climbed higher and higher, pushing McGee's thermometers through the 90's to 100°F., the second hottest day of those fateful eight. The buzzards hopped close. They waited. Pablo's consciousness, "his innermost self," as Dr. McGee expressed it, hovered near, unwilling to leave the drying husk of his body. This strange illusion of apartness between Pablo's ego and his broken body persisted. The sun moved toward the zenith until the shade of the shrubs covered only part of the naked body. Still the ugly buzzards waited. Still they sensed the spark of life in the inert body.

The sun moved westward. Gradually clouds floated up from the distant gulf until the sky was 70 per cent overcast, the relative humidity 37.5 per cent, and the thermometers on their sheltered racks dropped to 90°F. The buzzards lifted their clumsy bodies from the hot sands to abandon the ghoulish vigil for the night.

Darkness fell. The chill of the desert night bathed and cooled the fevered body beneath the bushes. It stirred, as Pablo seemed to watch it. Strange how that husk, apart from him, crawled and struggled along the desert floor. Almost aimlessly the body moved among the cactus and the chaparral. Torn, but never bleeding, the body kept the general direction of El Camino del Diablo. Dante, himself, saw no bodies worse tortured than that witnessed by Pablo Valencia. He knew the naked body was his own, but he seemed only to watch it. Seldom did he feel himself within that ghastly purple-gray skin. But there were some moments when he was "half alive, enduring an agonizing struggle to separate the body and his spirit."

Through the cool night, forces outside his body seemed to drive it forward toward Tinajas Altas. Pablo knew a voice was trying to call for rescue, but he could not associate that voice with himself. So the night dragged on, even as the grotesque body with blackened face and shrunken flesh was dragged across the desert floor. The lips and the gums were dried and shrunken back. Teeth showed, a ghastly scar in a black mask. The nose was shrunken to half its size—its lining black, no longer red and lifelike. Even the eyelids had disappeared; shriveled back, they showed the eyeballs like whitish marbles in deep blackened pits.

Then came the dawn of August 23. That grotesque shape of parchment skin and jointed bones again became part of Pablo. Somehow he knew that he was close to the meteorologist's camp and rescue. He heard his own voice break from his body in a bull-like bellow. With a final surge of energy he crawled the last fifty yards of the Devil's Highway down into the arroyo and lay below the Mesa of the Forty Graves.

At McGee's camp a quarter of a mile away, the day sounds had not begun. No bird chirped; no wind stirred in the chaparral. Silence blanketed the dead world of the desert. McGee and Papago Jose were still asleep. Suddenly that dead silence was shattered. The canyon walls reverberated with a roar. McGee started from a vivid dream of a herd of cattle led by a huge bull. Jose was on his feet.

"Was it a big zoo lion?" he asked.

"Pablo," said McGee. "Get a canteen!"

Jose ran down the canyon. McGee followed with his medicine

case and another canteen. Under an ironwood tree was the wrecked body of Pablo. His ribs and the joints of his arms and legs showed through a skin as hard and stiff as dry rawhide. Cuts and deep scratches were but slashes in this dry leather. Jose tried to give him water from the big canteen, but Pablo could not swallow. Neither could he speak. He was blind except to light and darkness; deaf except to shouts. His tongue was a shrunken, shapeless mass of black.

They sloshed water over the body and massaged it until the skin began to soften and take up water just as rawhide softens in the rain. Diluted whiskey was forced into his mouth and rubbed onto his chest. The whiskey seemed to take effect, and Dr. McGee believed this was because the man was unaccustomed to alcohol in any form. Even so, it was half an hour before feeble swallowing movements began in Pablo's throat, and an hour before he really could drink, and then much of the water was expelled from his stomach. Two hours after his rescue, a couple of ounces of a bird broth with rice and shredded bacon was given to him. In three hours, with the help of McGee and Jose, he walked to camp, the circulation in his limbs being restored. His wounds began to redden, then exude blood and serum. As his voice returned, cracked and changing like a teen-ager's, he begged for "Agua, agua," and protested against the "dust they were forcing him to sip." The rest of his recovery is medical history. But Pablo Valencia lived. He lived by the Grace of God and the will to survive.

An Epilogue

Jesus Rios, unreliable as he was, did not abandon Pablo. He returned to Dr. McGee's camp with the horses as Pablo had directed. He watered the animals, ate, and departed at 3:30 A.M. on August 16 with five gallons of water. He reached the rendezvous and left the canteens although not where they could have been easily found. He saw no trace of Pablo and believed that he had gone on to Agua Salada. Rios was back at camp the morning of August 17, completely exhausted after riding 150 miles in fifty-two hours.

Papago Jose took the Tucker horse at 10:00 A.M. on August 17, and rode to the point where Rios left Pablo on the 15th. He followed Pablo's trail on foot for about seven miles into the sand, then returned to the horse. It was 11:50 A.M. when he reached camp August 18. He, too, was worn out by his fourteen-mile walk and seventy-mile ride in desert heat. McGee had studied hundreds of cases of "desert thirst" or dehydration, and he believed that unless Pablo had gone on to Agua Salada he must have died from lack of water. Accordingly, he sent Jesus Rios back to Jim Tucker with the horses and a letter explaining the situation.

Tucker set out from Yuma by horse and wagon to go in search of Pablo's body. He reached McGee's camp after the rescue—and almost killed the survivor with rich food. McGee decided to accompany the sick man back to civilization in the wagon, and for a while it looked doubtful that he would pull through; but when they finally got a supply of watermelons, Pablo began to improve rapidly and his recovery was assured.

XX

....
....
....
....
.....

Twentieth-Century Desert Survival

PABLO VALENCIA SURVIVED BECAUSE OF A SUPERB PHYSICAL BODY, a phenomenal strength of will-to-survive, and luck in the form of mild weather and the presence of Dr. McGee. By all the laws of physiology and all the statistics on death from dehydration, or thirst, if you prefer to call it that, Pablo should have died on the fifth day of his ordeal. He did many things wrong, things which in ordinary individuals would outweigh the few things which he did correctly.

His worst error was common to the thinking of his time. When he found his water getting low, he began to hoard it in the canteen instead of in his belly where it would have kept him mentally and physically more fit at the beginning of his journey.

It is more than half a century since Pablo's journey. Even at that time physiologists knew that the human body must have water to function properly, but the general public believed in hoarding water in their canteens as if it were gold which would be more valuable later on. The American army has operated in the desert for a century and lost both men and campaigns for lack of water, but it was not until 1943 that a Surgeon General Circular Letter indicated that inadequate water supply is regarded as a patent error. That letter stated that water deficits must be repaid within twelve hours or risk heat exhaustion. In spite of this knowledge the vicious advice to hoard water persisted. Military manuals continued to support the nineteenth-century fallacy by saying, "Don't drink for the first twenty-four hours."

It is now thirteen years since the standard text, *Physiology of Man in the Desert,* was published by Dr. E. F. Adolph and his associates. This book states that even a little dehydration is dangerous. In spite of all the warnings, however, I recently received an advertisement in the mail for a desert-survival manual, "Prepared by Experts," in which the age-old error is cited as good advice. When will the "experts" catch up?

Pablo's next worst error was in traveling so often during the heat of the day. If he had just waited until sunset after Rios left him before starting through the sand——; if he had waited for the cool of evening to do his work at the mine——; if he had always hunted shade *before* the sun got too hot——; if he had kept his clothes and serape to insulate him against the hot desert air and radiant heat of the sun——; if he had used his urine to wet his clothing and cool his body by its evaporation, instead of adding its salt and poisonous wastes to his already overburdened body——. Each of these "ifs" would have helped to keep up his strength and his mental alertness. Only his fantastic trail sense which kept him from wandering in circles, as so many have done, and the fact that he did find some shade, did lie sleeping or inert during much of the heat— only these actions contributed, together with his good physical condition at the start, to keeping him alive and moving towards his friends.

Civilization has progressed since the time of Pablo. Now you can go to Yuma by airplane, bus, or private air-conditioned automobile, and so avoid all the discomforts of desert travel common at the turn of the century. That is, you can generally avoid them, but every summer spectacular desert tragedies and near-tragedies reach the metropolitan newspapers. The sheriffs' offices in the southwestern United States report many more. Death by dehydration is just as sure in the twentieth century as it was in the nineteenth.

Only a couple of years ago, a Wisconsin student, his French companion, and their Egyptian guide died in the desert of upper Egypt. In southeastern Utah a Mr. and Mrs. Scott with six children were stranded by a broken-down automobile, and it was two days before modern rescue services found them. Fortunately they had practiced good survival tactics and were in pretty fair condition when rescued. In 1957 Mr. and Mrs. Clifford White, traveling in their air-conditioned ranch wagon got stuck in the sand in Big Bend National Park, in west Texas. She started out for help and got lost, but survived in a mountain cave near a spring. He, later, left the car with its stock of water and food. Rescuers found him dead a few miles away. In 1955 it was Bill Falls, twenty-two years old, lost while flying from San Diego, California, to Phoenix, Arizona. He crashed, out of gas, in Mexico near the Gulf of California. Three weeks later, sportsmen flying home from a Mexican fishing trip spotted the wrecked plane and landed. Fall's diary told the story of death from dehydration.

Every year one or more Arabs working in Arabia leave their stalled trucks. Search planes go out as soon as the truck misses its ETA (estimated time of arrival), but in at least one case I know of, the Arab was found dead of dehydration only eighteen hours after he had left the truck. In another case, two Arabs were found dead. They had been stealing gasoline by hiding it in their water tanks.

The rangers at Grand Canyon National Park are called out every summer to find lost hikers who have started without adequate water on trails where no water exists for forty miles or more. Sometimes they find the hikers wandering in delirium. Sometimes they bring back the bodies.

Even a bus ride in the desert has its dangers. A neighbor of mine and her sister once started for Death Valley Scottie's Castle. The east-west bus dropped them at the crossroads where they were to transfer to the north-south bus.

"The other bus will be along in fifteen minutes," said the driver. "You just stay here."

"But the north-bound bus was late," my neighbor explained. "It was over thirty minutes before it came along."

Fortunately the girls sat on their suitcases and held umbrellas over their heads. It is thirty to forty degrees cooler a foot above the desert ground, and at least thirty degrees cooler in the shade than in the sun. Even so, they soon exhausted their thermos of drinking water, and when the bus finally got them to their hotel they were so near panic from thirst that they could not understand the bellboy's explanation that water was available.

There is no telling when accurate knowledge of desert survival may come in handy. Tourists and businessmen, prospectors, geologists, diplomats, and those who fly for fun will continue to cross deserts. In an emergency, they will find no shelter in the desert world, no water, and no telephone to summon help. If you travel at all, "it can happen to you" even as it happened to others since the days of Genghis Khan.

Those who travel the desert by automobile or fly their own planes, even those who only leave the central camping ground to hike in a national park should remember the "Siamese twins" of twentieth-century desert survival. These inseparable "twins" are a gallon canteen of water and a signal mirror. In the desert anything less than a gallon canteen is only a toy, and desert travel is not play. It is serious business. If one can provide more than the minimum, then the "quintuplets" of desert equipment are water, signal mirror, flashlight, compass—and more water. Plenty of water and signal equipment are absolute essentials for desert survival.

"A column of smoke by day, a pillar of fire by night" is a Biblical quotation no desert traveler should ever forget. Both are excellent signals, but they are not always possible in the desert because there is no fuel. Sometimes, however, one can kick up a dust which makes an excellent "column of smoke." If a strong wind is blowing the dust may hang so close to the ground that it can be seen only a short distance. I have seen this happen with red smoke bombs. But there is nothing that can be seen farther on land or sea if there is a little sunlight than a signal mirror. Its blinding flash will knock a pilot out of the cockpit, even when he is so far away that one can neither see nor hear the airplane. If there is no fuel in the desert for the "pillar of fire," the tiny spark of an electric torch can be seen for miles in the blackness of the desert night. The signal mirror can be flashed at the horizon all day long, but flashlight batteries should be saved until the rescue plane or automobile is either sighted or can be heard.

When the mirror flash has hit a rescuer it should be held on him until the pilot or driver turns your way. The mirror should not be moved erratically, for the pilot may confuse the signal with gun fire and hasten to get away. On the other hand, if a plane or rescue car comes toward you, do not blind the pilot. Give him a flash now and then as a guide to your location. Even after he is near you on the desert, he will need an occasional guiding signal to your location, but not a continuous blinding glare.

Those who carry more than the minimum equipment on their desert journey should include material to make black shade. A single sheet of parachute cloth will produce only light shade, but heavy cloth or several layers of parachute will make the shade black enough to keep out the rays of the burning sun. Desert travelers should not skimp on clothing either. Long pants and long sleeves may not *seem* comfortable in the midday sun but they will let sweat evaporate efficiently. They will keep the body temperature nearer normal and prevent sunburn which can be painful. Even those who already have a good coat of tan can still get sunburned and suffer.

Food is a survival "luxury" to be considered only if unlimited water is available. A man can live weeks, even for two months or more, without food but only a few hours without water.

Desert survival and rescue are most successful if the victims are on a trail. Desert trails in the Old World have been followed for millenniums. Those in America are centuries old. If there is water in a desert, it is on or near a trail; and if there are people traveling on a desert, they will be on trails. This is why it is advisable to keep the trails in sight, whether one travels by plane, jeep, air-conditioned auto, or on foot. If one must leave the trail, *he should file a flght plan,* that is, let his friends or the authorities know where he is going, and then stick to that plan. Should he be overdue, the wheels of private and official rescue services will get into motion. Usually "the lost shall be found" unless they are far off course and without signal equipment, as Bill Falls was.

A wrecked plane or automobile is more easily seen in the desert than a man on foot. Both will provide essential shade and sometimes more water than a man can carry. The shelter and signal equipment of a plane or vehicle generally makes it advisable to stay with the wreck. But if one should decide to walk in the desert, it should only be after the sun goes down and in the cool of early morning. Rest in the shade from "nine to five" is good advice; and when you do walk, don't hurry. Remember the Arab, his movements are slow and easy. He lives in slow motion—not because he is lazy, but because the desert makes him move that way. He is not just surviving in the desert. He lives there and seems to like it, but he lives according to the laws of physiology in the desert. He practices what we have been preaching. If there is plenty of water, two or three gallons for each man a day, one can work as hard as he likes, providing he drinks that water as often as he gets thirsty. Actually, he should drink more and oftener than he thinks his thirst requires, because a man can quench his thirst before he has drunk enough water to replace that already lost by dehydration.

"Where there is water there is life. Where no water is, is death," is an inexorable law of the desert; and no violator has ever escaped punishment for ignoring this law. This is why survivors are told to ration their sweat by working in slow motion and to hoard water in their bellies where it will do some good.

During World War II there were hundreds of military personnel stranded in deserts by wrecked planes, tanks, trucks, jeeps, etc. In spite of ignorance and faulty training for desert living, about three-quarters of them survived. One reason for the high percentage of rescues was that most of this activity did not take place during the hot summer months when neither men nor machines could function efficiently. In the accounts of these war-time survival episodes, one curious fact appears. Many times the only survivors of a party were the weaklings. The ones who lived were those who could not keep up with the husky men. Time and again the man who could not keep up crawled into a hole or found some shade. The strong ones went on—and were never heard from again unless their bodies were recovered at the end of their trails.

Why did the strong men die of thirst and the weak survive desert hardships? The answer lies in the general ignorance of basic physiological facts and the insidious nature of thirst, both of which have fostered the stupid practice of hoarding water in a canteen instead of using it as it was needed in the body.

The normal body temperature for man is 98.6°F., with a normal range from 97.2°F. to 99.5°F. Any variation, even as little as a couple of degrees from the normal range, reduces one's efficiency. Patients have survived after a few minutes of body temperature as low as twenty degrees below normal (78.8°F. and 75.2°F.), although their consciousness became clouded at half that drop.

In contrast, an increase in body temperature of six to eight degrees above the normal for any extended period causes death. Body temperature in a healthy person can be raised to the danger point either by absorbing heat or by generating it faster than the body can get rid of it. The human body absorbs heat from the air if the air is above 92°F. It can receive it from direct sunlight striking the body—radiant heat—even if the air is relatively cool. It can absorb reflected heat from the ground, or it can receive it by direct contact, as when one is lying down. Any kind of exercise, of course, produces body heat. In fact, the body produces so much heat, *even when at rest,* that unless this heat is lost a person will have two degrees of fever in one hour.

Regardless of where the heat comes from, the body must get rid of the excess and keep the body temperature in the normal range. This is done by evaporating sweat on the skin surface. It is a very effective and efficient process, and it is also the *only* cooling system the body has. In order to keep the body temperature normal, every hundred calories of heat generated in the body and absorbed from the air, sun, or ground, must be balanced by the evaporation of 173 grams (about six ounces) of sweat. This can mean more than one quart of sweat per hour.

When one sweats, the body loses water. Loss of body water is called dehydration. True, the body is about two-thirds water, but it is equally true that all this water is needed for circulation and other body functions. Therefore when one dehydrates, when he loses body water by sweating, this loss must be replaced by drinking water or the body goes into "water debt." Unless the water debt is quickly repaid, the body must pay for the loss in reduced efficiency. Actual scientifically controlled experiments on men working in hot deserts have given us some figures on loss of efficiency compared to the percentage of dehydration, or loss of body water.

For instance, when a man has lost 2½ per cent of his body weight by sweating (about two quarts of water), he loses 25 per cent of his efficiency. It has also been found that working in air temperatures of 110°F. cuts down a man's normal ability about 25 per cent. This means that if a person's body is short two quarts of water and the air around it is 110°F., that person is only half a man. He can do only about half as much work as he normally does. He can walk only half as far as he could with plenty of water in temperatures under 90°F.

Most people can get accustomed to working in high temperatures whether in the stokehold of a ship or in harvest fields on the Kansas prairie. It may take a good man from two days to a week before his circulation, his breathing, his heart action, and his sweat glands all become attuned to work in hot climates. Some people never do adjust to hot weather; others adjust quickly.

Although the body may acclimatize to hot weather, it still *must have water* to form sweat and supply liquid for circulation. When the body dehydrates, the blood loses more than its share of water. Blood becomes thicker and is diminished in volume. The result is more work for the heart and less efficiency in circulation.

Efficiency lost by dehydration is quickly restored by drinking water. Replacing water will even restore a man who has collapsed from dehydration in only a few minutes.

Most people drink the liquid they need at mealtimes. In hot climates they tend to dehydrate between meals and are restored to normal when they eat and drink. Such people often claim that they are tired, but in reality their loss of energy is due to dehydration.

There is no permanent harm done to a man who dehydrates even up to 10 per cent of his weight. If he weighs 150 pounds, he can sweat off fifteen pounds if he drinks enough water to gain it back later. Many individuals, however, will not be able to walk to the drinking fountain if they dehydrate that much; but if they can stagger over somehow and drink a quart or two of cool water, they will be back on their feet in a few minutes.*

Ice-cold water may cause stomach distress if drunk too rapidly, but warm or cool water may be swallowed as fast as you like.

There is no evidence that anyone can acclimatize to dehydration.† Some men have been dehydrated fifteen or twenty times under experimental conditions. *It took just as much water to bring them back to normal efficiency after the last dehydration as it did after the first.* During their dehydration, the same symptoms, the same loss of efficiency, always occurred at the same stages or percentages of water loss.

Here is how a man feels when he dehydrates. First, he is thirsty and uncomfortable. Then he starts taking it easy—sort of in slow

* Two U. S. aviators who were made prisoners in Italy by the Germans in World War II escaped into an attic and survived six days on one pint of water. They lay almost inert for fear of recapture and finally fell out of their hiding place when the building was blown up. It was several minutes before they could stagger over to water, but once there they drank three pints each right away and were able to walk. "I could actually feel energy returning," one of them told me in a personal conversation.

† Some writers claim that Arabs have acclimatized to dehydration. We can find no evidence to support this claim. We do find that desert natives conserve body water by following the rules stated in this chapter. For equal work in equal temperatures, the Arabs require as much water as other people. There is a record of two Arab soldiers in the Sahara who were proud of their desert ability and who believed the legend of the desert robber. He could go for two or three days without water just like his camel. These soldiers tried to imitate the legendary hero, but collapsed after thirty-six hours. They were revived by drinking water.

motion—and has no appetite. As he loses more water, he gets sleepy, his temperature goes up, and by the time he is dehydrated to 5 per cent of his body weight he gets sick at his stomach.

With from 6 to 10 per cent dehydration, the following symptoms may be expected: tingling in arms and legs, dry mouth, body becomes bluish, speech is indistinct, and increasing inability to walk. From this point on one needs help! If you are watching some fellow with less water than you have, you will find his symptoms in the tables at the end of this chapter. They range from being delirious to a numb skin. In any case, get water into him—but quick!

It is probable that man can survive 25 per cent dehydration in air temperature of 85°F. or cooler. At temperatures up in the 90's and higher, 15 per cent dehydration is probably fatal. Pablo Valencia was lucky in that night and early morning free air temperatures were below 92°F., the temperature at which the body begins to absorb heat from the air instead of losing its generated heat to the surrounding atmosphere.

Thirst is only the first symptom of dehydration. It is a signal that water debt is beginning. The insidious fact is that thirst is such a weak signal that it is easily ignored. A swallow or so of water, chewing gum, a few drags on a cigarette, placing pebbles in the mouth, even a little will power—all can stop the sensation of thirst *but they do not stop dehydration.* As dehydration progresses, the later symptoms, the aches and pains that follow and overshadow thirst, confuse the patient so that he believes he is not thirsty and blames his trouble on everything and anything *except* the lack of water. This is why so many have died of thirst with water in their canteens. Thirst is such a weak sensation, a signal so easily ignored, that people dehydrate even in cold areas like the Arctic. American soldiers in Korea would not drink enough water because they did not get "thirsty enough," and getting water sometimes involved a little extra work. The best plan is to drink water whenever you are the least bit thirsty as well as at mealtimes.

There is no substitute for water in preventing dehydration unless you want to consider milk, tea, coffee, soft drinks, and fruit juices.

All of these are, of course, mostly water and will replace body water. But alcohol, salt water, gasoline, blood, and urine—any of these liquids which desert and sea castaway romances say men have used as substitutes for water—only increase dehydration. This is because they all contain waste products which the body must get rid of through the kidneys. More water is required to carry off the waste through the body than is contained in the liquids mentioned. For example, sea water is more salty than urine; therefore, when sea water is drunk, the body must add more water to carry away the extra salt.

Recent studies on the salt needs of the body indicate that a little extra salt on food at mealtimes may be necessary for the first few days that one is working in hot climates. *But unless plenty of water is available, salt will do the body definite harm.* There is salt in sweat, but the body is able to conserve salt by regulating the amount that goes into sweat. One should not worry about salt requirements. Food salted to the taste will meet requirements in any climate unless the individual has not or will not acclimatize to hot weather.

In hot deserts a man needs a gallon of water a day. If he follows the rules at the beginning of this chapter and walks in the "cool" desert night, he can get about twenty miles from this daily gallon. If he does his walking in the daytime heat, he will be lucky to get half that. But whether he sits out his desert survival or walks home to mother, he will need water—at least four quarts a day.

Once in a desert "survival situation," water economy and signalling are the all-important factors in bringing about a happy ending. It is far better, of course, not to get into a survival situation, but even the best preparations sometimes do not prevent accidents. Advance knowledge of potential difficulties will reduce the chances of getting into trouble. This knowledge should include all one can learn about the particular area of travel: the pattern of its trails, the customs of its people, the location of wells, oases, and other types of water holes, etc. It should also include as much as possible about outdoor living and how to keep healthy without civilized comforts. Survival experts say that farm boys and city folks who have had a lot of Scout training are most successful at survival.

Most desert terrain is so easily traversed either by motor vehicle or on foot that few realize how suddenly a break in the level route can occur. It is quite possible to race all over the desert in any direction, as hunters do when they chase gazelle, but such a wild chase may perhaps drop the car into a hole and break an axle. Or an unexpected rock may rip the underside of the motor and spill the oil. I have experienced both accidents myself, but we carried spare parts and our mechanics were equal to the major repairs. Because of the possibility of this type of accident, it is wise to travel only in daylight and let the driver keep his eyes on the road no matter how flat and level it seems.

During World War II, in Arabia, three men were sent out in a jeep to patrol an area at night. They were told to cover area "A" and never drive faster than thirty-five miles per hour. For some unknown reason, they covered area "C" and ignored the specified speed. Search planes and ground parties went out when the jeep failed to report in the morning, and, of course, they combed area "A" without finding the lost party. It was three days before the search parties located the tragedy.

The jeep had hit a ditch and ripped out its transmission. Tracks in the sand showed how the men had walked back and forth in the wide cone of the vehicle's headlights. One man had walked a mile or two but, like so many who are lost and do not know how to follow a compass line, he had walked in a wide circle. His body was found only a little distance beyond where his tracks had completed the circle. A second man was dead in the shade under the jeep. The third, also dead, was found sitting against the front wheel. These men had died of dehydration—when water was within three feet of them. The radiator was still full of water! Apparently "the agony of thirst" was such a mild sensation that they did not even think they needed water.

Desert flying can be equally hazardous. Once I hitchhiked a plane ride from Bahrein Island in the Persian Gulf to Dhahran in Saudi Arabia. The distance was twenty-two miles and the flight seemed to take an unusually long time, but we finally landed. As I thanked the pilot he apologized for the long ride.

"Sorry," he said, "but I couldn't get down on the first pass. The midday desert is so hot that the air rising from the field just wouldn't let me get down."

Two years later, we had to shorten our stay at Gao, about two hundred miles downstream from Timbuktu on the Niger River, because if we did not get into the air before the desert field got hot we would have to wait until the next day.

Not only are there up-draughts which keep a plane from landing on its usual approach and from taking off during the heat of the day, but there are also tricky down-draughts. These are especially dangerous to light planes flying in desert canyon country. It is a fascinating experience to fly along in a deep canyon; but when the plane tries to lift suddenly at the end, it may encounter a down-draught so strong that it can make no headway at all. One pilot said it was like trying to swim up a waterfall. Of course, if one is crossing the mountains from the other direction, that waterfall-like down-draught can dash the plane against the canyon floor.

Much desert plain is suitable for forced landings; but a little loose sand, a few unexpected rocks, abrupt arroyo banks, or the thin crust over the soft mud on the floor of a dry salt lake can all turn the perfect landing into a no-take-off tragedy. The desert, like the sea, dictates rugged terms for those who try to cross it unprepared.

In temperate climates, good campers stop long enough before dark to make themselves comfortable and to find a supply of fuel and water. The desert traveler should also make himself comfortable, but he will most often find fuel and water only in the supplies he carries with him.

Cooking fires are tiny affairs in the desert world. Any thorny bush, some few twigs from a dead branch, a handful of roots found beneath the dead stub of a desert plant will boil the teakettle. Near an oasis, palm leaves and stems are used for fires but often on the *bled*, or open desert, there is nothing but the dried droppings of the camels. These, like the buffalo chips of our western plains, have boiled the tea and cooked the meat of desert peoples for countless generations. In the Gobi, cow dung and sheep dung are also used. Both burn with a smoky yellow flame. There the cow dung is often made into bricks and built into walls for corrals; and as winter cold increases, the top bricks are used for fuel to heat the yurts. Heifer dung, recognized by its symmetrical shape in contrast to the broad-splashed pattern of cow dung, burns with a hot blue flame. Desert travelers generally stop to pick up any bit of good fuel wherever they see it and carry it to their next stop, rather than try to make the stop at a fuel supply.

Wild food is even more scarce in the desert than fuel. There is plenty of food in the oases, just as there is on a farm in any other part of the world, but desert travelers between oases cannot expect to live off the land. There is a long list of edible desert plants, espe-cially for the American deserts, but their numbers on any given trail will be too few to make a full meal. If the traveler finds an edible morsel here and there, it may serve as a vitamin supplement to the supplies he carries; but the wise traveler does not count on foraging to keep his stomach full.

Some edible plants of the desert world have been discussed in earlier chapters, but special mention should be made of *Citrullus colocynthis*. This lush, moisture-filled gourd, which looks like a watermelon, is a poisonous emetic. It is found in both the Sahara and Arabian Deserts, and either it or a related species is probably the gourd Pablo Valencia tried to eat in the desert along the Mexi-can border. Those who have tasted *colocynthis* have found that it causes violent vomiting. This, of course, increases dehydration by expelling large quantities of stomach fluids.

In the Kalahari Desert of Africa there is a gourd which, from the descriptions I have seen, closely resembles *colocynthis*. Unlike its northern cousin, the Kalahari species has been reported as safe to eat and is a recognized source of drinking water. But, north of the equator, beware of the "pretty little desert watermelon."

All forms of animal life described in Chapter VIII are edible— if one can catch them! If it hops, crawls, jumps, runs, or flies, you can eat it, although you may have to get rid of some of your "civilized" food prejudices first. Meat will give more energy per pound than vegetable foods in general, but it also takes more body water to carry away the waste products. Unless one has plenty of water to drink, it is better to go easy on any food, and on meat in particular. It takes weeks to starve to death, but only hours to die of dehydration.

Deserts are generally healthy places. Hot, dry air is not a favorable environment for bacteria, and wounds usually heal quickly either with or without treatment. In some oases in all deserts and in the crowded yurts of the Gobi, the natives are subject to venereal diseases and tuberculosis; but in a survival situation one is not likely to spend enough time with the natives to be contaminated. Scurvy and dysentery can be avoided by following a normal diet, and the innoculations all travelers must have will protect one against the contagious diseases which sometimes are found.

Desert travelers are much more likely to suffer from photophthalmia (snow blindness) than from typhoid fever. The color of the desert ground varies, but where there is light sand, the ground may reflect as much as 80 per cent of the light which falls. This is close to the amount reflected by snow. There is a little higher percentage of ultraviolet light near the equator, so some desert areas may reflect a damaging concentration of these light rays at eye level.

Short, infrared light rays, as well as the visible rays, can produce solar retinitis in desert areas. Unless one looks directly at the sun or spends considerable time scanning the heavens near the sun, he will not be bothered with this particular eye trouble. However, sun glasses are useful in the desert. Even if the glare does not seem painful, the very high intensity of desert light will cause a decrease in your night vision.

The easy answer to the sun-glass problem in the desert is a pair of flying glasses in large frames, to help keep out the dust as well as glare. The glass should be of neutral density with 12–16 per cent transmission. If glasses are not available, a cloth mask with narrow eye slits will help, or one can blacken the skin around the eyes with a burnt stick.

Sandstorms have received much romantic attention as desert

hazards. As we pointed out in the chapter on climate and weather, a man will not be buried alive by a sandstorm, but if he tries to travel in the zero visibility of wind-borne dust he may quickly lose his way. When one is lost in the desert, tragedy is apt to follow. The best advice is to sleep out the storm with one's back to the wind—but don't forget to DRINK WATER!

Symptoms of dehydration at deficits of body water of

1-5% of body weight	6-10% of body weight	11-20% of body weight
Thirst	Dizziness	Delirium
Vague discomfort	Headache	Spasticity
Economy of movement	Dyspnea (labored	Swollen tongue
Anorexia (no appetite)	breathing)	Inability to swallow
Flushed skin	Tingling in limbs	Deafness
Impatience	Decreased blood	Dim vision
Sleepiness	volume	Shriveled skin
Increased pulse rate	Increased blood	Painful micturition
Increased rectal temp.	concentration	Numb skin
Nausea	Absence of saliva-	Anuria (defective
	tion	micturition or
	Cyanosis (body blue)	none)
	Indistinct speech	
	Inability to walk	

Days of expected survival under two conditions:

Condition	Max daily shade Temp °F	Available water per man, U. S. quarts					
		0	1	2	4	10	20
No walking at all	120	2	2	2	2.5	3	4.5
	110	3	3	3.5	4	5	7
	100	5	5.5	6	7	9.5	13.5
	90	7	8	9	10.5	15	23
	80	9	10	11	13	19	29
	70	10	11	12	14	20.5	32
	60	10	11	12	14	21	32
	50	10	11	12	14.5	21	32
Walking at night until exhausted and resting thereafter	120	1	2	2	2.5	3	
	110	2	2	2.5	3	3.5	
	100	3	3.5	3.5	4.5	5.5	
	90	5	5.5	5.5	6.5	8	
	80	7	7.5	8	9.5	11.5	
	70	7.5	8	9	10.5	13.5	
	60	8	8.5	9	11	14	
	50	8	8.5	9	11	14	

XXI

. . . .

. . . .

. . . .

. . . .

. . . . .

Will the Desert Bloom Again?

WILL THE DESERT BLOOM AGAIN? THE QUESTION HAS CHALLENGED dreamers for centuries. Many schemes have been proposed to reclaim the wastelands of the world on a gigantic scale, and huge, spectacular projects designed to stagger the imagination have been worked out on paper. In theory, each would modify the face of half a continent, and bring verdant crops and prosperity to the people of many nations. Some of the more modest dreams which keep within the boundaries and the budget of a single nation are actually being put into operation. But those schemes based on the water of great rivers like the Nile, the Tigris, the Euphrates, or even the little Jordan, find that rivers are no respecters of nationality. Desert nations, like desert families and individuals, are jealous of their rights. Most of them are more interested in keeping for themselves that which is theirs than in sacrificing even a small part of their national sovereignty to the theory of "the greatest good for the greatest number."

Long before the heroic dreamers, there were little dreamers. They were practical men who cared little for the glory of big projects, but who wanted little gardens of their own. These ordinary people have already made patches of green vegetation in their corners of the desert world. They have given us ample evidence that the desert can produce better than it does.

Twice I have seen tiny, isolated green gardens in the desert—gardens which were built by a single individual with no equipment but a big hoe. One was deep in the Sahara at the foot of a barren cliff. A man had scraped out a little spring there and scratched a ditch away from the cliff to nearly level ground where he grew enough vegetables for his own use. The other was in a rocky canyon on the northern edge of the desert. There a man had built a mud-walled ditch from a spring on the rocky floor. The ditch ran for nearly half a mile and leaked away almost half the water, but enough was left to keep a garden and some fig trees in good health.

Two hundred miles south of the Mediterranean Sea in the Libyan Desert is a narrow, gently sloping river bed. The nomads of the region have built terrace walls a foot or so high in this bed, and when it rains, even a little, these walls trap water and fine silt. The silt builds a flat garden bed, and the water stands for a little while after the storm, so each terrace soaks up a good supply of moisture. The nomads scatter seed grain on the mud flats, then move on to pastures with their flocks. The unattended little fields green up. The grain grows. When it is ready to harvest, the nomads come back and gather the crop.

In the Negev of Israel, I saw a one-man experiment on a similar river-bottom project. The man was a refugee from another part of the world, and apparently he had never heard of the age-old Arab technique of flood-bottom agriculture. All by himself he was working out a system. His farm included the broad, sandy valley of a dry wash with a slope even more gentle than that the Sahara nomads used. If the winter rains came to the Negev, there would be a few hours when the valley floor was covered by a foot or so of water. With a hand shovel the man had built a dirt wall across a part of the river bed. The wall was only a few inches high, but high enough to divert enough of the water to sheet-flood an acre or two on the edge of the valley. Just before the rains, the man scattered seed by hand over the area to be flooded.

The flood came. It washed out the seeds and carried them farther out on the flood plain. Someone had driven a truck over the area and water followed the wheel tracks, leaving the seeds thick in the little channels. The grain was growing all right when I saw the field, but in some places it was in thick, dense patches and elsewhere it was sparse or non-existent.

"Next year," the refugee said, "I'll wait and scatter the seed after the flood instead of before. Then it will grow evenly where I want it and be easier to harvest."

In the Gobi, rains are scanty but still enough for grasslands. Herds of horses and camels, flocks of sheep and goats, even large herds of antelope, all keep the grass short on thousands of acres. In contrast to the scanty vegetation of the overgrazed plains, we once found a large mesa that looked like an American hayfield. The grass was waist-high and thick. No more rain fell on that hayfield than on the surrounding plain, and we wondered why the mesa had such luxuriant vegetation. Eventually the Mongols told us that the place was sacred and that no Mongol herdsman would dare to pasture his flocks on that Holy Mesa. Without grazing, the grasses had opportunity to grow and go to seed. There was no attempt to harvest either seed or hay, but there was nothing to prevent the seed from blowing from the sacred ground to the secular plain around it. I do not know whether or not the lamas of the near-by monastery realized that by creating a Holy Mesa they were being practical conservationists. Western scientists recognize the sacred field as just one more proof that certain parts of the desert world will bloom again if given half a chance.

Once I stood on the ruins of Pueblo Wupatki in northern Arizona with Dr. Len Hargrave of the Museum of Northern Arizona. All around us was barren desert as far as we could see. Even the broad valley of an old stream bed was bare of vegetation.

"Would you believe that two hundred years ago a lush, marshy meadow covered all that flat land?" asked Dr. Hargrave.

"It looks as if it had always been desert," I replied.

"No," said Hargrave. "We have the diaries of early explorers who traveled through here. In those days this ruined pueblo was a living village. The Indians who lived here were agriculturists. Their fields were over there on the edge of the marshy meadow."

Today it takes a vivid imagination to believe this, but the record is clear. In the days before white men claimed the region, there were colonies of beaver in Arizona. Beavers dammed the creeks, held back the flood waters, and made marshes lush with vegetation. Indians as well as the beaver prospered in the area. Then came the fashion for men's beaver hats, and the beavers were trapped by the thousands to supply the demand for skins. In the valley at Pueblo Wupatki they were trapped out entirely, so that when a heavy rain washed out the beaver dams, there were no animals left to repair the damage. The Indians lacked both the necessary know-how and the labor force. After the dams were gone, other floods washed away the meadows, and in time all storm waters rushed farther out and disappeared in the desert. This loss of water stopped Indian agriculture. Starvation faced the people and they were forced to leave the pueblo.

Throughout the desert world it is the same story in one way or another. In the Middle East the hordes of Genghis Khan destroyed the dams of irrigation projects. They slaughtered thousands of the people. There was not enough labor left to rebuild those projects which had grown through the centuries with the civilizations. On the northern edge of the Sahara, the fall of Rome left North Africa without a strong government authority capable of providing repair and upkeep on the water projects. Those men with engineering knowledge and those with ability to direct and manage the labor needed to control the floods all left the region. With the loss of managers, the dams and irrigation ditches, even the huge cisterns which had trapped the run-off from tile-roofed buildings, fell into ruin. The floods, once trapped and useful, raced on to be lost in the desert.

Many of the ancient water projects were part of desert civilizations which had developed over centuries of time. They had grown from small beginnings. They were started before dense population and consequent over-use had destroyed the native vegetation. Consequently, the destruction of those ancient works left the land more barren than it was before they were ever built.

During years of abundant rain, a pasture will feed many head of sheep and goats, but herdsmen in the desert world are individualists. Each one always tries to keep the same large flocks through years of drought. They soon so overgraze the vegetation that even a few years of good rains cannot repair the damage.

In every corner of the desert world there are scientists and "practical conservationists," like the Mongol lamas of Holy Mesa in the Gobi, who know how to make the desert produce better than it does. But, just as certainly, the majority of herdsmen and farmers refuse to follow their advice. Government authority in many cases has been reluctant to enforce the good advice against the ignorance and misguided selfishness of the majorities. Nevertheless, year by year both the little dreamers and the scientists are expanding fertile acres in the desert world. Sometimes they do it by reducing grazing pressure, and sometimes they bring in vegetation better suited to the desert area. Most often they make the biggest showing with new supplies of water.

Water wells are now as common in the Arabian Desert as the oil wells we hear so much about. The Bedouins no longer need to migrate far to the north in summer, because their herds can now be watered at concrete tanks filled from deep wells. In the Algerian Sahara, a deep vein of ground water was discovered a few years ago, and modern well drills have tapped this vast new supply. It flows to the surface or comes within easy pumping distance and irrigates date palms and garden patches where only a few years ago there was only barren, hard, clay desert floor. At Beersheba, in the Negev, a pipeline carries water from wells in coastal Israel to the desert.

A few years ago, not far from the shores of the Dead Sea, in Jordan, the Arabs consulted Western engineers about digging for water on that salty desert. They were told that the idea was fruitless. They would get no water and nothing would grow on the salty soil anyway. However, a handful of little dreamers pooled their resources and hand-dug a well 300 feet deep in the valley of the Dead Sea.

They reached water in abundance. They brought it to the surface and flushed a patch of the desert. The salt was leached away. Crops grow there now. Watered trees grow three feet a year where no trees grew before. Arab refugees now live in modest homes close to their fields.

The desert will bloom wherever enough water can be spread across the arid acres. In the Nile valley the story of irrigation is so old and well known that one seldom thinks of the region as a desert. But when one flies to Cairo he has vivid proof that man has made the desert bloom. The desert stops on a surveyor's line at the edge of watered fields. In Egypt, as in the provinces of ancient Rome, strong, central authority has developed and maintained large water-conservation projects.

Even when large amounts of water are available, power is generally needed to get it over the land. Along the Nile, men walk on treadmill water wheels to lift the water. Gradually these are being replaced by faster, more efficient water lifts with bicycle pedals. Well-sweeps in Sahara gardens are moved up and down by man power. In Arabia, huge skin bags of water are lifted from the wells by donkeys or camels hitched to the well-ropes. This lifting power of man and beast has its limitations and it takes long hours to water a few small gardens. Near the oil fields modern power pumps are coming into use, but they require a capital investment the small gardener cannot always make. New and more efficient windmill designs are being produced for other desert regions, and experiments with solar heat are advancing rapidly. Already practical solar cook-stoves are in use in desert Egypt and India. As one Arab said, "The sun is our atomic pile, we don't need your atom-smashers"; and some day soon direct sunlight will be converted into power with which to water gardens. However, the supply of water from dammed-up floods, from deep or shallow wells, from rainfall trapped in cisterns is all together not enough to irrigate the desert world and make lush pastures or large fields of waving grain.

Perhaps the day is not far off when a cheap and easy process will be found to take the salt from sea water and make it sweet.

Already there are pilot plants for two or three such processes being put into operation. When the break-through really comes, then the heroic dreamers may at last bring water to half a continent. Then it may even be practical to pipe Mediterranean water some forty miles across the desert to let it plunge 165 feet into the Qattara Depression of the Libyan Sahara. As that water falls below sea level, it could turn huge generators and produce the power necessary to make some of the salt water fresh enough for irrigation then and pump it on into irrigation canals. When that day comes the desert world will have vast garden spots indeed, but even then there will be endless barren plains and sun-scorched mountains. There will always be a desert world until the winds of heaven cease their present pattern and the mountains in their pathways disappear.

Index

acacias, 106
accretion, 52
Adolph, Dr. E. F., 315
agave (century plant), 284
air funnels, 67
Akamouk (*amenokal* of Hoggar Federation), 210, 212–24
Ala Shan Desert, 60, 68; temperatures, 87
alfalfa grass, 113
Altriplex cana, 105
Amenokal (elected chief), 210
American Deserts, 15; (*see* also N. American Deserts)
American Indians, 16, 280–85; agriculture, 290–93; baths, sweat, 294–95; cliff-dwellers, 290–91; clothing, 286–87; decorative arts, 287, 293–94; dyes, 287; food, 281–85; game, 281–82; irrigation & dams, 285, 291–92; Navajo, 289, 293, 294; Papago, 102, 109; Piute, 283, 285, 287, 294; Pueblo Wupatki, 332–33; rabbit drives, 282; religion, 292–93; witches, belief in, 294; vegetation, 281
American Museum of Natural History, *see* Central Asiatic Expedition
Anabasis articulata, 106
Andrews, Dr. Roy Chapman, 14, 60, 118, 195
animals, 110–124; birth control, 114–15; as food, 119
Anopheles (mosquito), 124

antelope, 110–12, 124
Arabian-American Oil Co., 130
Arabian Desert, area, 14; fog, 84; food, 253–54, 255, 272–74; history, 252; industry, 253–54, 255, 256; irrigation, 254, 334; name, use of, 13; religion, 260–62; seasons, 81; *shamal* (wind), 91–92; temperature, 74, 76; trade & barter, 253–54, 256, 264–65; water wells, 334; (*see* also Saudi Arabia)
Archean Period, 64
Armoise, 105
arrak, 232
artemisias, 106
Atacama Desert, area, 14
Aures Mountains, 105
Australia, "brick-fielder" (wind), 93; desert area, 14; food, 120, 273; sand dunes, 54; water holes ("soaks"), 167, 274; water, 115

Bagnold, R. A., 49, 50, 53, 56, 99–100
Baikal, Lake, temperatures, 85
baobab tree, 276–77
basins, in Gobi, 59–69
Bedouins, 201, 252–56; raiding, 263
Belaid (author's interpreter), 217–22
Benguela Current, 72
Berkey, Dr. Charles P., 199
bi, 278
Bidon Cinque, 17
birds, 112, 113, 114; as food, 119
Bis naga, 286